THE PUBLISHED WRITINGS OF WILBUR AND ORVILLE WRIGHT

SMITHSONIAN HISTORY OF AVIATION SERIES

VON HARDESTY, Series Editor

On December 17, 1903, human flight became a reality when Orville Wright piloted the *Wright Flyer* across a 120-foot course above the sands at Kitty Hawk, North Carolina. That awe-inspiring twelve seconds of powered flight inaugurated a new era. The airplane quickly evolved as a means of transportation and a weapon of war. Flying faster, farther, and higher, airplanes soon encircled the globe, dramatically altering human perceptions of time and space. The dream of flight appeared to be without bounds. Having conquered the skies, the heirs of the Wrights eventually orbited the Earth and landed on the Moon.

Aerospace history is punctuated with extraordinary feats of heroism and technological achievement. But that same history also showcases the devastating impact of aviation technology in modern warfare. The airplane—as with many other important technological breakthroughs—has provided safe, reliable, and inexpensive travel for millions. Vertical flight continues to play a key role in rescue and communications.

International in scope, this scholarly series includes original monographs, biographies, reprints of out-of-print classics, translations, and reference works. Both civil and military themes are included, along with studies related to the cultural impact of the airplane. Together, these diverse titles contribute to our overall understanding of aeronautical technology and its evolution.

THE PUBLISHED WRITINGS OF WILBUR AND ORVILLE WRIGHT

EDITED BY
PETER L. JAKAB AND
RICK YOUNG

SMITHSONIAN INSTITUTION PRESS
Washington and London

Copy editor: D. Teddy Diggs
Production editor: Ruth Thomson
Designer: Janice Wheeler

Library of Congress Cataloging-in-Publication Data
Wright, Wilbur, 1867–1912.
[Selections. 2000]
The published writings of Wilbur and Orville Wright / edited by Peter L. Jakab and Rick Young.
p. cm. — (Smithsonian history of aviation series)
Includes bibliographical references and index.
ISBN 1-56098-938-6 (cloth : alk. paper)
1. Wright, Wilbur, 1867–1912 Archives. 2. Wright, Orville, 1871–1948 Archives.
3. Aeronautics—United States—History Sources. I. Wright, Orville, 1871–1948. II. Jakab, Peter L.
III. Young, Rick (Richard Leo). IV. Title. V. Series.
TL540.W7A25 2000
629.13′092′2—dc21
[B] 99-39653

British Library Cataloguing-in-Publication Data are available

Manufactured in the United States of America
07 06 05 04 03 02 01 00 5 4 3 2 1

♾ The paper used in this publication meets the minimum requirements of the American National Standard for Information Sciences—Permanence of Paper for Printed Library Materials ANSI Z39.48-1984.

AVIATION HAS GONE BEYOND MY DREAMS.

—Orville Wright, June 1929

CONTENTS

Acknowledgments xi

Introduction 1

1 • "THE AGE OF THE FLYING MACHINE HAD COME"

The Wrights Tell Their Story 11

1. Statement by the Wright Brothers to the Associated Press 14
2. Statement to the Aero Club of America 16
3. Our Recent Experiments in North Carolina 19
4. Our Aeroplane Tests at Kitty Hawk 21
5. The Wright Brothers' Aëroplane 24
6. Ohio in Aviation 35
7. Presentation of Langley Medal to Messrs. Wilbur and Orville Wright 36
8. The Earliest Wright Flights—A Letter from Wilbur Wright 37
9. A Letter from Orville and Wilbur Wright 39
10. How We Made the First Flight 40
11. My Narrowest Escape in the Air 49
12. How I Learned to Fly 51
13. The Work of Orville Wright 57
14. Wright's First Statement since the War 58
15. Orville Wright: An Interview 59

16. Our Early Flying Machine Developments 63

17. The Wright-Langley Controversy: Both Sides Presented by Orville Wright and Dr. Walcott 66

18. Winged Pioneers: A Thumbnail History of Aviation by the Men Who Have Made It 72

19. Why the 1903 Wright Airplane Is Sent to a British Museum 73

20. Orville Wright Declines—Naturally: With the Smithsonian These Days Life Is Just One Statement—and Label—after Another 76

21. Wilbur Wright 79

22. What's Going On Here? An Answer by Our Traveling Reporter, Fred C. Kelly 81

23. Our Life in Camp at Kitty Hawk 84

24. Orville Wright Ordered Return to America of Original Airplane 92

25. Orville Wright—"First Man to Fly" 98

2 • "SOME AERONAUTICAL EXPERIMENTS"

Technical Articles by the Wrights 107

26. Angle of Incidence 109

27. The Horizontal Position during Gliding Flight 112

28. Some Aeronautical Experiments 114

29. Experiments and Observations in Soaring Flight 132

30. The Relations of Weight, Speed, and Power of Flyers 147

31. Inverted Aeroplane Stresses 148

32. Stability of Aeroplanes 149

33. Possibilities of Soaring Flight 157

3 • "THE GREATEST OF THE PRECURSORS"

The Wrights Assess Their Contemporaries 163

34. He Can Half Fly 165

35. Air Ship Soon to Fly 166

36. Wright's Statement Concerning Johnstone's Fatal Fall 167

37. The Life and Work of Octave Chanute 168

38. What Mouillard Did 171

39. What Clement Ader Did 176

40. Otto Lilienthal 184

41. The Mythical Whitehead Flight 188

4 • "IT IS NEVER SAFE TO PROPHESY"

The Wrights on the Future of Aviation 191

42. Flying as a Sport—Its Possibilities 194

43. The Aeroplane: What It Will Be Like in Five Years Time, Opinions of Prominent Aeroists 196

44. The Future of the Aeroplane 200

45. Flying from London to Manchester 201

46. Airship Safe: Air Motoring No More Dangerous Than Land Motoring 205

47. A Talk with Wilbur Wright 206

48. W. Wright on Altitude and Fancy Flying 208

49. In Honor of the Army and Aviation 210

50. Wright Considers High Speed Too Dangerous 211

51. Wilbur Wright Favors Reliability Tests 213

52. Wright Finds Ocean Crossing Risky Now 213

53. Flying Machines and the War 214

54. Address by Orville Wright at the National Parks Conference, under the Auspices of the Department of the Interior, Washington, D.C., January 5, the Day's Program Being Devoted to the Subject of "Motor Travel to the Parks," and under the Direction of the American Automobile Association 219

55. The Safe and Useful Aeroplane 221

56. Orville Wright Says 10,000 Aeroplanes Would End the War within Ten Weeks 231

57. Says Aircraft Will Win War 238

58. Wright to Make Aeros for Commercial Use 238

59. The Future of Civil Flying **239**

60. Sporting Future of the Airplane: Reduced Landing Speeds an Essential Factor **242**

61. The Commercial Airplane **244**

62. Low-Speed Landing Is First Need of Aviation **246**

63. Inventor of the Airplane Details Some of Early Experiences in Radio Message to World **247**

64. Orville Wright Forecasts Aircraft Expansion **252**

65. What Is Ahead in Aviation: America's Foremost Leaders in Many Branches of Flying Give Remarkable Forecasts of the Future **256**

66. Sun Power Motor **257**

67. Orville Wright Foresees Great Progress in Next Decade **258**

68. Orville Wright Takes Look Back on 40 Years since First Flight; Despite Air War, Has No Regrets **261**

69. Wright Favors Free Competition on Postwar Foreign Air Routes **267**

APPENDIX • "THEN WE QUIT LAUGHING"

Witnesses to the Birth of Flight **271**

70. Then We Quit Laughing **274**

71. With the Wrights at Kitty Hawk: Anniversary of First Flight Twenty-five Years Ago **278**

72. I Was Host to Wright Brothers at Kitty Hawk **283**

73. My Story of the Wright Brothers **285**

74. The First Airplane—After 1903 **296**

Bibliography **301**

Photography Credits **307**

Index **309**

ACKNOWLEDGMENTS

AT THE COMPLETION OF ANY book project there are always many debts. Some are great, some small, but all equally deserving of recognition. The following individuals and organizations were particularly helpful in the preparation of *The Published Writings of Wilbur and Orville Wright.* First and foremost, Rick Young, his brother Bill Young, and his wife, Sue Young, and Lee Mintz merit a resounding thank-you. They collected and transcribed nearly all of the articles in part 1 through part 4, forming the core of the book. Their labors are heartily appreciated.

Mark G. Hirsch of the Smithsonian Institution Press and Von D. Hardesty, curator at the National Air and Space Museum (NASM) and editor of the Smithsonian History of Aviation book series, offered initial interest and support for the project. Von also, along with NASM curators Michael J. Neufeld and Tom D. Crouch, provided useful advice on format and editorial questions. Dominick A. Pisano, chairman of the Aeronautics Division, NASM, and John D. Anderson, also a member of the Aeronautics Division, contributed a helpful review of the introduction and a number of the more complex annotations. John H. Morrow Jr., of the University of Georgia, and Marc Rothenberg, Editor, Joseph Henry Papers Project, Smithsonian Institution, made useful overall comments on the manuscript. NASM volunteer Theodore M. Hamady provided valuable research assistance. Elaine Cline, NASM librarian, shared her expertise regarding copyright issues for previously published historical material.

Libraries and archives are of course the lifeblood of any scholar. Several institutions were critical to the success of this project. The Library of Congress, Wright State

University Libraries, the National Air and Space Museum Library and Archives, the Smithsonian Institution Archives, Roesch Library at the University of Dayton, and the Dayton and Montgomery County Public Library each played an important role.

Finally, thanks go to the NASM Photography Department for reproducing the illustrations.

Peter L. Jakab

THE PUBLISHED WRITINGS OF WILBUR AND ORVILLE WRIGHT

INTRODUCTION

THE INVENTION OF THE AIRPLANE by Wilbur and Orville Wright is one of the great stories in American history. It entails the creation of a world-changing technology at the opening of an exciting new century, an era full of promise and confidence in the future. At the center of this tale are two talented, yet modest, midwestern bicycle-shop proprietors whose inventive labors and achievement transformed them from respected small-town businessmen into international celebrities. The account of the brothers' aeronautical work is a treat for the student of intellectual and technical creativity. The influence of their invention on the twentieth century is beyond measure. The transport by air of material and people, quickly and over great distances, and the military applications of flight technology have had an incalculable economic, geopolitical, and cultural impact all over the globe. The Wrights' invention not only solved a long-studied technical problem but helped fashion a new world.

The compelling story of the Wright brothers has been told in no fewer than eight full-scale biographies. The most detailed and textured account of their lives can be found in Tom D. Crouch's *The Bishop's Boys: A Life of Wilbur and Orville Wright.* Fred Howard's *Wilbur and Orville: A Biography of the Wright Brothers* and Harry Combs's *Kill Devil Hill: Discovering the Secret of the Wright Brothers* also offer accurate and useful overviews of the Wrights' achievement. The most complete discussion of the brothers' inventive process and their aeronautical work is Peter L. Jakab's *Visions of a Flying Machine: The Wright Brothers and the Process of Invention.* These books go far toward chronicling and interpreting the life and work of the Wrights, but they are, of course, secondary treatments. Fortunately for all of those interested in the detail of the Wright story, Wilbur and Orville left behind a vast amount of primary material.

After Orville Wright's death on January 30, 1948, his estate took charge of two of the world's greatest aviation treasures: the first airplane flown—on December 17, 1903—which is currently the centerpiece of the Smithsonian Institution's National Air and Space Museum in Washington, D.C.; and the Wright Papers, the brothers' many notebooks, diaries, and personal correspondence in which they recorded their path to human flight. The latter were deposited in the Library of Congress in 1949 with the condition that the papers be published in edited form before the collection was opened to the public. The product of this condition, *The Papers of Wilbur and Orville Wright,* edited by Marvin W. McFarland, appeared in 1953 and remains one of the finest pieces of historical editing ever published. McFarland's skillful selection and annotation of the primary material resulted in a nearly seamless telling, in the Wright brothers' own words, of the invention of the airplane. Nearly fifty years after the initial publication of the McFarland collection, the two large volumes of *The Papers of Wilbur and Orville Wright* endure as the central resource for any serious investigation of the brothers' aeronautical work. A useful supplement to *The Papers* had been published two years earlier: *Miracle at Kitty Hawk: The Letters of Wilbur and Orville Wright,* edited by Fred C. Kelly. Kelly was a personal friend of Orville Wright's and was the only researcher given significant access to the brothers' personal papers before the papers were donated to the Library of Congress. Even though *Miracle at Kitty Hawk* is a much smaller work than *The Papers,* it does include a fair number of letters, mostly of a more personal nature, that are not in the McFarland volumes.

The Aeronautics Division, later the Science and Technology Division, of the Library of Congress subsequently produced three other important reference works concerning the Wright brothers. Compiled by Arthur G. Renstrom, one of McFarland's associates, they are *Wilbur and Orville Wright: A Bibliography* (1968), *Wilbur and Orville Wright: A Chronology* (1975), and *Wilbur & Orville Wright: Pictorial Materials, a Documentary Guide.* (1982). These three publications contain a vast amount of information and a myriad of references to material on virtually every aspect of the Wright story. They are a marvelous complement to the brothers' edited personal papers.

The secondary historical accounts, *The Papers, Miracle at Kitty Hawk,* and the Renstrom volumes document the Wright story in exhaustive detail. Still, there is one further body of relevant materials that have never been brought together into a usable, coherent form: the Wright brothers' *own* published writings. This book fills the remaining gap in scholarly resources on the Wrights. The brothers jointly and individually authored dozens of articles on their inventive work and other aeronautical matters during their lifetimes. Most of the articles were published in what are today long-defunct journals and magazines, obscure newspapers, or otherwise difficult-to-find publications. This book, for the first time, brings these wide-ranging pieces together into a single, annotated reference. Also included are a number of published remarks offered by the Wrights at events in their honor, at ceremonies, or at other public gatherings, as well as letters to editors, congressional testimony, and extended published interviews. The book seeks to document how the Wright brothers *themselves* chose to record their achievement and shape their legacy, as well as to present their public views regarding pertinent aviation issues of their time.

When poring over the Wright brothers collection in the manuscript reading room at the Library of Congress, one is immediately impressed by the technical detail and sophistication running through their expansive letters and diary entries. But beyond the wealth of information and insight the material offers regarding the Wrights' engineering acumen, it also reveals the brothers' considerable skill as writers. The care and clarity of their technical descriptions and engineering arguments in their correspondence with fellow experimenters, and the artful expression and frequent humor in their letters sent home to family members, demonstrate a literary ability rarely seen in engineers and technically minded people.

Writing and publishing were a part of Wilbur and Orville's lives very early on. Their father, Milton Wright, a bishop in a midwestern Protestant sect called the Church of the United Brethren in Christ, served as the editor and publisher of several of the church newspapers and other religious publications. On occasion, when Milton Wright became embroiled in political battles within the church, Wilbur contributed to pamphlets, published by the bishop, supporting the elder Wright's position.

The United Brethren Printing Establishment was located in Dayton, Ohio, where the Wright family lived, and Milton Wright had an office in the building that housed the printing facilities. As boys, Wilbur and Orville enjoyed frequent access to the pressrooms; the brothers, Orville in particular, were fascinated by the printing process. As teenagers, Orville and a boyhood friend, Ed Sines, began a small job-printing business operated out of their homes. In 1886 "Sines & Wright" attempted to produce a small school newspaper, the *Weekly Midget,* but only one issue was printed and it was never distributed. Shortly thereafter, following a dispute between the boys, Orville bought out Sines's part of the business, though Sines continued to work for him as an employee. In March 1889, when Orville was seventeen, he launched another newspaper, a more substantial local weekly called the *West Side News.* By the end of April, Orville was publishing the *West Side News* from a small office a few blocks from his home and Wilbur had joined the operation as editor. A year later the paper became a daily under the moniker the *Evening Item.* Interestingly, in the issue of July 17, 1890, a brief, partly humorous, item appeared about the German aeronautical pioneer Otto Lilienthal. The inclusion is significant considering how central Lilienthal's work would be to the brothers' early research into flight after they began study of the problem following Lilienthal's death in a glider accident in 1896. The short Lilienthal mention was repeated nine days later. It appears in part 3 of this book.

The *Evening Item* was a good local paper, but competition was stiff, with a dozen newspapers available to Dayton residents at that time. On July 30, 1890, after seventy-eight issues, the *Item* ceased publication. Apart from the heavy workload of producing a daily newspaper, the brothers determined that it was simply far more profitable to do only job printing.

As job printers, the brothers had one more brief newspaper experience. Paul Laurence Dunbar, who would later achieve fame as one of the country's greatest African-American poets, was a neighbor and high school classmate of Orville's. In December 1890 Dunbar began a short-lived weekly, called the *Dayton Tattler,* oriented to the city's black community. He hired the Wrights to print it. Only three issues appeared, but in the final one an interesting item appeared that was almost certainly contributed by Wilbur or Orville, if not actually written by one of them. Entitled "Air Ship Soon to Fly," it was a short article that noted the announcement in Chicago of a planned cross-country flight by a dirigible airship. It is also included in part 3.

The Wrights began their better-known pre-aeronautical livelihood of bicycle repair and manufacture in 1892, but they maintained their printing firm until 1899. They sold the latter business and equipment that year after Sines, who had been doing most of the day-to-day work for quite some time, left the Wrights' employ.

Although both the brothers were skilled with a pen, Wilbur had a genuine affinity for writing, whereas Orville found it a chore. As Orville explained to a fellow aeronautical experimenter in 1903, "Will seems to enjoy writing, so I leave all the literary part of our work to him."[1] Wilbur's obvious pleasure at this form of self-expression runs through his extensive correspondence with the Wrights' friend and colleague Octave Chanute. Chanute, the elder statesmen of the aeronautical community at the close of the nineteenth century, received his first letter from Wilbur in May 1900. By the time of Chanute's death in 1910, some four hundred letters had been exchanged between them; in great measure, these letters documented the invention of the airplane. The Wright-Chanute correspondence forms the core of McFarland's *Papers of Wilbur and Orville Wright.* The precision and delight with which Wilbur conveys the details of the brothers' aeronautical work in these letters reveals a person for whom this is not merely an act of communication. The technical work was of course the central concern, but the correspondence itself was clearly a creative outlet for Wilbur. For Orville, on the other hand, a conscious literary effort was never a motivation. He wrote grudgingly and only when something needed to be said, and he did so with the utmost economy of language. Despite a demonstrated writing ability, Orville early convinced himself that he lacked talent for writing, an idea that reinforced his distaste for the pursuit.

These contrasting attitudes toward writing reflected the brothers' personalities. Wilbur was the spokesman for the pair. He delivered all the papers and addresses, wrote most of the correspondence to other aeronautical experimenters and business associates, and gave the interviews after the brothers gained fame. As the older brother, Wilbur took a natural leadership role, but assuming this position was also much more in his character than Orville's. Orville was painfully shy with anyone outside his immediate family. Much to his relief, he could always retreat behind Wilbur's strong presence when the outside world intruded.

Wilbur and Orville had always planned to write a detailed, thorough treatment of their inventive achievement. Toward this end they carefully guarded their personal papers and technical notebooks, offering only the most limited access to outsiders. Their first significant published account of their experiments after the successful powered flights at Kitty Hawk was an article entitled "The Wright Brothers' Aëroplane," which appeared in *Century Magazine* in September 1908. Ironically, the article was written entirely by Orville early that summer, since Wilbur, busy preparing for the Wrights' upcoming first public demonstration of their airplane in France, was on his way to Europe through New York. Orville's article was intended primarily for publicity. Four and a half years after Kitty Hawk, and two and a half years since making their last flights, the Wrights were now ready to unveil their creation to the world. To pave the way for popular understanding of the depth of their accomplishment and to avoid confusion with lesser efforts then beginning to grab public attention, the brothers felt that the need for an authoritative statement had become critical. In spite of the pragmatic purpose of the article, "The Wright Brothers' Aëroplane" remains one of the best short descriptions of the invention of the airplane. Still, it was not the book-length account the Wrights ultimately intended to prepare. Typical of Orville's low assessment of his literary skills, he offered to return part of the $500 paid to him by *Century Magazine.* "The Wright Brothers' Aëroplane" appears in part 1.

Wilbur Wright's sudden and untimely death from typhoid fever in May 1912 at the age of forty-five ended any realistic hope that the Wright brothers would produce a book of their own. In his will, Wilbur cited his younger brother as the person "who has been associated with me in all the hopes and labors both of childhood and manhood, and who, I am sure, will use the property [referring to their papers] in very much the same manner as we would use it together in case we would both survive until old age."[2] Orville took this responsibility seriously, yet it became an increasing personal burden during the remaining thirty-six years of his life. His psychological block toward writing and his growing procrastination thwarted Orville's best intentions to get on with the book that he and Wilbur had planned to do together. His anguish over his inability to fulfill his brother's wishes was compounded by his frustration with the efforts of others to tell the Wright story. Extremely particular over the smallest detail and insistent that only the technical story be told, without personal biographical information he considered private, Orville was dissatisfied with all attempts of would-be Wright biographers. For decades, numerous friends and colleagues, including Charles Lindbergh, urged Orville to write his autobiography. Eventually it became painfully clear to all that the book would never be written.

Finally, in 1939 a journalist and longtime friend of Orville's, Fred C. Kelly, persuaded Orville to cooperate with him on an authorized biography. This appeared as *The Wright Brothers: A Biography Authorized by Orville Wright* in 1943 and has remained in print to the present day. It was not Orville's own account, but it was at least a version he could live with. Even if he had written the long-sought autobiography, it likely would not have revealed many personal insights about the brothers. Orville's shyness and the Wright family's general attitude toward privacy would have precluded anything but a strictly technical, though very accurate, telling of the invention of the airplane—nothing more, nothing less. Thus, of Wilbur and Orville's own published words, all we have are the articles reproduced here. Though not the comprehensive autobiography the world has craved, the pieces the Wrights did author provide a useful window onto how the brothers wanted to tell their story and what they saw as their legacy.

Organization and Editorial Considerations

This book is organized into four broad subject areas. The articles that cover the invention of the airplane and the Wrights' personal history, including the controversy with the Smithsonian Institution over the work of Samuel P. Langley, compose part 1. Part 2 presents the Wrights' published technical papers on aeronautics, including Wilbur's pathbreaking 1901 article "Some Aeronautical Experiments." Part 3 gathers the few pieces the Wrights wrote about fellow experimenters. Here we have their assessments of pivotal figures in their inventive work, people such as Chanute and Lilienthal. Part 4 includes material that will certainly be the least familiar to general and specialist audiences alike. After Wilbur and Orville became firmly established as the founders of the aerial age, their opinions on the aviation issues of the day were often sought. As the technology they gave birth to flourished and matured, issues ranging from the military application of the airplane to its commercial viability and direction were the subject of vigorous debate. Frequently the brothers—especially Orville, since he lived until 1948—were asked to give their sage views on such matters. The articles and other materials in part 4 are the public record of the Wrights' commentary on the state of aviation as it advanced.

Within each section, the material is presented chronologically by date of first publication. Some of the articles appeared in multiple publications or were reprinted elsewhere. Only the main citation is given here. A complete listing of citations for those articles that appeared in more than one place can be found in Renstrom's *Wilbur and Orville Wright: A Bibliography.* Journal and magazine titles appear as they did at the time the individual articles were published; in some cases the titles changed over time.

Note number 1 for each document provides the bibliographic citation for the article. Subsequent notes are explanatory notes and annotations. Obvious typographical errors in the original publications have been corrected, but the original spelling, accents, capitalization, punctuation, style, and usage have been retained. Editor's notes and other supplemental elements originally published with the Wrights' text have been retained. Some of the articles appeared with photographs. These pictures have been omitted, since nearly all of them were commonly seen and frequently published images and are not essential to understanding the content of the text. There would also be a fair amount of redundancy if the pictures were placed with the articles in their original format. The photos prepared for this book, however, do include virtually all of these images.

Materials considered appropriate for inclusion in the book were the following: (a) published articles authored individually or jointly by the Wrights; (b) published transcriptions of spoken addresses given by Wilbur or Orville; (c) the brothers' published letters written to newspaper editors; (d) published transcriptions of testimony given before congressional committees; and (e) published interviews that extensively quote the Wrights on substantive issues.

Documents deemed inappropriate for this book included the following: depositions given in the Wrights' numerous patent-infringement cases, which are in the published court record; interviews of a brief and inconsequential nature; essays or book introductions that are short and that contain no substantive commentary or were likely only signed by one of the Wrights; and passing announcements, published in trade journals, from the Wrights' manufacturing company with one or two quotes of an insignificant nature. The few pieces that Wilbur helped his father prepare on church matters have also been omitted, since Wilbur appeared as the author on only one. That item was written in 1888 and is listed in the bibliography.

Four documents attributed to the Wright brothers but not actually written by them have been excluded from this work. "How We Invented the Airplane," by Orville Wright, with an introduction and commentary by Fred C. Kelly, appeared as a small book in 1953 and also in *Harper's Magazine* in June of that year. The text was not drafted by Orville but was compiled by Kelly using excerpts from Orville's court depositions given in patent-infringement cases in 1920 and 1921. It is a useful essay, but it is beyond the scope of this book. Further, it is available in published form in the 1953 book released by the David McKay Company.

In 1920 an article entitled "The Story of the Wright Brothers' Early Developments" appeared in a General Motors Corporation publication under Orville's name. On his personal copy in the Wright Papers in the Library of Congress, Orville crossed out his own name and noted that F. C. Makeley was the true author.

In the March 5, 1909, issue of the *New York Herald* appeared a piece with the headline "Story of Our Lives," by Wilbur and Orville Wright. There is little doubt that the brothers had nothing to do with this item. To begin with, many passages are pulled directly or are closely paraphrased from the text of the *Century Magazine* article published a few months earlier. The *Century Magazine* piece had typographical errors concerning three key dates, and these errors also appeared in the *Herald* article. It is hard to imagine that the same errors would be repeated in a genuinely new article. In addition, what is not drawn verbatim from the *Century Magazine* text is riddled with factual errors. Also, the title, "Story of Our Lives," does not fit well with the content of the article. It would have been out of character for the Wrights to be so imprecise. For these reasons, it is a sound assumption that this article was not authored by the brothers.

Finally, in 1904 a popular magazine called the *Independent* published "The Experiments of a Flying Man," by Wilbur Wright. In a June 28, 1908, letter to Orville commenting on the draft of the *Century Magazine* article, Wilbur instructed him to note in the text or in a footnote that the *Independent* article was a "forgery."

One transcript of testimony has not been included. On October 3, 1918, Orville was interrogated by Judge Charles Evans Hughes in connection with a government investigation of the U.S. aircraft industry during World War I. The questioning focused on Orville's involvement with the Dayton-Wright Airplane Company, which had a wartime government contract to produce aircraft. The transcript offers little information beyond determining that Orville had no financial interest in the firm and that he provided little technical consultation to the company. He did little more than lend his prestigious name to a concern formed by several Dayton business colleagues. Since the transcript has limited value and was published in *The Papers of Wilbur and Orville Wright,* it has been omitted here.

One other piece absent from this collection deserves comment. In the Wright Papers in the Library of Congress is a typed manuscript, with editorial marks and additions in Wilbur's handwriting, entitled "Comparison of Airships with Flyers." Although a formal paper, it does not appear to have been published. Copies of the finished paper were circulated to individuals involved in negotiations concerning the sale of the Wright airplane in Germany in 1907, but no published version seems to exist. Considering that the Germans had a heavy investment in lighter-than-air dirigible airships in this period, this manuscript was apparently prepared by Wilbur to clarify the advantages of heavier-than-air flying machines in an effort to bolster the Wrights' chances for a deal with the Germans. Since it was not formally published and since McFarland included it in *The Papers of Wilbur and Orville Wright,* "Comparison of Airships with Flyers" has not been reproduced here.

Rounding out the book is an appendix containing a small number of articles not written by the Wrights. These are articles written by people who had a direct connection to the brothers and who played a key personal role in the Wright story. The published reminiscences of these associates provide a unique perspective on Wilbur and Orville and the first flight. Given the fact that the articles appeared in obscure magazines and journals and the fact that there are few such publications by historical players connected to the invention of the airplane and the epic events at Kitty Hawk, they merit inclusion in this collection.

1. O. Wright to George A. Spratt, June 7, 1903, in Marvin W. McFarland, ed., *The Papers of Wilbur and Orville Wright,* 2 vols. (New York: McGraw-Hill, 1953), 1:310–15.
2. Quoted in introduction to ibid., 1:xi.

THE WRIGHTS TELL THEIR STORY

WHEN WILBUR AND ORVILLE WRIGHT began their aeronautical research and experiments, they did not set out to be the inventors of the airplane. In the now famous letter that Wilbur wrote to the Smithsonian on May 30, 1899, explaining his interest in flight and requesting "such papers as the Smithsonian Institution has published on this subject," he expressed only his hope that he could make a contribution. "I wish to avail myself of all that is already known and then if possible add my mite to help on the future worker who will attain final success," Wilbur declared.[1] By the summer of 1902, however, after three years of serious investigation and trials with three full-sized gliders, the Wrights were convinced that *they,* not a "future worker," would attain "final success" in inventing the airplane. In a response to Octave Chanute concerning a request to publish drawings of the brothers' latest glider, Wilbur stated, "I do not think that drawings will reveal very much of the principles of operation of our machines, unless accompanied with somewhat extended explanations, so our secrets are safe enough."[2] Clearly, by now the brothers realized that their findings had to be guarded to prevent someone else from gaining fame and fortune based on their breakthrough research and hard work.

This comment was among the earliest references to a sentiment that after 1905 became a near obsession of the Wrights. After achieving success in 1903, they spent a great deal of time trying to ensure public recognition of the magnitude of their contribution to aeronautics and to establish that they were the true inventors of the airplane. Often in the history of invention, after a long-thought-insoluble technical problem is conquered, numerous competing experimenters either claim to have solved the problem first or attempt to diminish the achievements of the actual inventor. This happened with the airplane, in part because the Wrights chose to release news and details of their success in a very careful, controlled way. They sought to secure patent protection and lock up financial arrangements concerning the sale of their invention before sharing too many details with the world. In the absence of a lot of specific information, skepticism regarding the Wrights' accomplishment began to grow. Moreover, those who did attempt to recognize the Wrights' triumph published uninformed or erroneous descriptions of the brothers' airplane. Compounding the problem were an increasing number of equally erroneous accounts describing other experimenters' work and typically crediting them with far more than they actually accomplished.

Facing what they perceived as a growing public relations crisis, the Wrights began a campaign to set the public straight on what they had truly done, as well as to make clear how distinct their achievement was from the work of others. The articles and statements that Wilbur and Orville published through 1908 expressly had this goal behind them, particularly the *Century Magazine* piece from 1908. The first group of articles in part 1 of the book fall into this category.

In the late summer and fall of 1908, all doubts were dispelled regarding the claims of the Wrights. In August near Le Mans, France, Wilbur began a series of flights that bowled over the aviation community and instantly turned him into an international celebrity. Beginning slowly, with short flights, Wilbur ultimately performed aerial spectacles of extended duration, turning and circling with awe-inspiring grace and ease. (One prize-winning flight made in December lasted more than two hours.) At the same time, Orville was matching Wilbur's sensational performances with flights at Fort Myer, Virginia, where he was beginning flight trials to fulfill the requirements of a U.S. Army contract for the sale of aircraft to the U.S. government. Although these were the first official public flights by the brothers, the Wrights had in fact made such long-duration flights as early as 1905 near their home in Dayton, Ohio. With the 1908 demonstrations and further public flights in 1909, Wilbur and Orville Wright had established themselves as aviation's leading figures. There would be future attempts to dispute their stature as the fathers of flight, but by 1910 the Wright brothers had taken their place in the pantheon of great American inventors.

The Wrights formed a flying exhibition team and aircraft manufacturing company in late 1909, and they made a handsome profit from their invention. But money was not a primary motivation for the brothers, especially after 1910. What became increasingly important to them was protecting their reputation as the inventors of the airplane. They believed, and legitimately so, that they had done something quite original and fundamentally revolutionary, and had done so essentially alone. After this time, the articles and statements by the Wrights about their aeronautical work were largely intended to protect and nurture their priority of invention. After Wilbur's death in 1912, this became an even greater preoccupation for Orville. As the surviving member of the pair, Orville felt a powerful sense of obligation to husband the reputation that he and Wilbur together had built and to vigilantly guard it from detractors.

The most egregious and sustained attack on the Wrights' achievement came in the form of the Wright/Smithsonian controversy over the work of Samuel P. Langley, secretary of the Smithsonian Institution. In the 1890s and the first years of the twentieth century, Langley successfully flew a series of unpiloted, steam- and gasoline-powered models of substantial size. In 1903 he followed up these experiments with a full-sized, man-carrying version of his design, known as the *Great Aerodrome.* Two highly publicized attempts to fly the craft, the second just nine days before the Wrights' success at Kitty Hawk on December 17, resulted in disaster and made Langley the subject of vicious ridicule for the remaining three years of his life. In 1914, eight years after Langley's death and four years after the Wrights had been awarded the inaugural Langley Medal, given by the Smithsonian to honor aeronautical achievement (see document 7), the Smithsonian contracted with the Wrights' principal aeronautical rival in the United States, Glenn Curtiss, to rebuild the old Langley machine, in an effort to demonstrate its basic inherent airworthiness and, in so doing, to restore Langley's tarnished reputation. The aircraft, drastically modified by Curtiss, was coaxed into the air for a number of brief hops and was then returned to the Smithsonian. The Institution next restored the aircraft to its *failed* 1903 configuration and publicly displayed it with a misleading label that identified the Langley airplane as the world's first "capable of sustained free flight," in light of the fact that the original trials preceded those of the Wrights' powered Flyer. This specious characterization, to say the least, outraged Orville (Wilbur was deceased).

The actions of the Smithsonian undermined an already shaky relationship between the Institution and the Wrights; the brothers felt they had been slighted by the Smithsonian in some earlier dealings. The resulting feud lasted for decades. The defining moment came in 1928 when Orville sent the Wright Flyer to the Science Museum in London in a gesture of protest over the Smithsonian's persistent refusal to make an honest accounting of the Langley matter. Sending this powerful symbol of American ingenuity abroad, Orville believed, would bring public pressure on the situation. The deadlock was finally broken in 1942 when in its annual report the Smithsonian published details of the Langley modifications and an unequivocal statement crediting the Wright brothers with having invented the airplane. Vindicated, Orville set about bringing the Wright Flyer home for donation to and display in the Smithsonian museum.

Because of the war in Europe and other factors, the historic airplane did not arrive back in the United States until after Orville's death in 1948. In a grand ceremony on December 17 of that year, the Wrights' airplane took its place of honor in the Smithsonian's National Air Museum. Four documents containing Orville's published comments on the long controversy appear in this section of the book. For a detailed version of the story, see Tom D. Crouch, "Capable of Flight: The Saga of the 1903 Wright Airplane," or Crouch, *The Bishop's Boys: A Life of Wilbur and Orville Wright.*

As discussed in the introduction, the Wrights never produced their planned magnum opus on their world-changing invention. What we do have are the articles and published interviews and statements gathered here. As individual pieces, they leave many unanswered questions. But as a collection, they provide a good sense of what the Wrights believed was important about their work, of how they saw their place in history, and of the degree to which they felt this legacy needed fostering and protecting. Paired with the biographies and historical monographs, this material presents yet another avenue by which to gain insight into the endlessly fascinating Wilbur and Orville Wright.

1. W. Wright to the Smithsonian Institution, May 30, 1899, in Marvin W. McFarland, ed., *The Papers of Wilbur and Orville Wright,* 2 vols. (New York: McGraw-Hill, 1953), 1:4–5.
2. W. Wright to Octave Chanute, May 29, 1902, in ibid., 1:234–35.

1 • STATEMENT BY THE WRIGHT BROTHERS TO THE ASSOCIATED PRESS[1]

It had not been our intention to make any detailed public statement concerning the private trials of our power "Flyer" on the 17th of December last; but since the contents of a private telegram, announcing to our folks at home the success of our trials, was dishonestly communicated to the newspapermen at the Norfolk office, and led to the imposition upon the public, by persons who never saw the "Flyer" or its flights, of a fictitious story incorrect in almost every detail; and since this story together with several pretended interviews or statements, which were fakes pure and simple, have been very widely disseminated, we feel impelled to make some correction. The real facts were as follows:

On the morning of December 17th, between the hours of 10:30 o'clock and noon, four flights were made, two by Orville Wright and two by Wilbur Wright.[2] The starts were all made from a point on the level sand about two hundred feet west of our camp, which is located a quarter of a mile north of the Kill Devil sand hill, in Dare County, North Carolina. The wind at the time of the flights had a velocity of 27 miles an hour at ten o'clock, and 24 miles an hour at noon, as recorded by the anemometer at the Kitty Hawk Weather Bureau Station. The anemometer is thirty feet from the ground. Our own measurements, made with a hand anemometer at a height of four feet from the ground, showed a velocity of about 22 miles when the first flight was made, and 20½ miles at the time of the last one. The flights were directly against the wind. Each time the machine started from the level ground by its own power alone with no assistance from gravity, or any other source whatever. After a run of about 40 feet along a monorail track, which held the machine eight inches from the ground, it rose from the track and under the direction of the operator climbed upward on an inclined course till a height of eight or ten feet from the ground was reached, after which the course was kept as near horizontal as the wind gusts and the limited skill of the operator would permit. Into the teeth of a December gale the "Flyer" made its way forward with a speed of ten miles an hour over the ground and thirty to thirty-five miles an hour through the air. It had previously been decided that for reasons of personal safety these first trials should be made as close to the ground as possible. The height chosen was scarcely sufficient for maneuvering in so gusty a wind and with no previous acquaintance with the conduct of the machine and its controlling mechanisms. Consequently the first flight was short. The succeeding flights rapidly increased in length and at the fourth trial a flight of fifty-nine seconds was made, in which time the machine flew a little more than a half mile through the air, and a distance of 852 feet over the ground. The landing was due to a slight error of judgment on the part of the aviator. After passing over a little hummock of sand, in attempting to bring the machine down to the desired height, the operator turned the rudder too far; and the machine turned downward more quickly than had been expected. The reverse movement of the rudder was a fraction of a second too late to prevent the machine from touching the ground and thus ending the flight. The whole occurrence occupied little, if any, more than one second of time.

Only those who are acquainted with practical aeronautics can appreciate the difficulties of attempting the first trials of a flying machine in a twenty-five mile gale. As winter was already well set in, we should have postponed our trials to a more favorable season, but for the fact that we were determined, before returning home, to know whether the machine possessed sufficient power to fly, sufficient strength to withstand the shocks of landings, and sufficient capacity of control to make flight safe in boisterous winds, as well as in calm air. When these points had been definitely established, we at once packed our goods and returned home, knowing that the age of the flying machine had come, at last.

From the beginning we have employed entirely new principles of control; and as all the experiments have been conducted at our own expense without assistance from any individual or institution, we do not feel ready at present to give out any pictures or detailed description of the machine.

---

1. This statement was filed on January 5, 1904, and appeared in numerous newspapers on January 6. Only the *Dayton Press*, however, included the opening paragraph.
2. The precise time of takeoff for the first flight, with Orville at the controls, was 10:35 A.M.

2 • STATEMENT TO THE AERO CLUB OF AMERICA[1]

Wilbur and Orville Wright

March 12, 1906

The following statement has been made to the Aero Club of America:

Though America, through the labors of Professor Langley, Mr. Chanute, and others, had acquired not less than ten years ago the recognized leadership in that branch of aeronautics which pertains to bird-like flight, it has not heretofore been possible for American workers to present a summary of each year's experiments to a society of their own country devoted exclusively to the promotion of aeronautical studies and sports. It is with great pleasure, therefore, that we now find ourselves able to make a report to such a society.

Previous to the year 1905 we had experimented at Kitty Hawk, North Carolina, with man-carrying gliding machines in the years 1900, 1901, 1902 and 1903; and with a man-carrying motor flyer, which, on the 17th day of December, 1903, sustained itself in the air for 59 seconds, during which time it advanced against a 20-mile wind a distance of 852 feet. Flights to the number of more than 100 had also been made at Dayton, Ohio, in 1904, with a second motor flyer. Of these flights, a complete circle made for the first time on the 20th of September, and two flights of 3 miles each made on the 9th of November and the 1st of December, respectively, were the more notable performances.

The object of the 1905 experiments was to determine the cause and discover remedies for several obscure and somewhat rare difficulties which had been encountered in some of the 1904 flights, and which it was necessary to overcome before it would be safe to employ flyers for practical purposes.[2] The experiments were made in a swampy meadow about 8 miles east of Dayton, Ohio,[3] and continued from June until the early days of October, when the impossibility of longer maintaining privacy necessitated their discontinuance.

Owing to frequent experimental changes in the machine and the resulting differences in its management, the earlier flights were short; but, towards the middle of September means of correcting the obscure troubles were found, and the flyer was at last brought under satisfactory control. From this time forward almost every flight established a new record. In the following schedule the duration, distance and cause of stopping are given for some of the later flights.

Date.	*Distance.*	*Time.*	*Cause of Stopping.*
Sept. 26	17,961 meters (11 1/8 miles)	18 min. 9 sec.	Exhaustion of fuel.
Sept. 29	19,570 meters (12 miles)	19 min. 55 sec.	Exhaustion of fuel.
Sept. 30	....	17 min. 15 sec.	Hot bearing.
Oct. 3	24,535 meters (15 1/4 miles)	25 min. 5 sec.	Hot bearing.
Oct. 4	33,456 meters (20 3/4 miles)	33 min. 17 sec.	Hot bearing.
Oct. 5	38,956 meters (24 1/5 miles)	38 min. 3 sec.	Exhaustion of fuel.

It will be seen that an average speed of a little more than 38 miles an hour was maintained in the last flight. All of the flights were made over a circular course of about three-fourths of a mile to the lap, which reduced the speed somewhat. The machine increased its velocity on the straight parts of the course and slowed down on the curves. It is believed that in straight flight the normal speed is more than 40 miles an hour. In the earlier of the flights named above less than 6 pounds of gasoline was carried. In the later ones a tank was fitted large enough to hold fuel for an hour, but by oversight it was not completely filled before the flight of October 5.

In the past three years a total of 160 flights have been made with our motor-driven flyers, and a total distance of almost exactly 160 miles covered, an average of a mile to each flight, but until the machine had received its final improvements the flights were mostly short, as is evidenced by the fact that the flight of October 5th was longer than the 105 flights of the year 1904 together.

The lengths of the flights were measured by a Richard anemometer which was attached to the machine. The records were found to agree closely with the distances measured over the ground when the flights were made in calm air over a straight course; but when the flights were made in circles a close comparison was impossible because it was not practicable to accurately trace the course over the ground. In the flight of October 5th a total of 29.7 circuits of the field was made. The times here taken with stop-watches. In operating the machine it has been our custom for many years to alternate in making flights, and such care has been observed that neither of us has suffered any serious injury, though in the earlier flights our ignorance and the inadequacy of the means of control made the work exceedingly dangerous.

The 1905 flyer had a total weight of about 925 pounds, including the operator, and was of such substantial construction as to be able to make landings at high speed without being strained or broken. From the beginning the prime object was to devise a machine of practical utility, rather than a useless and extravagant toy. For this reason extreme lightness of construction has always been resolutely rejected. On the other hand, every effort has been made to increase the scientific efficiency of the wings and screws in order that even heavily built machines may be carried with a moderate expenditure of power. The favorable results which have been obtained have been due to improvements in flying quality resulting from more scientific design and to improved methods of balancing and steering. The motor and machinery possess no extraordinary qualities. The best dividends on the labor invested have invariably come from seeking more knowledge rather than more power.

Very respectfully,
(Signed) Orville Wright
(Signed) Wilbur Wright

Addenda

In view of the fact that all of the flights which have been mentioned were made in private, it is proper that the names of persons who witnessed one or more of them should be given. We therefore name:

Mr. E. W. Ellis, Assistant Auditor of the City of Dayton.
Mr. Torrence Huffman, President of the Fourth National Bank.[4]
Mr. C. S. Billman, Secretary of the West Side Building Association.
Mr. Henry Webbert.
Mr. W. H. Shank.
Mr. William Fouts.
Mr. Frank Hamburger.
Mr. Charles Webbert.[5]
Mr. Howard M. Myers.
Mr. Bernard H. Lambers.
Mr. William Webbert.
Mr. Reuben Schindler.
Mr. William Weber.
All of Dayton, Ohio.
Mr. O. F. Jamieson, East Germantown, Ind.
Mr. Theodore Waddell, Census Department, Washington, D.C.
Mr. David Beard, Osborn, Ohio.
Mr. Amos Stauffer, Osborn, Ohio.

---

1. This statement was published as a circular by the Aero Club of America on March 12, 1906. An original copy is located in the Wright brothers biographical file, Archives Division, National Air and Space Museum, Smithsonian Institution, Washington, D.C.
2. These "difficulties" primarily concerned continued pitch instability problems of the type experienced with the 1903 Flyer at Kitty Hawk. The elevator control on the first powered airplane was very sensitive, making it nearly impossible for Wilbur and Orville to maintain steady, level flight. The Wrights attempted to smooth out the erratic up-and-down oscillation of the aircraft in pitch by adding ballast to the front of the machine and by locating the forward elevator assembly farther out in front of the wings. These modifications, made during 1904 and 1905, did not completely cure the stability problem. But they did reduce the severity of the problem to the point where the aircraft could be flown with reasonable control and consistency for indefinite periods.
3. The field was known locally as Huffman Prairie.
4. Torrence Huffman was the owner of the field that the Wrights used for their 1904 and 1905 flights. He charged the brothers no rent or fee but merely asked that they drive the grazing cows and horses outside the fence before doing any flying.
5. Charles Webbert was the Wrights' landlord at their bicycle shop on 1127 West Third Street in Dayton, Ohio, the site where the majority of the design and fabrication of their aircraft took place.

3 • OUR RECENT EXPERIMENTS IN NORTH CAROLINA[1]

Wilbur and Orville Wright

For those readers whose acquaintance with aeronautics is limited to the last few years, this account of our recent experiments in North Carolina is prefaced with a short account of our previous work.

Up to the year 1900, our interest in the subject had been confined mostly to reading and theorizing. But in the Fall of that year we began out-door experiments on the coast of North Carolina, near Kitty Hawk. Here we attempted, at first, to fly our machine as a kite; but later made some short glides on the slopes of the Kill Devil Hill.

The gliding experiments were continued in the years 1901 and 1902. A number of flights were made of over a minute's duration. The rate of descent was reduced to an angle of 7 degrees.

The account of these experiments given by Mr. Chanute in talks before scientific societies in Europe, and in articles contributed to technical papers, created some interest. A number of persons took up experiments in France with machines built on the drawings and descriptions furnished in Mr. Chanute's articles. Among these were the well-known aviators Archdeacon, Esnault-Pelterie and the Voisin Brothers, builders of the Farman and Delagrange aeroplanes. Captain Ferber had already been experimenting for some months with what he termed a "Chanute-Wright" machine.[2]

Schedule of Flights during May, 1908.

Date	*No. Passengers*	*Distance*	*Time*	*Velocity of Wind*
May 6	One	1008 feet	0:22 s.	8 to 12 miles an hour
May 8	One	956 feet	0:31 s.	20 miles an hour
	One	2186 feet	0:59½	16 miles an hour
May 11	One	0.78 miles	1:11	8 miles an hour
	One	1.80 miles	2:28	No record
	One	1.55 miles	2:11	No record
May 13	One	0.60 miles	0:51 s.	No record
	One	1.85 miles	2:44	16 to 18 miles
	One	....	2:40	14 to 16 miles
	One	2.40 miles	3:20	14 to 16 miles
May 14	Two	0.45 miles	0:29	No record
	Two	2.50 miles	3:40	18 to 19 miles
	One	5.00 miles	7:20	No record (about 15 miles)

In 1903 we added a motor to our machine, and on the 17th of December made four flights with it. The longest of these covered a distance of 852 feet in 59 seconds against a 20 mile wind.

In 1904 we continued the experiments on a new ground near Dayton, Ohio. The longest flights of that year were two of five minutes each, covering distances of 3 miles.

Experiments were resumed in the summer of 1905 at our grounds near Dayton. Five flights were made in September and October of that year, covering distances of from 11 to 24 miles. The account of these flights, published in l'Aerophile, of Paris, in December, 1905, created a sensation in France, and many more persons took up experiments with enthusiasm. Among these were Santos-Dumont, Delagrange, and later, Farman.[3] The news of these flights was received by the daily press as a "clap of thunder out of a clear sky," and some discussion arose as to the truthfulness of the report. A number of persons from France, England and Germany, as well as from different parts of our own country, made trips to Dayton to make personal investigation of the matter. Though many came incredulous, not one returned in doubt.

Our recent experiments were conducted upon the grounds, near Kitty Hawk, North Carolina, where we experimented in 1900, 1901, 1902 and 1903. The flyer used in these experiments was the one with which we made the flights in September and October, 1905, near Dayton, Ohio. The means of control remained the same as in those flights, but the position of the controlling levers and their directions of motion had to be altered in order to permit the operator to take a sitting position. A seat for a passenger was added. The engine used in 1905 was replaced by a later model, one of which was exhibited at the Aero Club Show at New York in 1906.[4] Larger gasoline reservoirs and radiators were also installed.

We undertook these experiments in order to test the carrying capacity of the machine, and to ascertain its speed with two men on board, as well as to regain familiarity in the handling of the machine after a period of almost three years without practice. No attempt was made to beat our record of distance, made in 1905.[5]

The first flights were made over a straight course against winds of 8 to 18 miles an hour. The equilibrium of the machine proving satisfactory in these flights, we began to describe circles, returning and landing at the starting point. These flights covered distances of from 1 to 2½ miles.

On the 14th of May a passenger was taken on board.[6] In the first flight the motor was shut off at the end of 29 seconds to prevent running into a sand hill, towards which the machine was started. But in a second, the machine carried the passenger and operator for a flight of three minutes and forty seconds, making a complete circle, and landing near the starting point. The wind, measured at a height of six feet from the ground while the machine was in flight, had a velocity of 18 to 19 miles an hour. The distance traveled through the air, as registered by an anemometer attached to the machine, was a little over four kilometers (2.50 miles), which indicated a speed of about 41 miles an hour. A speed as high as 44 miles an hour was reached in an earlier flight, with only one man on board.

In a later flight, on May 14th, a false movement of a controlling lever caused the machine to plunge into the ground when traveling with the wind at a speed of about 55 miles an hour. The repairs of the machine would have necessitated a delay of five or six days, and as that would have consumed more time than we had allowed for the experiments, we discontinued them for the present.

---

1. *Aeronautics*, June 1908, 4–6.
2. Ernest Archdeacon was not himself a pilot, although he was a leading promoter of aviation in France. A wealthy lawyer and a dominant voice in the Aéro-Club de France, Archdeacon contributed to a number of major financial prizes for aviation accomplishments in the pioneer era.

   Robert Esnault-Pelterie began his aeronautical work building biplane gliders based on secondhand information about the Wrights' aircraft. Since his knowledge of the brothers' design was incomplete, performance of his gliders was poor, and this led him to conclude erroneously that the Wrights' claims of success were inflated. Esnault-Pelterie later built and flew successful aircraft of his own design. He was even more successful as a designer and manufacturer of aircraft engines. He was also one of the earliest experimenters with rocket fuels and reaction motors, and he authored several visionary papers on space travel.

   Charles and Gabriel Voisin were among Europe's earliest successful aviators. They were flying gliders in 1904 and 1905, and by 1907 they were manufacturing powered aircraft for sale. Most of the prominent aviators in 1908 and 1909 were flying Voisin biplanes.
3. For information on Alberto Santos-Dumont, see document 38, note 7.

   Léon Delagrange, a noted Paris sculptor, became interested in aviation in 1905 and acquired his first airplane, a Voisin biplane, in 1907. On July 8, 1908, in Turin, Italy, he took one of his art students, Thérèse Peltier, up for a brief flight, making Peltier the first women to fly as a passenger in an airplane. Delagrange was one of Europe's most celebrated pilots at the time of his death in a crash in January 1910.

   Henri Farman was the son of an affluent English newspaper correspondent based in Paris. While studying painting at the École des Beaux Arts, he became interested in racing-bicycles, motorcycles, and automobiles, and he took up flying in 1907. He purchased a Voisin biplane, and on January 13, 1908, won a 50,000-franc prize for the first flight of a one-kilometer circuit in Europe. (The Wrights had flown many times this distance in 1905, including one circling flight of twenty-four miles, but had not as yet flown publicly.)
4. This engine, a vertical four-cylinder engine of 30–40 horsepower, became the standard power plant in Wright aircraft from 1908 until 1912, when the Wright six-cylinder motor was introduced.
5. The record was 24½ miles in 39 minutes on October 5, 1905.
6. The passenger was Charles W. Furnas, the Wrights' mechanic. This was the first airplane flight ever to carry a passenger.

4 • OUR AEROPLANE TESTS AT KITTY HAWK[1]

Wilbur and Orville Wright

The spring of 1908 found us with contracts on hand, the conditions of which required performance not entirely met by our flights in 1905. The best flight of that year, on October 5, covered a distance of a little over 24 miles, at a speed of 38 miles an hour with only one person on board. The contracts call for a machine with a speed of 40 miles an hour, and capable of carrying two men and fuel supplies sufficient for a flight of 125 miles.[2] Our recent experiments were undertaken with a view of testing our flyer in these particulars, and to enable us to become familiar with the use of the controlling levers as arranged in our latest machines.

After tedious delays in repairing our old camp at Kill Devil Hills, near Kitty Hawk, N.C., we were ready for experiments early in May. We used the same machine with which we made flights near Dayton, Ohio in 1905; but several modifications were instituted to allow the operator to assume a sitting position, and to provide a seat for a passenger. These changes necessitated an entirely new arrangement of the controlling levers. Two of them were given motions so different from those used in 1905 that their operation had to be completely relearned.

We preferred to make the first flights, with the new arrangement of controlling levers, in calm air; but our few weeks' stay had convinced us that in the spring time we could not expect any practice at that place in winds of less than 8 to 10 miles an hour, and that the greater part of our experiments must be made in winds of 15 to 20 miles.

The engine used in 1905 was replaced by a motor of a later model, one of which was exhibited at the New York Aero Club show in 1906.[3] The cylinders are four in number, water cooled, of 4¼-inch bore and 4-inch stroke. An erroneous statement, that the motor was of French manufacture, has appeared in some papers. This is, no doubt, due to the fact that we are having duplicates of this motor built by a well-known Paris firm, for use in European countries.

The longer flights this year were measured by a Richard anemometer attached to the machine in the same manner as in 1905. Except in the first few flights, made over regular courses, it was found impracticable to secure accurate measurements in any other way. These records show the distances traveled through the air. The measurements of the velocity of the wind were made at a height of six feet from the ground at the starting point, and were usually taken during the time the machine was in flight.

The first flight was made on the 6th of May, in a wind varying from 8 to 12 miles an hour. After covering a distance of 1,008 feet measured over the ground, the operator brought the machine down to avoid passing over a patch of ground covered with ragged stumps of trees.

In the morning of May 8 several short flights were made in winds of 9 to 18 miles an hour. In the afternoon the machine flew 956 feet in 31 seconds, against a wind of a little over 20 miles an hour; and later, at a distance of 2,186 feet in 59½ seconds, against a wind of 16 miles. These distances were measured over the ground.

On May 11 the Richard anemometer was attached to the machine. From this time on the flights were not over definite courses, and the distances traveled were measured by this instrument. Three flights were made on this day in winds varying from 6 to 9 miles. The distances were: 0.78 miles, 1.80 miles, and 1.55 miles.

On May 13 four flights were made. The anemometer on the machine registered a distance of 0.60 mile in the first; 1.85 miles in the second; no distance measurement in the third—time, 2 minutes and 40 seconds; and 2.40 miles in the fourth. The velocity of the wind was 16 to 18 miles an hour.

On May 14 Mr. C. W. Furnas, of Dayton, Ohio, who was assisting in the experiments, was taken as a passenger.[4] In the first trial, a turn was not commenced soon enough, and to avoid a sand hill, toward which the start was made, the power was shut off. The second flight, with passenger on board, was in a wind of 18 to 19 miles an hour. The anemometer recorded a distance traveled through the air of a little over 4 kilometers (2.50 miles) in 3 minutes and 40 seconds.

The last flight was made with operator only on board. After a flight of 7 minutes and 29 seconds, while busied in making a turn, the operator inadvertently moved the fore-and-aft controlling lever. The machine plunged into the ground, while traveling with the wind, at a speed of approximately 55 miles an hour. The anemometer showed a distance of a little over 8 kilometers (5 miles).

The frame supporting the front rudder was broken; the central section of the upper main bearing surface was broken and torn; but beyond this, the main surfaces and rudders received but slight damage. The motor, radiators, and machinery came through uninjured. Repairs could have been made in a week's time, but the time allowed for these experiments having elapsed, we were compelled to close experiments for the present.

These flights were witnessed by the men of the Kill Devil life-saving station, to whom we were indebted for much assistance, by a number of newspaper men, and by some other persons who were hunting and fishing in the vicinity.

The machine showed a speed of nearly 41 miles an hour with two men on board, and a little over 44 miles with one man. The control was very satisfactory in winds of 15 to 20 miles an hour, and there was no distinguishable difference in control when traveling with, against, or across the wind.

---

1. *Scientific American*, June 13, 1908, 423.
2. The contracts referred to were with the U.S. Army Signal Corps for the Wrights' first sale of an airplane. To complete the transaction, the Wrights had to meet certain performance standards specified by the Signal Corps. Flight trials to demonstrate that the Wright airplane could meet these performance specifications were scheduled to begin in September 1908 at Fort Myer, Virginia, near Washington, D.C. In the spring of 1908, the Wrights modified their 1905 powered Flyer and took it to Kitty Hawk to prepare for the trials. They had not flown at all in two-and-a-half years. The trials were interrupted on September 17, 1908, when Orville Wright crashed while carrying the army's representa-

tive, Lieutenant Thomas E. Selfridge. Orville was severely injured, and Selfridge was killed. The Wrights returned to Fort Myer with a new airplane in 1909 and completed the trials. Their airplane exceeded the Signal Corps' minimum performance requirements, the contract was fulfilled, and the Wrights were paid $30,000 for their airplane.

3. See document 3, note 2.
4. See document 3, note 4.

5 • THE WRIGHT BROTHERS' AËROPLANE[1]

Wilbur and Orville Wright[2]

The article which follows is the first popular account of their experiments prepared by the inventors. Their accounts heretofore have been brief statements of bare accomplishments, without explanation of the manner in which results were attained. The article will be found of special interest, in view of the fact that they have contracted to deliver to the United States Government a complete machine, the trials of which are expected to take place about the time of the appearance of this number of *The Century*.—The Editor

Though the subject of aerial navigation is generally considered new, it has occupied the minds of men more or less from the earliest ages. Our personal interest in it dates from our childhood days. Late in the autumn of 1878, our father came into the house one evening with some object partly concealed in his hands, and before we could see what it was, he tossed it into the air. Instead of falling to the floor, as we expected, it flew across the room till it struck the ceiling, where it fluttered awhile, and finally sank to the floor. It was a little toy, known to scientists as a "hélicoptère," but which we, with sublime disregard for science, at once dubbed a "bat." It was a light frame of cork and bamboo, covered with paper, which formed two screws, driven in opposite directions by rubber bands under torsion. A toy so delicate lasted only a short time in the hands of small boys, but its memory was abiding.[3]

Several years later we began building these hélicoptères for ourselves, making each one larger than that preceding. But, to our astonishment, we found that the larger the "bat," the less it flew. We did not know that a machine having only twice the linear dimensions of another would require eight times the power. We finally became discouraged, and returned to kite-flying, a sport to which we had devoted so much attention that we were regarded as experts. But as we became older, we had to give up this fascinating sport as unbecoming to boys of our ages.

It was not till the news of the sad death of Lilienthal reached America in the summer of 1896 that we again gave more than passing attention to the subject of flying.[4] We then studied with great interest Chanute's "Progress in Flying Machines," Langley's "Experiments in Aërodynamics," the "Aëronautical Annuals" of 1895, 1896, and 1897,[5] and pamphlets published by the Smithsonian Institution, especially articles by Lilienthal and extracts from Mouillard's "Empire of the Air." The larger works gave us a good understanding of the nature of the flying problem, and the difficulties in past attempts to solve it, while Mouillard and Lilienthal, the great missionaries of the flying cause, infected us with their own unquenchable enthusiasm, and transformed idle curiosity into the active zeal of workers.[6]

In the field of aviation there were two schools. The first, represented by such men as Professor Langley and Sir Hiram Maxim,[7] gave chief attention to power flight; the second, represented by Lilienthal, Mouillard, and Chanute, to soaring flight. Our sympathies were with the latter school, partly from impatience at the wasteful extravagance of mounting delicate and costly machinery on wings which no one knew how to manage, and partly, no doubt, from the extraordinary charm and enthusiasm with which the apostles of soaring flight set forth the beauties of sailing through the air on fixed wings, deriving the motive power from the wind itself.

The balancing of a flyer may seem, at first thought, to be a very simple matter, yet almost every experimenter had found in this the one point which he could not satisfactorily master. Many different methods were tried. Some experimenters placed the center of gravity far below the wings, in the belief that the weight would naturally seek to remain at the lowest point. It was true, that, like the pendulum, it tended to seek the lowest point; but also, like the pendulum, it tended to oscillate in a manner destructive of all stability. A more satisfactory system, especially for lateral balance, was that of arranging the wings in the shape of a broad V, to form a dihedral angle, with the center low and wing-tips elevated. In theory this was an automatic system, but in practice it had two serious defects: first, it tended to keep the machine oscillating; and, second, its usefulness was restricted to calm air.

In a slightly modified form the same system was applied to the fore-and-aft balance. The main aëroplane was set at a positive angle, and a horizontal tail at a negative angle, while the center of gravity was placed far forward. As in the case of lateral control, there was a tendency to constant undulation, and the very forces which caused a restoration of balance in calms, caused a disturbance of the balance in winds. Notwithstanding the known limitations of this principle, it had been embodied in almost every prominent flying-machine which had been built.

After considering the practical effect of the dihedral principle, we reached the conclusion that a flyer founded upon it might be of interest from a scientific point of view, but could be of no value in a practical way. We therefore resolved to try a fundamentally different principle. We would arrange the machine so that it would not tend to right itself. We would make it as inert as possible to the effects of change of direction or speed, and thus reduce the effects of wind-gusts to a minimum. We would do this in the fore-and-aft stability by giving the aëroplanes a peculiar shape;

and in the lateral balance, by arching the surfaces from tip to tip, just the reverse of what our predecessors had done. Then by some suitable contrivance, actuated by the operator, forces should be brought into play to regulate the balance.

Lilienthal and Chanute had guided and balanced their machines by shifting the weight of the operator's body. But this method seemed to us incapable of expansion to meet large conditions, because the weight to be moved and the distance of possible motion were limited, while the disturbing forces steadily increased, both with wing area and with wind velocity. In order to meet the needs of large machines, we wished to employ some system whereby the operator could vary at will the inclination of different parts of the wings, and thus obtain from the wind forces to restore the balance which the wind itself had disturbed. This could easily be done by using wings capable of being warped, and by supplementary adjustable surfaces in the shape of rudders. As the forces obtainable for control would necessarily increase in the same ratio as the disturbing forces, the method seemed capable of expansion to an almost unlimited extent. A happy device was discovered whereby the apparently rigid system of superposed surfaces, invented by Wenham,[8] and improved by Stringfellow[9] and Chanute, could be warped in a most unexpected way, so that the aëroplanes could be presented on the right and left sides at different angles to the wind. This, with an adjustable, horizontal front rudder, formed the main feature of our first glider.

The period from 1885 to 1900 was one of unexampled activity in aëronautics, and for a time there was high hope that the age of flying was at hand. But Maxim, after spending $100,000, abandoned the work; the Ader machine,[10] built at the expense of the French Government, was a failure; Lilienthal and Pilcher[11] were killed in experiments; and Chanute and many others, from one cause or another, had relaxed their efforts, though it subsequently became known that Professor Langley was still secretly at work on a machine for the United States Government. The public, discouraged by the failures and tragedies just witnessed, considered flight beyond the reach of man, and classed its adherents with the inventors of perpetual motion.

We began our active experiments at the close of this period, in October, 1900, at Kitty Hawk, North Carolina. Our machine was designed to be flown as a kite, with a man on board, in winds of from fifteen to twenty miles an hour. But, upon trial, it was found that much stronger winds were required to lift it. Suitable winds not being plentiful, we found it necessary, in order to test the new balancing system, to fly the machine as a kite without a man on board, operating the levers through cords from the ground. This did not give the practice anticipated, but it inspired confidence in the new system of balance.

In the summer of 1901 we became personally acquainted with Mr. Chanute.[12] When he learned that we were interested in flying as a sport, and not with any expectation of recovering the money we were expending on it, he gave us much encouragement. At our invitation, he spent several weeks with us at our camp at Kill Devil Hill, four miles south of Kitty Hawk, during our experiments of that and the two succeeding years. He also witnessed one flight of the power machine near Dayton, Ohio, in October, 1904.

The machine of 1901 was built with the shape of surface used by Lilienthal, curved from front to rear like the segment of a parabola, with a curvature $1/12$ the depth of its cord; but to make doubly sure that it would have sufficient lifting capacity when flown as a kite in fifteen- or twenty-mile winds, we increased the area from 165 square feet, used in 1900, to 308 square feet—a size much larger than Lilienthal, Pilcher, or Chanute had deemed safe. Upon trial, however, the lifting capacity again fell very far short of calculation, so that the idea of securing practice while flying as a kite, had to be abandoned. Mr. Chanute, who witnessed the experiments, told us that the trouble was not due to poor construction of the machine. We saw only one other explanation—that the tables of air-pressures in general use were incorrect.

We then turned to gliding—coasting down hill on the air—as the only method of getting the desired practice in balancing a machine. After a few minutes' practice we were able to make glides of over 300 feet, and in a few days were safely operating in twenty-seven-mile[13] winds. In these experiments we met with several unexpected phenomena. We found that, contrary to the teachings of the books, the center of pressure on a curved surface traveled backward when the surface was inclined, at small angles, more and more edgewise to the wind. We also discovered that in free flight, when the wind on one side of the machine was presented to the wind at a greater angle than the one on the other side, the wing with the greater angle descended, and the machine turned in a direction just the reverse of what we were led to expect when flying the machine as a kite. The larger angle gave more resistance to forward motion, and reduced the speed of the wing on that side. The decrease in speed more than counterbalanced the effect of the larger angle. The addition of a fixed vertical vane in the rear increased the trouble, and made the machine absolutely dangerous. It was some time before a remedy was discovered. This consisted of movable rudders working in conjunction with the twisting of the wings. The details of this arrangement are given in our patent specifications, published several years ago.[14]

The experiments of 1901 were far from encouraging. Although Mr. Chanute assured us that, both in control and in weight carried per horse-power, the results obtained were better than those of any of our predecessors, yet we saw that the calculations upon which all flying-machines had been based were unreliable, and that all were simply groping in the dark. Having set out with absolute faith in the existing scientific data, we were driven to doubt one thing after another, till finally, after two years of experiment, we cast it all aside, and decided to rely entirely upon our own investigations. Truth and error were everywhere so intimately mixed as to be undistinguishable. Nevertheless, the time expended in preliminary study of books was not misspent, for they gave us a good general understanding of the subject, and enabled us at the outset to avoid effort in many directions in which results would have been hopeless.

The standard for measurements of wind-pressures is the force produced by a current of air of one mile per hour velocity striking square against a plane of one square-foot area. The practical difficulties of obtaining an exact measurement of this force have been great. The measurements by different recognized authorities vary fifty per cent. When this simplest of measurements presents so great difficulties, what shall be said of the troubles encountered by those who attempt to find the pressure at each angle as the plane is inclined more and more edgewise to the wind? In the eighteenth century the French Academy prepared tables giving such information, and at a later date the Aëronautical Society of Great Britain made similar experiments. Many persons likewise published measurements and formulas; but the results were so discordant that Professor Langley undertook a new series of measurements, the results of which form the basis of his celebrated work, "Experiments in Aërodynamics." Yet a critical examination of the data upon which he based his conclusions as to the pressure at small angles shows results so various as to make many of his conclusions little better than guess-work.

To work intelligently, one needs to know the effects of a multitude of variations that could be incorporated in the surfaces of flying-machines. The pressures on squares are different from those on rectangles, circles, triangles, or ellipses; arched surfaces differ from planes, and vary among themselves according to the depth of curvature; true arcs differ from parabolas, and the latter differ among themselves; thick surfaces differ from thin, and surfaces thicker in one place than another vary in pressure when positions of maximum thickness are different; some surfaces are most efficient at one angle, others at other angles. The shape of the edge also makes a difference, so that thousands of combinations are possible in so simple a thing as a wing.

We had taken up aëronautics merely as a sport. We reluctantly entered upon the scientific side of it. But we soon found the work so fascinating that we were drawn into it deeper and deeper. Two testing-machines were built, which we believed would avoid the errors to which the measurements of others had been subject. After making preliminary measurements on a great number of different-shaped surfaces, to secure a general understanding of the subject, we began systematic measurements of standard surfaces, so varied in design as to bring out the underlying causes of differences noted in their pressures. Measurements were tabulated on nearly fifty of these at all angles from zero to 45 degrees, at intervals of 2½ degrees.

Measurements were also secured showing the effects on each other when surfaces were superposed, or when they follow one another.

Some strange results were obtained. One surface, with a heavy roll at the front edge, showed the same lift for all angles from 7½ to 45 degrees. A square plane, contrary to the measurements of all our predecessors, gave a greater pressure at 30 degrees than at 45 degrees. This seemed so anomalous that we were almost ready to doubt our own measurements, when a simple test was suggested. A weather-vane, with two planes attached to the pointer at an angle of 80 degrees with each other, was made. According to our tables, such a vane would be in unstable equilibrium when pointing directly into the wind; for if by chance the wind should happen to strike one plane at 39 degrees and the other at 41 degrees, the plane with the smaller angle would have the greater pressure, and the pointer would be turned still farther out of the course of the wind until the two vanes again secured equal pressures, which would be at approximately 30 and 50 degrees. But the vane performed in this very manner. Further corroboration of the tables was obtained in experiments with a new glider at Kill Devil Hill the next season.[15]

In September and October, 1902, nearly one thousand gliding flights were made, several of which covered distances of over 600 feet. Some, made against a wind of thirty-six miles an hour, gave proof of the effectiveness of the devices for control. With this machine, in the autumn of 1903, we made a number of flights in which we remained in the air for over a minute, often soaring for a considerable time in one spot, without any descent at all. Little wonder that our unscientific assistant should think the only thing needed to keep it indefinitely in the air would be a coat of feathers to make it light!

With accurate data for making calculations, and a system of balance effective in winds as well as in calms, we were now in position, we thought, to build a successful power-flyer. The first designs provided for a total weight of 600 pounds, including the operator and an eight horse-power motor. But, upon completion, the motor gave more power than had been estimated, and this allowed 150 pounds to be added for strengthening the wings and other parts.

Our tables made the designing of the wings an easy matter; and as screw-propellers are simply wings traveling in a spiral course, we anticipated no trouble from this source. We had thought of getting the theory of the screw-propeller from the marine engineers, and then, by applying our tables of air-pressures to their formulas of designing air-propellers suitable for our purpose. But so far as we could learn, the marine engineers possessed only empirical formulas, and the exact action of the screw-propeller, after a century of use, was still very obscure. As we were not in a position to undertake a long series of practical experiments to discover a propeller suitable for our machine, it seemed necessary to obtain such a thorough understanding of the theory of its reactions as would enable us to design them from calculation alone. What at first seemed a simple problem became more complex the longer we studied it. With the machine moving forward, the air flying backward, the propellers turning sidewise, and nothing standing still, it seemed impossible to find a starting-point from which to trace the various simultaneous reactions. Contemplation of it was confusing. After long arguments, we often found ourselves in the ludicrous position of each having been converted to the other's side, with no more agreement than when the discussion began.

It was not till several months had passed, and every phase of the problem had been thrashed over and over, that the various reactions began to untangle themselves. When once a clear understanding had been obtained, there was no difficulty in designing suitable propellers, with proper diameter, pitch, and area of blade, to meet the requirements of the flyer. High efficiency in a screw-propeller is not dependent upon any particular or peculiar shape, and there is no such thing as a "best" screw. A propeller giving a high dynamic efficiency when used upon one machine, may be almost worthless when used upon another. The propeller should in every case be designed to meet the particular conditions of the machine to which it is to be applied. Our first propellers, built entirely from calculation, gave in useful work 66 per cent. of the power expended. This was about one third more than had been secured by Maxim or Langley.[16]

The first flights with the power-machine were made on the 17th of December, 1903. Only five persons besides ourselves were present. These were Messrs. John T. Daniels, W. S. Dough, and A. D. Etheridge of the Kill Devil Life Saving Station; Mr. W. C. Brinkley of Manteo, and Mr. John Ward[17] of Naghead [Nags Head]. Although a general invitation had been extended to people living within five or six miles, not many were willing to face the rigors of a cold December wind in order to see, as they no doubt thought, another flying-machine not fly. The first flight lasted only twelve seconds, a flight very modest compared with that of birds, but it was, nevertheless, the first in the history of the world in which a machine carrying a man had raised itself by its own power into the air in free flight, had sailed forward on a level course without reduction of speed, and had finally landed without being wrecked. The second and third flights were a little longer, and the fourth lasted fifty-nine seconds, covering a distance of 852 feet over the ground against a twenty-mile wind.

After the last flight, the machine was carried back to camp and set down in what was thought to be a safe place. But a few minutes later, while we were engaged in conversation about the flights, a sudden gust of wind struck the machine, and started to turn it over. All made a rush to stop it, but we were too late. Mr. Daniels, a giant in stature and strength, was lifted off his feet, and falling inside, between the surfaces, was shaken about like a rattle in a box as the machine rolled over and over. He finally fell out upon the sand with nothing worse than painful bruises, but the damage to the machine caused a discontinuance of experiments.[18]

In the spring of 1904, through the kindness of Mr. Torrence Huffman of Dayton, Ohio, we were permitted to erect a shed, and to continue experiments, on what is known as the Huffman Prairie, at Simms Station, eight miles east of Dayton. The new machine was heavier and stronger, but similar to the one flown at Kill Devil Hill. When it was ready for its first trial, every newspaper in Dayton was notified, and about a dozen representatives of the press were present. Our only request was that no pictures be taken, and that the reports be unsensational, so as not to attract crowds to our experiment-grounds. There were probably fifty persons altogether on the ground. When preparations had been completed, a wind of only three or four miles was blowing,—insufficient for starting on so short a track,—but since many had come a long way to see the machine in action, an attempt was made. To add to the other difficulty, the engine refused to work properly. The machine, after running the length of the track, slid off the end without rising into the air at all. Several of the newspaper men returned the next day, but were again disappointed. The engine performed badly, and after a glide of only sixty feet, the machine came to the ground. Further trial was postponed till the motor could be put in better running condition. The reporters had now, no doubt, lost confidence in the machine, though their reports, in kindness, concealed it. Later, when they heard that we were making flights of several minutes' duration, knowing that longer flights had been made with air-ships, and not knowing any essential difference between air-ships and flying-machines, they were but little interested.

We had not been flying long in 1904 before we found that the problem of equilibrium had not as yet been entirely solved. Sometimes, in making a circle, the machine would turn over sidewise despite anything the operator could do, although, under the same conditions in ordinary straight flight, it could have been righted in an instant. In one flight, in 1905, while circling around a honey locust-tree at a height of about fifty feet, the machine suddenly began to turn up on one wing, and took a course toward the tree. The operator, not relishing the idea of landing in a thorn-tree, attempted to reach the ground. The left wing, however, struck the tree at a height of ten or twelve feet from the ground, and carried away several branches; but the flight, which had already covered a distance of six miles, was continued to the starting-point.

The causes of these troubles—too technical for explanation here—were not entirely overcome till the end of September, 1905. The flights then rapidly increased in length, till experiments were discontinued after the 5th of October, on account of the number of people attracted to the field. Although made on a ground open on every side, and bordered on two sides by much traveled thoroughfares, with electric cars passing every hour, and seen by all the people living in the neighborhood for miles around, and by several hundred others, yet these flights have been made by some newspapers the subject of a great "mystery."

A practical flyer having been finally realized, we spent the years 1906 and 1907 in constructing new machines and in business negotiations. It was not till May of this year that experiments (discontinued in October, 1905) were resumed at Kill Devil Hill, North Carolina.[19] The recent flights were made to test the ability of our machine to meet the requirements of a contract with the United States Government to furnish a flyer capable of carrying two men and sufficient fuel supplies for a flight of 125 miles, with a speed of forty miles an hour. The machine used in these tests was the same one with which the flights were made at Simms Station in 1905, though several changes had been made to meet present requirements. The operator assumed a sitting position, instead of lying prone, as in 1905, and a seat was added for a passenger. A larger motor was installed,[20] and radiators and gasolene reservoirs of larger capacity replaced those previously used. No attempt was made to make high or long flights.

In order to show the general reader the way in which the machine operates, let us fancy ourselves ready for the start. The machine is placed upon a single rail track facing the wind, and is securely fastened with a cable. The engine is put in motion, and the propellers in the rear whir. You take your seat at the center of the machine beside the operator. He slips the cable, and you shoot forward. An assistant who has been holding the machine in balance on the rail, starts forward with you, but before you have gone fifty feet the speed is too great for him, and he lets go. Before reaching the end of the tract the operator moves the front rudder, and the machine lifts from the rail like a kite supported by the pressure of the air underneath it. The ground under you is at first a perfect blur, but as you rise the objects become clearer. At a height of one hundred feet you feel hardly any motion at all, except for the wind which strikes your face. If you did not take the precaution to fasten your hat before starting, you have probably lost it by this time. The operator moves a lever: the right wing rises, and the machine swings about to the left. You make a very short turn, yet you do not feel the sensation of being thrown from your seat, so often experienced in automobile and railway travel. You find yourself facing toward the point from which you started. The objects on the ground now seem to be moving at much higher speed, though you perceive no change in the pressure of the wind on your face. You know then that you are traveling with the wind. When you near the starting-point, the operator stops the motor while still high in the air. The machine coasts down at an oblique angle to the ground, and after sliding fifty or a hundred feet comes to rest. Although the machine often lands when traveling at a speed of a mile a minute, you feel no shock whatever, and cannot, in fact, tell the exact moment at which it first touched the ground. The motor close beside you kept up an almost deafening roar during the whole flight, yet in your excitement, you did not notice it till it stopped!

Our experiments have been conducted entirely at our own expense.[21] In the beginning we had no thought of recovering what we were expending, which was not great, and was limited to what we could afford for recreation. Later, when a successful flight had been made with a motor, we gave up the business in which we were engaged, to devote our entire time and capital to the development of a machine for practical uses. As soon as our condition is such that constant attention to business is not required, we expect to prepare for publication the results of our laboratory experiments, which alone made an early solution of the flying problem possible.[22]

---

1. *Century Magazine,* September 1908, 641–50.
2. Although this article appeared under joint authorship, it was entirely the work of Orville Wright.
3. Several nineteenth-century aeronautical experimenters developed these small, rubber-band-powered toy helicopters. The one the Wrights' father gave them was designed by Alphonse Pénaud. Pénaud performed significant pioneering aerodynamic work in the area of inherent stability in the 1870s. The Wright brothers, after their success, credited Pénaud as one of their most important predecessors.
4. Otto Lilienthal died as a result of injuries sustained in a glider accident on August 9, 1896.
5. The original text of the article mistakenly printed the years of the *Aeronautical Annual* as 1905, 1906, and 1907.
6. See documents 38 and 40, Wilbur Wright's comments on the work of Louis-Pierre Mouillard and Otto Lilienthal.
7. Sir Hiram Maxim emphasized propulsion as the central challenge in the invention of a heavier-than-air flying machine. He asserted in 1892, "Scientists have long said, Give us a motor and we will very likely soon give you a successful flying machine" (Hiram Maxim, *The Cosmopolitan,* June 1892, quoted in Valerie Moolman, *The Road to Kitty Hawk* [Alexandria, Va.: Time-Life Books, 1980], 68). In 1894, Maxim attempted to fly an aircraft that weighed four tons and was powered by two 180-horsepower steam engines. It was little more than a complex engine test rig. The craft was tethered to an elaborate launching track equipped with guardrails to prevent it from rising more than a few inches. On its third trial on July 31, 1894, it rose slightly, traveled a few hundred feet, and crashed. Maxim had shown that with enough power, a winged craft could indeed be coaxed into the air. But his airplane was completely devoid of any of the other elements necessary for practical flight and thus contributed little to the eventual invention of the airplane.
8. Francis Herbert Wenham was a mid-nineteenth-century British aeronautical experimenter. His contributions regarding the curvature, profile, and outline of wing shapes foreshadowed modern aerodynamics. In 1866 he published a groundbreaking paper entitled "Aerial Locomotion," and in 1871, with John Browning, he built the first wind tunnel in which to test model wing shapes. He also experimented with full-size gliders to demonstrate the correctness of his theories on wing shape.
9. John Stringfellow, another British experimenter, worked in the same period as Wenham; however, his meaningful technical contributions were far more limited. He developed a number of sizable aircraft models and, more significantly, designed several

small steam engines to power them, but there is little evidence that any of these aircraft flew. He collaborated with Samuel Henson on some of these projects, most notably in 1842 on a modern-looking airplane conception called the Aerial Steam Carriage. Henson and Stringfellow had grandiose plans for the design, but the aircraft was never built or tested. See Harald Penrose, *An Ancient Air: A Biography of John Stringfellow of Chard* (Washington, D.C: Smithsonian Institution Press, 1989).

10. See document 39: "What Clement Ader Did."
11. Percy Pilcher, a Scottish glider pioneer, patterned his experiments after the work of Lilienthal. He was killed in 1899 in a gliding accident that was remarkably similar to the one in which Lilienthal was killed a few years before. See Philip Jarrett, *Another Icarus: Percy Pilcher and the Quest for Flight* (Washington, D.C.: Smithsonian Institution Press, 1987).
12. The Wrights had their first face-to-face meeting with Octave Chanute in June 1901 when Chanute visited them in Dayton. But Wilbur Wright had written to Chanute more than a year earlier, on May 13, 1900, to introduce himself to the then elder statesman of aeronautics and to share the results of the brothers' experiments up to that time. Chanute immediately recognized the potential of these new members of the aeronautical community and quickly responded with an encouraging reply. These were the first of over four hundred letters exchanged between the Wrights and Chanute until the latter's death in 1910.
13. [This footnote appeared with the original article:] The gliding flights were all made against the wind. The difficulty in high winds is in maintaining balance, not in traveling against the wind.
14. U.S. Patent 821,393, granted May 22, 1906.
15. For a detailed discussion of the Wright brothers' wind tunnel experiments, see appendix 2, "1901 Wind Tunnel," in Marvin W. McFarland, ed., *The Papers of Wilbur and Orville Wright,* 2 vols. (New York: McGraw-Hill, 1953), 1:547–93.
16. For a detailed discussion of the Wright brothers' propeller design and experiments, see appendix 3, "The Wright Propellers," in ibid., 1:594–640.
17. Orville mistakenly referred to Ward, whose actual first name was Jesse, when he meant Johnny Moore of Nags Head. Moore was the fifth person present at Kitty Hawk on December 17, when the first flights were made. Jesse Ward was a local resident who appeared at the Wright brothers' camp the next day, December 18, with a telegram from the Norfolk correspondent of the *New York World,* who was seeking exclusive rights for a story with pictures. The Wrights did not consent to the interview.
18. See John T. Daniels's own account of this event in document 70: "Then We Quit Laughing."
19. The Wrights did not make a single flight from October 1905 to May 1908.
20. See document 3, note 2.
21. From the beginning of their research to the success at Kitty Hawk in December 1903, the Wrights spent approximately $1,000 on their flying experiments. All of the money came from the proceeds of their bicycle business.
22. By "laboratory experiments" Orville means the pivotal wind tunnel research conducted in late 1901 and early 1902. Although it was always their intention, the Wrights in fact never published their wind tunnel data.

6 • OHIO IN AVIATION[1]

Wilbur Wright

Like every son of Ohio who has passed beyond the borders of the State, I have often been astonished at the great number of Ohio people I have met everywhere throughout the world. I confess, however, that I have never found them quite as thick as I have tonight. It is an old story that any time in the last forty years a man might go down to Washington and have at least three chances out of five at finding an Ohio man living in the White House. It has got to be such an old story to have an Ohio man as one of the candidates in our Presidential elections, that such elections have lost their thrill, and the people are beginning to demand something more exciting. Accordingly, in our election three years hence we are expecting to run two Ohio men, one as a Democrat and other as a Republican. And I venture to predict that if that race comes off it will be the most exciting race we have ever known. And I further predict that the result will be just the same as it has always been, an Ohio man will come out on top.

But what we find down in Washington we are liable to find all over the world. I know only one other State which turns out such a foreign colony as the State of Ohio. I refer, of course, to the State of Missouri. When my brother and I first poked our heads out of our seclusion, we found Missouri men wherever we went. Everyone seemed to be from Missouri. But as time went on the Missouri men became scarcer and scarcer and scarcer, until finally, about the time that Dr. Cook came back from his snow palace in the north,[2] there were no Missouri men. But the trouble with the Missouri men is that you cannot depend on them, sometimes they are here, and sometimes they are not. But Ohio men you can always depend on.

Ohio stands at the gateway between the East and the West, and her sons possess the boundless energy and enthusiasm of the West, and combine it with the salt of conservation of the East. The result is a combination that carries Ohio men to victory everywhere.

If I were giving a young man advice as to how he might succeed in life, I would say to him, pick out a good father and mother, and begin life in Ohio.

---

1. Remarks given by Wilbur Wright at the twenty-fourth annual banquet of the Ohio Society of New York on January 10, 1910, published in *Reports of Proceedings, 1910* (New York: Ohio Society of New York, 1910), 93–138.
2. The reference is to Dr. Frederick A. Cook's expedition to the North Pole in 1908. Cook's claim to have discovered the Pole was later disputed by Robert E. Peary, who reached the North Pole on April 6, 1909. Over time, Cook's penchant for exaggerating his claims for various achievements was revealed, and Peary's 1909 discovery of the North Pole was affirmed.

7 • PRESENTATION OF LANGLEY MEDAL TO MESSRS. WILBUR AND ORVILLE WRIGHT[1]

Wilbur Wright

REMARKS BY WILBUR WRIGHT

Mr. Chancellor, at different times my brother and myself have received recognition for the work which we have attempted to do in the line of aerial research, but in no instance has such recognition given us greater pleasure than that which we now receive from the Smithsonian Institution.[2] This is particularly the case because the Institution, through the studies and work of Professor Langley, has always taken especial interest in scientific research in matters relating to the physical properties of the air, and this interest has extended to practical attempts to fly. We are very much gratified, therefore, that the Institution has thought our work worthy of this honor, for which we desire to express our sincere thanks. A subject of research which has not yet been completed, and one to which Doctor Bell has called attention in the work of Professor Langley,[3] is the coefficient of air pressure; that is, the pressure of wind at a certain speed on a plane of a certain size. A great many investigations have been made by Professor Langley, and other people have also experimented in this art, but for the most part the results have not yet been brought into shape to be presented to the public. Our own work in this particular investigation we have been obliged to set aside for a while on account of the press of business matters, but it is our intention, as soon as these business details are arranged, to take it up again and present the results to the world. There is a great deal of work to do in this line, and a great many other researches to be taken up, which will keep a large number of investigators busy for a lifetime, and I venture to express the hope that the Smithsonian Institution will continue to encourage the labors of those engaged in these fields.[4]

---

1. Speech delivered on February 10, 1910, and published in "Proceedings of Regents," *Annual Report of the Board of Regents of the Smithsonian Institution, 1910* (Washington, D.C.: Government Printing Office, 1911), 109–10.
2. Samuel P. Langley died in 1906. To honor Langley's work in aeronautics, his successor as secretary of the Smithsonian Institution, Charles D. Walcott, established a Langley medal to recognize important contributions to aeronautics. The first Langley medals were presented to the Wright brothers at the Smithsonian Institution in Washington, D.C., on February 10, 1910. Walcott also founded the Langley Laboratory, which he hoped would become a national facility for aeronautical research.
3. Before the presentation of the Langley medals to the Wrights and before Wilbur's remarks, Dr. Alexander Graham Bell had delivered an address on Langley's aeronautical work. Bell was a member of the Smithsonian Board of Regents, the governing body of the Institution. He was an aeronautical experimenter and a friend and colleague of Langley's.

4. This same 1910 Smithsonian annual report printed (on page 23) a statement that was attributed to Wilbur Wright and that was made to appear to be part of his remarks given at the presentation of the Langley medal. The statement gave the misleading impression that the Wrights credited Langley with a critical role in their own success. This falsified quotation, paraphrased from a 1906 letter from Wilbur to Chanute commenting on Langley's death, was later used by the Wrights' opponents to undermine their standing as the true inventors of the airplane. The inaccurate statement attributed to Wilbur read as follows: "The knowledge that the head of the most prominent scientific institution of America believed in the possibility of human flight was one of the influences that led us to undertake the preliminary investigations that preceded our active work. He recommended to us the books which enabled us to form sane ideas at the outset. It was a helping hand at a critical time, and we shall always be grateful." See also document 19: "Why the 1903 Wright Airplane Is Sent to a British Museum," note 5.

8 • THE EARLIEST WRIGHT FLIGHTS—A LETTER FROM WILBUR WRIGHT[1]

Wilbur and Orville Wright

To the Editor of the *Scientific American:*

The *Scientific American* of June 25th contains an editorial which says: "Curtiss was using hinged wing tips in his earlier machines, with which he made public flights antedating the open flights of the Wrights." The use of the catch expression "open flights" is calculated to give to the general reader an entirely false impression regarding the real facts. The general construction of the Wright machines, and the method of control which has now become so widely copied, were well known to aviators in general and to Mr. Curtiss[2] in particular long before he began building aeroplanes. The *Scientific American* of February 22nd, 1902, contains several pictures of Wright machines, and gives an abstract of an illustrated article in the printed *Journal of the Western Society of Engineers,* containing an account of the construction of the machine and its novel methods of control. In 1903 Mr. O. Chanute visited Europe in the interests of the St. Louis Exposition, and while in Paris gave an illustrated lecture on aviation in America, setting forth what he had witnessed during visits to the Wright camp at Kitty Hawk in 1901 and 1902. In the same year (1903) he wrote an article for *L'Aerophile* giving scale drawings of the Wright 1902 machine. Aroused by this news, several members of the Aero Club of France decided to form a sub-commission on aviation, the club having been heretofore solely a balloon society. Mr. Archdeacon, the prime mover, gave an order to a French workman for the construction of a copy of the Wright 1902 glider. This "aeroplane du type de Wright," from which grew the Voisin, Farman, and earlier Blériot machines, was tested at Berck in April, 1904, by a young man from Lyons, M. Voisin, it being his debut in aviation. Pictures of this pioneer French-built machine of the "type Wright" were published in numerous French papers of that year and also in the

New York Press of March 20th, 1904. A second Archdeacon machine with a motor was illustrated in the *Scientific American* of December 17th, 1904, which says in the accompanying test, "It resembles the Wright aeroplane in its general principles, but contains certain modifications in detail." The French patent, explaining in detail the new Wright system of control, was published in 1904. The American patent was published in 1906. The *Scientific American* of April 7th, 1906, published numerous pictures of Wright machines, and after mentioning the horizontal front rudder, says, "There may also be other patentable improvements for maintaining the transverse stability, such as a method of twisting the planes slightly at either end." In 1907 Dr. Bell organized the Aerial Experiment Association, with Lieut. Selfridge as secretary, and Mr. Curtiss as chief of construction. Lieut. Selfridge wrote to the brothers Wright in behalf of the association, asking for information regarding the construction of gliders, and was referred to the drawings and description in the Wright American patent and to the drawings and description in the *Aerophile* article of 1903. Lieut. Selfridge in answer said he had obtained a copy of the patent, and hoped to obtain the other paper soon. At first only the general form of the Wright machine was copied in the machines constructed by Mr. Curtiss, but soon the adjustable tips began to appear, their necessity having become apparent. It was only in 1908 that Mr. Curtiss began using adjustable tips. Judge Hazel was aware of these facts, and in his decision mentioned this correspondence as one of the reasons for granting the temporary injunction.[3]

Wilbur Wright

---

1. *Scientific American*, July 16, 1910, 47.
2. Glenn Hammond Curtiss was the Wrights' principal competitor in the manufacture and sale of aircraft in the United States. For a full treatment of Curtiss's life and work, see C. R. Roseberry, *Glenn Curtiss: Pioneer of Flight* (Garden City, N.Y.: Doubleday, 1972).
3. To assert their priority of invention and to prevent others from unfairly profiting from their achievement, the Wrights filed a patent-infringement suit against Curtiss and his firm, the Herring-Curtiss Company. Judge John R. Hazel, of the federal circuit court in Buffalo, New York, issued an injunction on January 3, 1910, restraining the Herring-Curtiss Company from the manufacture, sale, or exhibition of airplanes. Curtiss immediately filed an appeal, which enabled him to continue operations at least until the appellate court issued a ruling. Despite the appeal, the Herring-Curtiss Company filed for bankruptcy in April 1910. On June 14, 1910, the U.S. Circuit Court of Appeals for the Second Circuit removed the injunction imposed by Judge Hazel, allowing Curtiss to pursue his business until the original patent-infringement suit filed by the Wrights was adjudicated. In December 1911 Curtiss, without Herring (see document 28, note 11), formed the Curtiss Aeroplane and Motor Company, which would become the largest producer of aircraft in the United States by 1914. The Wright-Curtiss patent war dragged on for several more years, ending in a murky resolution with the creation of a Manufacturers Aircraft Association and a series of cross-licensing agreements after the United States entered World War I in April 1917.

9 • A LETTER FROM ORVILLE AND WILBUR WRIGHT[1]
Wilbur and Orville Wright

We are in receipt of information from Germany, regarding the recent action of the German Patent Office, nullifying the main claim of the Wright German Patent.[2] A letter from our attorney says:

"After the discussion of all of these points, the Division took one hour and a half to deliberate, and then pronounced as their judgment that claim 1 should be annulled on the disclosure contained in *L'Aeronaut,* page 103, passage 5, in connection with *Automotor,* of February 15, 1902, page 197, column 1, lines 2 to 4. The full grounds were not verbally pronounced. It was said that they would be given in writing."

The citation from *L'Aeronaut,* is from a report of an address by Mr. Chanute before the Aero Club of France, in April, 1903, describing the experiments of the Wright brothers at Kitty Hawk, N.C., in 1902. The citation from the *Automotor,* is a synopsis of the address of Mr. Wilbur Wright before the Western Society of Engineers in 1901 describing the experiments at Kitty Hawk in 1901. The statement of Mr. Chanute which is cited as a disclosure of the Wright invention was as follows:

"To assure transverse equilibrium, the operator works two cords, which warp the right and left wings and at the same time adjust the vertical rear rudder."

Under the laws of Germany and France, a disclosure of an invention by the inventors, or by anyone else, who has knowledge of it, before the application for a patent is filed, is sufficient to render the patent void. The disclosure must be sufficient to enable anyone to understand how to build and use the invention.

The German Patent Office has taken the extreme position that these few words were sufficient to teach anyone how to build and operate a flying machine in 1903, and that they canceled the right of the inventors to any property in their invention in Germany. The Wright brothers do not believe that this action of the Patent Office is based on a proper interpretation of the law, and will take an appeal to a higher tribunal.

The address of Mr. Chanute, on which the German decision turned, was delivered about two weeks after the date of the French application, and, therefore, could not be used against the Wrights in the French trial, which they won. The German application was not filed until after the date of this address by Mr. Chanute.

Very truly yours,
Wright Brothers

---

1. *Aero,* March 23, 1912, 499.
2. In addition to the U.S. patent cases involving Curtiss and others, the Wrights also filed suit against their European competitors. Their patent was upheld in all the countries except Germany.

10 • HOW WE MADE THE FIRST FLIGHT[1]

Orville Wright

The flights of the 1902 glider had demonstrated the efficiency of our system of maintaining equilibrium, and also the accuracy of the laboratory work upon which the design of the glider was based. We then felt that we were prepared to calculate in advance the performance of machines with a degree of accuracy that had never been possible with the data and tables possessed by our predecessors. Before leaving camp[2] in 1902 we were already at work on the general design of a new machine which we proposed to propel with a motor.

Immediately upon our return to Dayton, we wrote to a number of automobile and motor builders, stating the purpose for which we desired a motor, and asking whether they could furnish one that would develop eight-brake horse power, with a weight complete not exceeding 200 pounds. Most of the companies answered that they were too busy with their regular business to undertake the building of such a motor for us; but one company replied that they had motors rated at 8 h.p., according to the French system of ratings, which weighed only 135 pounds, and that if we thought this motor would develop enough power for our purpose, they would be glad to sell us one. After an examination of the particulars of this motor, from which we learned that it had but a single cylinder of 4 inch bore and 5 inch stroke, we were afraid that it was much overrated. Unless the motor would develop a full 8 brake horse power, it would be useless for our purpose.

Finally we decided to undertake the building of the motor ourselves. We estimated that we could make one of four cylinders with 4 inch bore and 4 inch stroke, weighing not over two hundred pounds, including all accessories. Our only experience up to that time in the building of gasoline motors had been in the construction of an air-cooled motor, 5 inch bore and 7 inch stroke, which was used to run the machinery of our small workshop. To be certain that four cylinders of the size we had adopted (4" X 4") would develop the necessary 8 horse power, we first fitted them into a temporary frame of simple and cheap construction. In just six weeks from the time the design was started, we had the motor on the block testing its power. The ability to do this so quickly was largely due to the enthusiastic and efficient services of Mr. C. E. Taylor,[3] who did all the machine work in our shop for the first as well as the succeeding experimental machines. There was no provision for lubricating either cylinders or bearings while this motor was running. For that reason it was not possible to run it more than a minute or two at a time. In these short tests the motor developed about nine horse power. We were then satisfied that, with proper lubrication and better adjustments, a little more power could be expected. The completion of the motor according to drawing was, therefore, proceeded with at once.

While Mr. Taylor was engaged with this work, Wilbur and I were busy in completing the design of the machine itself. The preliminary tests of the motor having convinced us that more than 8 horse power would be secured, we felt free to add enough weight to build a more substantial machine than we had originally contemplated.

Our tables of air pressures and our experience in flying with the 1902 glider, enabled us, we thought, to calculate exactly the thrust necessary to sustain the machine in flight. But to design a propeller that would give this thrust with the power we had at our command, was a matter we had not as yet seriously considered.[4] No data on air propellers was available, but we had always understood that it was not a difficult matter to secure an efficiency of 50% with marine propellers. All that would be necessary would be to learn the theory of the operation of marine propellers from books on marine engineering, and then substitute air pressures for water pressures. Accordingly we secured several such books from the Dayton Public Library. Much to our surprise, all the formulae on propellers contained in these books were of an empirical nature. There was no way of adapting them to calculations of aerial propellers. As we could afford neither the time nor expense of a long series of experiments to find by trial a propeller suitable for our machine, we decided to rely more on theory than was the practice with marine engineers.

It was apparent that a propeller was simply an aeroplane traveling in a spiral course. As we could calculate the effect of an aeroplane traveling in a straight course, why should we not be able to calculate the effect of one traveling in a spiral course? At first glance this does not appear difficult, but on further consideration it is hard to find even a point from which to make a start; for nothing about a propeller, or the medium in which it acts, stands still for a moment. The thrust depends upon the speed and the angle at which the blade strikes the air; the angle at which the blade strikes the air depends upon the speed at which the propeller is turning, the speed the machine is traveling forward, and the speed at which the air is slipping backward; the slip of the air backward depends upon the thrust exerted by the propeller, and the amount of air acted upon. When any one of these changes, it changes all the rest, as they are all interdependent upon one another. But these are only a few of the many factors that must be considered and determined in calculating and designing propellers. Our minds became so obsessed with it that we could do little other work. We engaged in innumerable discussions, and often after an hour or so of heated argument, we would discover that we were as far from agreement as when we started, but that both had changed to the other's original position in the discussion. After a couple of months of this study and discussion, we were able to follow the various reactions in their intricate relations long enough to begin to understand them. We realized that the thrust generated by a propeller when standing stationary was no indication of the thrust when in motion. The only way to really test the efficiency of a propeller would be to actually try it on the machine.

For two reasons we decided to use two propellers. In the first place we could, by the use of two propellers, secure a reaction against a greater quantity of air, and at the same time use a larger pitch angle than was possible with one propeller; and in the second place by having the propellers turn in opposite direction, the gyroscopic action of one would neutralize that of the other. The method we adopted of driving the propellers in opposite directions by means of chains is now too well known to need description here.[5] We decided to place the motor to one side of the man, so that in case of a plunge headfirst, the motor could not fall upon him. In our gliding experiments we had had a number of experiences in which we had landed upon one wing, but the crushing of the wing had absorbed the shock, so that we were not uneasy about the motor in case of a landing of that kind. To provide against the machine rolling over forward in landing, we designed skids like sled runners, extending out in front of the main surfaces. Otherwise the general construction and operation of the machine was to be similar to that of the 1902 glider.

When the motor was completed and tested, we found that it would develop sixteen horse power for a few seconds, but that the power rapidly dropped till, at the end of a minute, it was only 12 horse power. Ignorant of what a motor of this size ought to develop, we were greatly pleased with its performance. More experience showed us that we did not get one-half of the power we should have had.

With twelve horse power at our command, we considered that we could permit the weight of the machine with operator to rise to 750 or 800 pounds, and still have as much surplus power as we had originally allowed for in the first estimate of 550 pounds.

Before leaving for our camp at Kitty Hawk we tested the chain drive for the propellers in our shop at Dayton, and found it satisfactory. We found, however, that our first propeller shafts, which were constructed of heavy gauge steel tubing, were not strong enough to stand the shocks received from a gasoline motor with light fly wheel, although they would have been able to transmit three or four times the power uniformly applied. We therefore built a new set of shafts of heavier tubing, which we tested and thought to be abundantly strong.

We left Dayton, September 23, and arrived at our camp at Kill Devil Hill on Friday, the 25th. We found there provisions and tools, which had been shipped by freight several weeks in advance. The building, erected in 1901 and enlarged in 1902, was found to have been blown by a storm from its foundation posts a few months previously. While we were awaiting the arrival of the shipment of machinery and parts from Dayton, we were busy putting the old building in repair, and erecting a new building to serve as a workshop for assembling and housing the new machine.

Just as the building was being completed, the parts and material for the machines arrived simultaneously with one of the worst storms that had visited Kitty Hawk in years. The storm came on suddenly, blowing 30 to 40 miles an hour. It increased during the night, and the next day was blowing over seventy-five miles an hour. In order to save the tar-paper roof, we decided it would be necessary to get out in this wind and nail down more securely certain parts that were especially exposed. When I ascended the ladder and reached the edge of the roof, the wind caught under my large coat, blew it up around my head and bound my arms till I was perfectly helpless. Wilbur came to my assistance and held down my coat while I tried to drive the nails. But the wind was so strong I could not guide the hammer and succeeded in striking my fingers as often as the nails.

The next three weeks were spent in setting the motor-machine together. On days with more favorable winds we gained additional experience in handling a flyer by gliding with the 1902 machine, which we had found in pretty fair condition in the old building, where we had left it the year before.

Mr. Chanute and Dr. Spratt,[6] who had been guests in our camp in 1901 and 1902, spent some time with us, but neither one was able to remain to see the test of the motor-machine, on account of the delays caused by trouble which developed in the propeller shafts.

While Mr. Chanute was with us, a good deal of time was spent in discussion of the mathematical calculations upon which we had based our machine. He informed us that, in designing machinery, about 20 per cent. was usually allowed for the loss in the transmission of power. As we had allowed only 5 per cent., a figure we had arrived at by some crude measurements of the friction of one of the chains when carrying only a very light load, we were much alarmed. More than the whole surplus in power, allowed in our calculations would, according to Mr. Chanute's estimate, be consumed in friction in the driving chains. After Mr. Chanute's departure, we suspended one of the drive chains over a sprocket, hanging bags of sand on either side of the sprocket of a weight approximately equal to the pull that would be exerted on the chains when driving the propellers. By measuring the extra amount of weight needed on one side to lift the weight on the other, we calculated the loss in transmission. This indicated that the loss in power from this source would be only 5 per cent., as we originally estimated. But while we could see no serious error in this method of determining the loss, we were very uneasy until we had a chance to run the propellers with the motor to see whether we could get the estimated number of turns.

The first run of the motor on the machine developed a flaw in one of the propeller shafts which had not been discovered in the test at Dayton. The shafts were sent at once to Dayton for repair, and were not received again until November 20, having been gone two weeks. We immediately put them in the machine and made another test. A new trouble developed. The sprockets which were screwed on the shafts, and locked with nuts of opposite thread, persisted in coming loose. After many futile attempts to get them fast, we had to give it up for that day, and went to bed much discouraged. However, after a night's rest, we got up the next morning in better spirits and resolved to try again.

While in the bicycle business we had become well acquainted with the use of hard tire cement for fastening tires on the rims. We had once used it successfully in repairing a stop watch after several watchsmiths had told us it could not be repaired. If tire cement was good for fastening the hands on a stop watch, why should it not be good for fastening the sprockets on the propeller shaft of a flying machine? We decided to try it. We heated the shafts and sprockets, melted cement into the threads, and screwed them together again. This trouble was over. The sprockets stayed fast.

Just as the machine was ready for test, bad weather set in. It had been disagreeably cold for several weeks, so cold that we could scarcely work on the machine some days. But now we began to have rain and snow, and a wind of 25 to 30 miles blew for several days from the north. While we were being delayed by the weather we arranged a mechanism to measure automatically the duration of a flight from the time the machine started to move forward to the time it stopped, the distance traveled through the air in that time, and the number of revolutions made by the motor and propeller. A stop watch took the time; an anemometer measured the air traveled through; and a counter took the lumber of revolutions made by the propellers. The watch, anemometer and revolution counter were all automatically started and stopped simultaneously. From data thus obtained we expected to prove or disprove the accuracy of our propeller calculations.

On November 28, while giving the motor a run indoors, we thought we again saw something wrong with one of the propeller shafts. On stopping the motor, we discovered that one of the tubular shafts had cracked!

Immediate preparation was made for returning to Dayton to build another set of shafts. We decided to abandon the use of tubes, as they did not afford enough spring to take up the shocks of premature or missed explosions of the motor. Solid tool-steel shafts of smaller diameter than the tubes previously used were decided upon. These would allow a certain amount of spring. The tubular shafts were many times stronger than would have been necessary to transmit the power of our motor if the strains upon them had been uniform. But the large hollow shafts had no spring in them to absorb the unequal strains.

Wilbur remained in camp while I went to get the new shafts. I did not get back to camp again till Friday, the 11th of December. Saturday afternoon the machine was again ready for trial, but the wind was so light, a start could not have been made from level ground with the run of only sixty feet permitted by our monorail track. Nor was there enough time before dark to take the machine to one of the hills, where, by placing the track on a steep incline, sufficient speed could be secured for starting in calm air.

Monday, December 14, was a beautiful day, but there was not enough wind to enable a start to be made from the level ground about camp. We therefore decided to attempt a flight from the side of the big Kill Devil Hill. We had arranged with the members of the Kill Devil Life Saving Station, which was located a little over a mile from our camp, to inform them when we were ready to make the first trial of the machine. We were soon joined by J. T. Daniels, Robert Westcott, Thomas Beachem, W. S. Dough and Uncle Benny O'Neal, of the Station, who helped us get the machine to the hill, a quarter mile away. We laid the track 150 feet up the side of the hill on a 9 degree slope. With the slope of the track, the thrust of the propellers and the machine starting directly into the wind, we did not anticipate any trouble in getting up flying speed on the 60 foot monorail track. But we did not feel certain the operator could keep the machine balanced on the track.

When the machine had been fastened with a wire to the track, so that it could not start until released by the operator, and the motor had been run to make sure that it was in condition, we tossed up a coin to decide who should have the first trial. Wilbur won. I took a position at one of the wings, intending to help balance the machine as it ran down the track. But when the restraining wire was slipped, the machine started off so quickly I could stay with it only a few feet. After a 35 to 40 foot run, it lifted from the rail. But it was allowed to turn up too much. It climbed a few feet, stalled, and then settled to the ground near the foot of the hill, 105 feet below. My stop watch showed that it had been in the air just 3½ seconds. In landing the left wing touched first. The machine swung around, dug the skids into the sand and broke one of them. Several other parts were also broken, but the damage to the machine was not serious. While the test had shown nothing as to whether the power of the motor was sufficient to keep the machine up, since the landing was made many feet below the starting point, the experiment had demonstrated that the method adopted for launching the machine was a safe and practical one. On the whole, we were much pleased.

Two days were consumed in making repairs, and the machine was not ready again till late in the afternoon of the 16th. While we had it out on the track in front of the building, making the final adjustments, a stranger came along. After looking at the machine a few seconds he inquired what it was. When we told him it was a flying machine he asked whether we intended to fly it. We said we did, as soon as we had a suitable wind. He looked at it several minutes longer and then, wishing to be courteous, remarked that it looked as if it would fly, if it had a "suitable wind." We were much amused, for, no doubt, he had in mind the recent 75 mile gale when he repeated our words, "a suitable wind"!

During the night of December 16, 1903, a strong cold wind blew from the north. When we arose on the morning of the 17th, the puddles of water, which had been standing about camp since the recent rains, were covered with ice. The wind had a velocity of 10 to 12 meters per second (22 to 27 miles an hour). We thought it would die down before long, and so remained indoors the early part of the morning. But when ten o'clock arrived, and the wind was as brisk as ever, we decided that we had better get the machine out and attempt a flight. We hung out the signal for the men of the Life Saving Station. We thought that by facing the flyer into a strong wind, there ought to be no trouble in launching it from the level ground about camp. We realized the difficulties of flying in so high a wind, but estimated that the added dangers in flight would be partly compensated for by the slower speed in landing.

We laid the track on a smooth stretch of ground about one hundred feet north of the new building. The biting cold wind made work difficult, and we had to warm up frequently in our living room, where we had a good fire in an improvised stove made of a large carbide can. By the time all was ready, J. T. Daniels, W. S. Dough and A. D. Etheridge, members of the Kill Devil Life Saving Station; W. C. Brinkley, of Manteo, and Johnny Moore, a boy from Nag's Head [Nags Head], had arrived.

We had a "Richard" hand anemometer with which we measured the velocity of the wind. Measurements made just before starting the first flight showed velocities of 11 to 12 meters per second, or 24 to 27 miles per hour. Measurements made just before the last flight gave between 9 and 10 meters per second. One made just after showed a little over 8 meters. The records of the Government Weather Bureau at Kitty Hawk gave the velocity of the wind between the hours of 10:30 and 12 o'clock, the time during which the four flights were made, as averaging 27 miles at the time of the first flight and 24 miles at the time of the last.

With all the knowledge and skill acquired in thousands of flights in the last ten years, I would hardly think today of making my first flight on a strange machine in a twenty-seven-mile wind, even if I knew that the machine had already been flown and was safe. After these years of experience I look with amazement upon our audacity in attempting flights with a new and untried machine under such circumstances. Yet faith in our calculations and the design of this first machine, based upon our tables of air pressures, secured by months of careful laboratory work, and confidence in our system of control developed by three years of actual experience in balancing gliders in the air had convinced us that the machine was capable of lifting and maintaining itself in the air, and that, with a little practice, it could be safely flown.

Wilbur, having used his turn in the unsuccessful attempt on the 14th, the right to the first trial now belonged to me. After running the motor a few minutes to heat it up, I released the wire that held the machine to the track, and the machine started forward into the wind. Wilbur ran at the side of the machine, holding the wing to balance it on the track. Unlike the start on the 14th, made in a calm, the machine, facing a 27-mile wind, started very slowly. Wilbur was able to stay with it till it lifted from the track after a forty-foot run. One of the Life Saving men snapped the camera for us,[7] taking a picture just as the machine had reached the end of the track and had risen to a height of about two feet.[8] The slow forward speed of the machine over the ground is clearly shown in the picture by Wilbur's attitude. He stayed along beside the machine without any effort.

The course of the flight up and down was exceedingly erratic, partly due to the irregularity of the air, and partly to lack of experience in handling this machine. The control of the front rudder was difficult on account of its being balanced too near the center. This gave it a tendency to turn itself when started; so that it turned too far on one side and then too far on the other. As a result the machine would rise suddenly to about ten feet, and then as suddenly dart for the ground. A sudden dart when a little over a hundred feet from the end of the track, or a little over 120 feet from the point at which it rose into the air, ended the flight. As the velocity of the wind was over 35 feet per second and the speed of the machine over the ground against this wind ten feet per second, the speed of the machine relative to the air was over 45 feet per second, and the length of the flight was equivalent to a flight of 540 feet made in calm air.[9] This flight lasted only 12 seconds, but it was nevertheless the first in the history of the world in which a machine carrying a man had raised itself by its own power into the air in full flight, had sailed forward without reduction of speed, and had finally landed at a point as high as that from which it started.

With the assistance of our visitors we carried the machine back to the track and prepared for another flight. The stingwind, however, had chilled us all through, so that before attempting a second flight, we all went to the building again to warm up. Johnny Ward,[10] seeing under the table a box filled with eggs, asked one of the Station men where we got so many of them. The people of the neighborhood eke out a bare existence by catching fish during the short fishing season, and their supplies of other articles of food are limited. He had probably never seen so many eggs at one time in his whole life. The one addressed jokingly asked him whether he hadn't noticed the small hen running about the outside of the building. "That chicken lays eight to ten eggs a day!" Ward, having just seen a piece of machinery lift itself from the ground and fly, a thing at that time considered as impossible as perpetual motion, was ready to believe nearly anything. But after going out and having a good look at the wonderful fowl, he returned with the remark, "It's only a common looking chicken!"

At twenty minutes after eleven Wilbur started on the second flight. The course of this flight was much like that of the first, very much up and down. The speed over the ground was somewhat faster than that of the first flight, due to the lesser wind. The duration of the flight was less than a second longer than the first, but the distance covered was about seventy-five feet greater.

Twenty minutes later the third flight started. This one was steadier than the first one an hour before. I was proceeding along pretty well when a sudden gust from the right lifted the machine up twelve to fifteen feet and turned it up sidewise in an alarming manner. It began a lively sidling off to the left. I warped the wings to try to recover the lateral balance and at the same time pointed the machine down to reach the ground as quickly as possible. The lateral control was more effective than I had imagined and before I reached the ground the right wing was lower than the left and struck first.[11] The time of this flight was fifteen seconds and the distance over the ground a little over 200 feet.

Wilbur started the fourth and last flight at just 12 o'clock. The first few hundred feet were up and down as before, but by the time three hundred feet had been covered, the machine was under much better control. The course for the next four or five hundred feet had but little undulation. However, when out about eight hundred feet the machine began pitching again, and, in one of its darts downward, struck the ground. The distance over the ground was measured and found to be 852 feet; the time of the flight 59 seconds. The frame supporting the front rudder was badly broken, but the main part of the machine was not injured at all. We estimated that the machine could be put in condition for flight again in a day or two.

While we were standing about discussing this last flight, a sudden strong gust of wind struck the machine and began to turn it over. Everybody made a rush for it. Wilbur, who was at one end, seized it in front, Mr. Daniels and I, who were behind, tried to stop it behind, tried to stop it by holding to the rear uprights. All our efforts were vain. The machine rolled over and over. Daniels, who had retained his grip, was carried along with it, and was thrown about head over heels inside of the machine. Fortunately he was not seriously injured, though badly bruised in falling about against the motor, chain guides, etc. The ribs in the surfaces of the machine were broken, the motor injured and the chain guides badly bent, so that all possibility of further flights with it for that year were at an end.[12]

---

1. *Flying*, December 1913, 10–12, 35–36.
2. The "camp" was at Kitty Hawk.
3. Charles E. Taylor, a machinist, was hired by the Wrights in June 1901 to assist with their bicycle business so that the brothers would have more time for their aeronautical experiments. Taylor played a key role in the fabrication of the engine of the 1903 Wright Flyer. See Taylor's reminiscence of his time with the Wrights in document 73: "My Story of the Wright Brothers."
4. See document 5, note 16.
5. An arrangement of chains and sprockets patterned after a bicycle transmission system was used to link the propellers to the crankshaft of the engine, which was mounted on the lower wing to the right of the pilot's position.
6. George A. Spratt, a young physician from Coatesville, Pennsylvania, contacted Chanute in 1899 with his ideas on flying machines and soon became one of the group of aeronautical enthusiasts fostered and supported by Chanute. He first visited the Wrights at Kitty Hawk in the summer of 1901, at Chanute's request, and the brothers found him a

"willing worker and a most congenial companion" (W. Wright to Octave Chanute, July 9, 1902, in Marvin W. McFarland, ed., *The Papers of Wilbur and Orville Wright,* 2 vols. [New York: McGraw-Hill, 1953], 1:237–38). Spratt previously had performed some aerodynamic research on his own. During discussions with the Wrights at Kitty Hawk about methods of measuring aerodynamic forces acting on model wing surfaces, Spratt suggested that measuring the ratio of lift to drag might be easier than trying to measure either force independently. The Wrights adopted the idea in their wind tunnel experiments of late 1901, although they used an instrument with a design entirely different from Spratt's. This was one of a few genuinely useful technical suggestions the brothers got from other experimenters. Spratt visited the Wrights at Kitty Hawk on the brothers' subsequent trips, and the three men maintained a warm and cordial friendship for many years.

7. This was John T. Daniels. His published reminiscence of the day of the first flight appears in document 70: "Then We Quit Laughing."
8. See photo 23.
9. This was equivalent to 6.8 mph ground speed, 31 mph airspeed, and an actual direct distance of 120 feet from takeoff to landing.
10. See document 5, note 17.
11. See photo 24. This and the famous photograph of the first flight takeoff (photo 23) are the only photographs of the Wright Flyer in the air.
12. The 1903 Wright Flyer was never flown again. The Wrights placed the airplane in storage in Dayton until 1916, when it was publicly exhibited at the Massachusetts Institute of Technology. From 1928 to 1948 it was on loan from Orville Wright to the Science Museum in London, and in 1948 it was deposited in the collection of the Smithsonian Institution. For further details on the material history of the Wright Flyer, see Mabel Beck's article published as document 74: "The First Airplane—After 1903."

11 • MY NARROWEST ESCAPE IN THE AIR[1]

Orville Wright, as told by him to Leslie W. Quirk for the readers of *Boys' Life*

"The conquest of the air accomplished through the genius of the Wright brothers is one of the most notable events of the century."

My narrowest escape may have been one of the times, back in 1901, when I attempted several flights in a glider that was scientifically correct in construction, according to all known figures, but that persistently upset them and me in actual trials. Or it may have been the day I waited in the calm for a wind to aid my ascent, watching it come by marking the lines of nodding daisies, and then discovering, as it lifted the wings of the machine, that it was not a mannerly, orderly breeze at all, but a boisterous whirlwind that tumbled me out on my head. Or my most hazardous experience may have been on that first flight with a motor-driven aeroplane, in 1903, when I flew for twelve seconds in the teeth of a gale, weaving jerkily up and down. Only once, however, have I actually lost control of my machine high in the air, and I presume that time might fairly be considered my narrowest escape.

The accident occurred at Fort Myer,[2] in 1908, and resulted in the death of my companion on the flight and the breaking of my own leg. I had been asked by the Government to make a flight with a passenger to prove the merit of our machine, and Lieutenant Selfridge[3] had been selected.

A crowd of perhaps 2,000 had turned out to watch the demonstration, attracted by the announcement that I was to take up a passenger with me. The weather was ideal, although there was a six-mile wind blowing.

The machine worked perfectly. After a run of about thirty feet on the ground we lifted into the air and began climbing in a spiral. At a height of perhaps 150 feet I heard a sudden snap behind me. Immediately the machine veered sharply downward and to the left, refusing to answer to its controls.

I learned afterward that the propeller had hit a wire. One blade was shattered altogether, but we did not fall because of that, as the newspapers stated at the time. If the accident had been no more serious than the breaking of a propeller shaft I could have glided to the ground in safety.

Unfortunately, however, the wire itself had also broken. It was one that held in position a vertical rudder. Before I could shut off the motor we had dived away from the field and were directly over a ravine, the worst possible place to descend. I was not unduly alarmed, however, and by utilizing an old system of control by which we had steered our first gliders I managed to work back to the middle of the field. From this position I counted upon landing easily and without danger.

All this time we had been dropping, of course, but I still believed I would get control of the machine in a second or two. A broken propeller blade was not enough to warrant any great amount of fear.

Then, behind me, I heard another ominous snap. The machine, which had been behaving nicely under the circumstances, turned nose downward and pitched toward the ground.

What had happened was simple. The broken wire controlled a vertical rudder at the rear. This rudder, loosed from its support, had swung into a horizontal position, where it caught the blanket of air as we descended and tilted the whole machine forward till it plunged nose down toward the ground.

We dropped sheer for perhaps ninety feet. Some twenty feet from the ground the rudder flapped back into its original vertical position, and once more I had perfect control. But it was too late to do more than deflect the machine slightly from its course. If we had been 1,000 feet in the air at the time of the accident I am sure it would have been no more serious than scores of others, granted, of course, that the rudder had snapped back into position as it did after the first fall of less than 100 feet. The broken propeller blade would have counted for nothing. I had already proved I could steer by the old system of control, and the gliding to the ground with the motor shut off would have been simple.

But our height was not enough. We crashed heavily when we struck, and after they had lifted the heavy machine and motor that pinned us down we were rushed to the hospital, where Lieutenant Selfridge died a few hours later.[4]

---

1. *Boys' Life*, August 1914, 5.
2. Fort Myer, Virginia, near Washington, D.C., was the site of the performance trials conducted by the Wrights to meet the specifications of their contract with the U.S. Army Signal Corps for the purchase of a powered airplane.
3. Lieutenant Thomas E. Selfridge's death in this accident on September 17, 1908, was the first in a heavier-than-air powered airplane.
4. The Wrights returned to Fort Myer in 1909 with a new airplane, successfully completed the trials, and were paid $30,000 for their aircraft by the U.S. Army.

12 • HOW I LEARNED TO FLY[1]

Orville Wright, as told by him to Leslie W. Quirk for the readers of *Boys' Life*[2]

I suppose my brother and I always wanted to fly. Every youngster wants to, doesn't he? But it was not till we were out of school that the ambition took definite form.

We had read a good deal on the subject and we had studied Lilienthal's tables of figures with awe. Then one day, as it were, we said to each other: "Why not? Here are scientific calculations, based upon actual tests, to show us the sustaining powers of planes. We can spare a few weeks each year. Suppose, instead of going off somewhere to loaf, we put in our vacations building and flying gliders." I don't believe we dared think beyond gliders at that time—not aloud, at least.

That year—it was 1900—we went down to North Carolina, near Kitty Hawk. There were hills there in plenty, and not too many people about to scoff. Building that first glider was the best fun we'd ever had, too, despite the fact that we put it together as accurately as a watchmaker assembles and adjusts his finest timepiece. You see, we knew how to work because Lilienthal had made his tables years before, and men like Chanute, for example, had verified them.

To our great disappointment, however, the glider was not the success we had expected. It didn't behave as the figures on which it was constructed vouched that it should. Something was wrong. We looked at each other silently, and at the machine, and at the mass of figures compiled by Lilienthal. Then we proved up on them to see if we had slipped somewhere. If we had, we couldn't find the error; so we packed up and went home. We were agreed that we hadn't built our glider according to the scientific specifications. But there was another year coming and we weren't discouraged. We had just begun.

We wrote to Chanute, who was an engineer in Chicago at the time. We told him about our glider; we drew sketches of it for him; we set down long rows of figures.

And then we wound up our letter by begging him to explain why the tables of Lilienthal, which he had verified by experiments of his own, could not be proved by our machine.

Chanute didn't know. He wrote back it might be due to a different curve or pitch of surfaces on the planes, or something like that. But he was interested just the same, and when we went down to Kitty Hawk in 1901 we invited him to visit our camp.

Chanute came. Just before he left Chicago, I recall his telling us, he had read and O.K.'d the proofs of an article on aeronautics which he had prepared for the *Encyclopedia Britannica,* and in which he again told us of verifying Lilienthal's tables.

Well, he came to Kitty Hawk, and after he had looked our glider over carefully he said frankly that the trouble was not with any errors of construction in our machine. And right then all of us, I suspect, began to lose faith in Lilienthal and his gospel figures.

We had made a few flights the first year, and we made about 700 in 1901. Then we went back to Dayton to begin all over. It was like groping in the dark. Lilienthal's figures were not to be relied upon. Nobody else had done any scientific experimenting along these lines. Worst of all, we did not have money enough to build our glider with various types and sizes of planes or wings, simply to determine, in actual practice, which was the best. There was only the alternative of working out tables of our own. So we set to work along this line.

We took little bits of metal and we fashioned planes from them.[3] I've still a deskful in my office in Dayton. There are flat ones, concave ones, convex ones, square ones, oblong ones and scores and scores of other shapes and sizes. Each model contains six square inches. When we built our third glider the following year, ignoring Lilienthal altogether and constructing it from our own figures, we made the planes just 7,200 times the size of those little metal models back at Dayton.[4]

It was hard work, of course, to get our figures right; to achieve the plane giving the greatest efficiency—and to know before we built that plane the exact proportion of efficiency we could expect. Of course, there were some books on the subject that were helpful. We went to the Dayton libraries and read what we could find there; afterwards, when we had reached the same ends by months and months of study and experiment, we heard of other books that would have smoothed the way.

But those metal models told us how to build. By this time, too, Chanute was convinced that Lilienthal's tables were obsolete or inaccurate, and was wishing his utmost that he was not on record in an encyclopedia as verifying them.

During 1902 we made upwards of 1,400 flights, sometimes going up a hundred times or more in a single day. Our runway was short, and it required a wind with velocity of at least twelve miles an hour to lift the machine. I recall sitting in it, ready to cast off, one still day when the breeze seemed approaching. It came presently, rippling the daisies in the field, and just as it reached me I started the glider on the runway. But the innocent-appearing breeze was a whirlwind. It jerked the front of the machine sharply upward. I tilted my rudder to descend. Then the breeze spun downward, driving the glider to the ground with a tremendous shock and spinning me out headfirst. That's just a sample of what we had to learn about air currents; nobody had ever heard of "holes" in the air at that time. We had to go ahead and discover everything for ourselves.

But we glided successfully that summer, and we began to dream of greater things. Moreover, we aided Chanute to discover the errors in Lilienthal's tables, which were due to experimental flights down a hill with a descent so acute that the wind swept up its side and out from its surface with false buoying power. On the proper incline, which would be one parallel with the flight of the machine, the tables would not work out. Chanute wrote the article on aeronautics for the last edition of that encyclopedia again, but he corrected his figures this time.

The next step, of course, was the natural one of installing an engine. Others were experimenting, and it now became a question of which would be the first to fly with an engine. But we felt reasonably secure, because we had worked out all own figures, and the others were still guessing or depending upon Lilienthal's or somebody's else that were inaccurate. Chanute knew we expected to try sustained flights later on, and while abroad that year mentioned the fact, so we had competition across the water, too.

We wrote to a number of automobile manufacturers about an engine. We demanded an eight-horse one of not over 200 pounds in weight. This was allowing twenty-five pounds to each horsepower and did not seem to us prohibitive.

Several answers came. Some of the manufacturers politely declined to consider the building of such an engine; the gasoline motor was comparatively new then, and they were having trouble enough with standard sizes. Some said it couldn't be built according to our specifications, which was amusing, because lighter engines of greater power had already been used. Some seemed to think we were demented—"Building a flying machine, eh?" But one concern, of which we had never heard, said it could turn out a motor such as we wanted, and forwarded us figures. We were suspicious of figures by this time, and we doubted this concern's ability to get the horsepower claimed, considering the bore of the cylinders, etc. Later, I may add, we discovered that such an engine was capable of giving much greater horsepower. But we didn't know that at the time; we had to learn our A, B, C's as we went along.

Finally, though, we had a motor built. We had discovered that we could allow much more weight than we had planned at first, and in the end the getting of the engine became comparatively simple. The next step was to figure out what we wanted in the way of a screw propeller.

We turned to our books again. All the figures available dealt with the marine propeller—the thrust of the screw against the water. We had only turned from the solution of one problem to the intricacies of another. And the more we experimented with our models the more complicated it became.

There was the size to be considered. There was the material to be decided. There was the matter of the number of blades. There was the delicate question of the pitch of the blades. And then, after we had made headway with these problems, we began to scent new difficulties. One pitch and one force applied to the thrust against still air; what about the suction, and the air in motion, and the vacuum, and the thousand and one changing conditions? They were trying out the turbine engines on the big ocean liners at that time, with an idea of determining the efficiency of this type. The results were amazing in the exact percentage of efficiency developed by fuel and engine and propeller combined. A little above 40 per cent. efficiency was considered wonderful. And the best we could do, after months of experimenting and studying, was to conceive and build a propeller that had to deliver 66 per cent. of efficiency, or fail us altogether. But we went down to Kitty Hawk pretty confident, just the same.[5]

There were the usual vexatious delays. But finally, in December, 1903, we were ready to make the first flight. My brother and I flipped a coin for the privilege of being the first to attempt a sustained flight in the air. Up to now, of course, we had merely taken turns. But this was a much bigger thing. He won.

The initial attempt was not a success. The machine fluttered for about 100 feet down the side of the hill, pretty much as gliders had done. Then it settled with a thud, snapping off the propeller shaft, and thus effectually ending any further experiments for the time being.

It was getting late in the fall. Already the gales off Hatteras were beginning to howl. So I went back to Dayton personally to get a new shaft, and to hurry along the work as rapidly as I could.

It was finished at last. As I went to the train that morning, I heard for the first time of the machine constructed by Langley, which had dropped into a river the day before. You see, others were working just as desperately as we were to perfect a flying machine.

We adjusted the new shaft as soon as I reached Kitty Hawk. By the time we had finished it was late in the afternoon, with a stiff wind blowing. Our facilities for handling the machine were of the crudest. In the past, with our gliders, we had depended largely upon the help of some men from a life saving station, a mile or two away. As none of them happened to be at our camp that afternoon, we decided to postpone the next trial till morning.

It was cold that night. A man named Brinkley—W. C. Brinkley—dropped in to warm himself. He was buying salvage on one or more of the ships that had sunk during a recent storm that raged outside Kitty Hawk Point. I remember his looking curiously at the great frame-work, with its engine and canvas wings, and asking,

"What's that?" We told him it was a flying machine which we were going to try out the next morning, and asked him if he thought it would be a success. He looked out toward the ocean, which was getting rough and which was battering the sunken ships in which he was interested. Then he said, "Well you never can tell what will happen—if conditions are favorable." Nevertheless, he asked permission to stay over-night and watch the attempted flight.

Morning brought with it a twenty-seven mile gale. Our instruments, which were more delicate and more accurate than the Government's, made it a little over twenty-four; but the official reading by the United States was twenty-seven miles an hour. As soon as it was light we ran up our signal flag for help from the life saving station. Three men were off duty that day, and came pounding over to camp. They were John T. Daniels, A. D. Etheridge and W. S. Dough. Before we were ready to make the flight a small boy of about thirteen or fourteen came walking past.

Daniels, who was a good deal of a joker, greeted him. The boy said his name was Johnny Moore, and was just strolling by. But he couldn't get his eyes off the machine that we had anchored in a sheltered place. He wanted to know what it was.

"Why, that's a duck-snarer," explained Daniels soberly. North Carolina, of course, is noted for its duck shooting. "You see, this man is going up in the air over a bay where there are hundreds of ducks on the water. When he is just over them, he will drop a big net and snare every last one. If you'll stick around a bit, Johnny, you can have a few ducks to take home."

So Johnny Moore was also a witness of our flights that day. I do not know whether the lack of any ducks to take away with him was a disappointment or not, but I suspect he did not feel compensated by what he saw.

The usual visitors did not come to watch us that day. Nobody imagined we would attempt a flight in such weather, for it was not only blowing hard, but it was also very cold. But just that fact, coupled with the knowledge that winter and its gales would be on top of us almost any time now, made us decide not to postpone the attempt any longer.

My brother climbed into the machine.[6] The motor was started. With a short dash down the runway, the machine lifted into the air and was flying. It was only a flight of twelve seconds, and it was an uncertain, wavy, creeping sort of a flight at best; but it was a real flight at last and not a glide.

Then it was my turn. I had learned a little from watching my brother, but I found the machine pointing upward and downward in jerky undulations. This erratic course was due in part to my utter lack of experience in controlling a flying machine and in part to a new system of controls we had adopted, whereby a slight touch accomplished what a hard jerk or tug made necessary in the past. Naturally, I overdid everything. But I flew for about the same time my brother had.

He tried it again, the minute the men had carried it back to the runway, and added perhaps three or four seconds to the records we had just made. Then, after a few secondary adjustments, I took my seat for the second time. By now I had learned something about the controls, and about how a machine acted during a sustained flight, and I managed to keep in the air for fifty-seven[7] seconds. I couldn't turn, of course—the hills wouldn't permit that—but I had no very great difficulty in handling it. When I came down I was eager to have another turn.

But it was getting late now, and we decided to postpone further trials until the next day. The wind had quieted, but it was very cold. In fact, it had been necessary for us to warm ourselves between each flight. Now we carried the machine back to a point near the camp, and stepped back to discuss what had happened.

My brother and I were not excited nor particularly exultant. We had been the first to fly successfully with a machine driven by an engine, but we had expected to be the first. We had known, down in our hearts, that the machine would fly just as it did. The proof was not astonishing to us. We were simply glad, that's all.

But the men from the life saving station were very excited. Brinkley appeared dazed. Johnny Moore took our flights as a matter of course, and was presumably disappointed because we had snared no ducks.

And then, quite without warning, a puff of wind caught the forward part of the machine and began to tip it. We all rushed forward, but only Daniels was at the front. He caught the plane and clung desperately to it, as though thoroughly aware as were we of the danger of an upset of the frail thing of rods and wings. Upward and upward it lifted, with Daniels clinging to the plane to ballast it. Then, with a convulsive shudder, it tipped backward, dashing the man in against the engine, in a great tangle of cloth and wood and metal. As it turned over, I caught a last glimpse of his legs kicking frantically over the plane's edge. I'll confess I never expected to see him alive again.[8]

But he did not even break a bone, although he was bruised from head to foot. When the machine had been pinned down at last, it was almost a complete wreck, necessitating many new parts and days and days of rebuilding. Winter was fairly on top of us, with Christmas only a few days off. We could do no more experimenting that year.

After all, though, it did not matter much. We could build better and stronger and more confidently another year. And we could go back home to Dayton and dream of time and distance and altitude records, and of machines for two or more passengers, and of the practical value of the heavier-than-air machine. For we had accomplished the ambition that stirred us as boys. We had learned to fly.

---

1. *Boys' Life,* September 1914, 2–4.
2. The content and the tone of Quirk's version of Orville's experiences are somewhat overly romanticized in places, no doubt to make the story appealing to the young readers of this publication.
3. The "planes" were actually model wing shapes.

4. See document 5, note 15.
5. See document 5, note 16.
6. Quirk mixed up the sequence in which the brothers alternated flights. It was actually Orville who made the twelve-second first flight on December 17, 1903, not his brother. Wilbur made the long fourth and final flight of the day, not Orville.
7. The airplane actually stayed in the air for fifty-nine seconds, and the flight covered a distance of 852 feet.
8. See John T. Daniels's own account of this event in document 70: "Then We Quit Laughing."

13 • THE WORK OF ORVILLE WRIGHT[1]

Interview with Orville Wright

Men say that the war must be won in the air, as if the idea were something new. But to Orville Wright it is not new.

Back in 1906 he and his brother Wilbur, now dead, planned the victory which must come soon.

On his front porch today he told of the vision of a lasting world peace that quickened their minds and guided their hands as he and his brother worked on their flying machine, which, as they planned, was to put an end to wars.

Not to win wars, but to win peace, they dreamed. And as they dreamed so it will come to pass. Of that he is certain. Because he says this is the last war.

For if the war is to be won in the air, as it must be, then it is to Orville Wright and his brother, Wilbur, to whom the world will build its grateful memorials.

"In your early experiments did you think of the aeroplane as a thing that would some time be a determining factor in war?"

"We always thought of it as an instrument for the making of permanent peace," said Wright. "That idea was constantly before us to inspire us. We never let it out of our sight. From the start we saw in it an unerring scout through which armies could detect each other's movements. An army movement can be successful only if veiled in the strictest secrecy. We saw that the aeroplane would give eyes to armies and the armies with the most eyes would win the war. We saw that when nations came to recognize what we saw, wars would end. And what we foresaw then is coming true now. The nation with the most eyes will win the war and put an end to war. That is what we planned and that is what will happen."

Thus spoke Orville Wright, who is Dayton's idol. Ask anyone how to get to Wright's home and they will reply, "Take the Oakwood car and get off at Harmon Avenue and walk two squares to the right until you come to the big white house on the hill."[2] And then you ask where Wright's workshop is. You are told at once to take a Third Street car and get off at Broadway, and that you will find Wright's shop "right behind the jewelry store on the corner."

1. *Aerial Age Weekly*, October 15, 1917, 195.
2. After their financial success with the airplane, the Wrights built a large mansion on the edge of town in Dayton. The residence, which they called Hawthorn Hill, was not completed until 1913, and Wilbur died before his brother, his sister, Katherine, and their father, Milton, moved in. Orville lived there until his death in 1948.

14 • WRIGHT'S FIRST STATEMENT SINCE THE WAR[1]

Orville Wright

Just eighteen years ago, on the 17th of December, 1903, after centuries of endeavor, man for the first time was lifted into the air by a power-propelled airplane. Flight seems so easy today that one naturally wonders at the long delay in its accomplishment. Yet eighteen years ago, on account of the thousands of failures, flying was classed with perpetual motion and the few who expressed belief in its possibilities were looked upon as mentally unbalanced. Up to 1900, only a few measurements of airplane wings had been made along successful lines. Most flying experiments up to that time had been made on the "cut and try" plan; and by that plan flight probably would not have been accomplished for centuries yet to come.

The problem was not one to be solved by guesswork. Duchemin, about the middle of the last century had published a formula for calculating the pressure on planes at different angles. Lilienthal in the eighties had published his measurements on curved surfaces with other valuable scientific work.[2] Langley in the nineties published his measurements of plane surfaces corroborating the earlier work of Duchemin.[3] It was to the work of Lilienthal that my brother and I were by far most deeply indebted. But owing to various defects in the systems of measuring all this work, we found it too inaccurate and too meagre for purposes of design.

In 1901 my brother Wilbur and I, having proved by actual gliding tests the inaccuracy of these tables, began a scientific study of the subject. We designed new types of measuring instruments and made measurements of hundreds of differing wing surfaces in a wind tunnel. It was due to the accuracy of these measurements that we were able, in 1903, to design a new type of biplane, almost entirely from calculation, which was able to lift itself and operator into the air with a crude motor weighing more than 12 pounds per horsepower. We had already developed a new system of control, the system with which our name has been so largely connected,[4] but this system of control would have been of little use without our wind tunnel work which enabled us to design a machine which would lift itself.

The longest flight on December 17, 1903, was 59 seconds duration at a speed of 30 miles an hour. Today continuous flights of more than 24 hours have been made and speeds in excess of 175 miles an hour reached. Many laboratories in all countries are now at work in this field of science. Who, then, will attempt to predict what airplanes can do at the end of another 18 years?

1. *U.S. Air Service,* December 1921, 8.
2. The results of Lilienthal's principal aerodynamic research were published in Otto Lilienthal, *Birdflight as the Basis of Aviation,* trans. A. W. Isenthal (New York: Longmans Green, 1911), originally published as *Der Vogelflug als Grundlage der Fliegekunst* in 1889, and in Hermann W. L. Moedebeck, *Pocket-Book of Aeronautics,* trans. W. Mansergh Varley (London: Whittaker and Co., 1907), 287–94, originally published as *Taschenbuch zum praktischen Gebrauch für Flugtechniker und Luftschiffer* in 1895.
3. The results of Langley's principal aerodynamic research were published in Samuel P. Langley, *Experiments in Aerodynamics* (Washington, D.C.: Smithsonian Institution, 1891), and Samuel P. Langley, *The Internal Work of the Wind* (Washington, D.C.: Smithsonian Institution, 1893).
4. This was the Wright system of three-axis control, the central feature of which was their wing-warping method for lateral balance control.

15 • ORVILLE WRIGHT: AN INTERVIEW[1]

Interview with Orville Wright by Carl J. Crane

Nature, the sculptor, was moulding a beautiful mantel of white over the crude outlines of a busy city one cold afternoon in February as I turned into the offices of Orville Wright. At five o'clock I was due. It was almost that time when the cheery smile of Mr. Wright greeted me and invited me into his private office. Here it was that Mr. Wright, seated behind his drawing board, gave me an insight into a most colorful career; one to which history itself can present no parallel.

Mr. Wright is a man of average stature, very erect and with sparkling blue eyes that sparkle all the more when speaking of matters pertaining to aeronautics and just what were the factors that rushed through my mind in the first few moments of conversation with Mr. Wright that it seemed at first that no definite one would persevere, but as I now write there is one that stands out more forcibly than the rest; it is the quiet and unassuming manner of speech and the genuine kindness and bigheartedness of the greatest genius of aeronautical activity the world has ever known.

"Mr. Wright, how did you become interested in aeronautics and just what were the factors that led up to your invention of the first heavier than air flying machine?", I ventured after a moment's deliberation.

"Well," said Mr. Wright, "my brother and I never really worked toward the end of perfecting an airplane, at least not in the early part of our experiments. We used to take a yearly vacation and it was during these vacations that we used our time in playing with gliders. It was just real play for we were interested in the big kites and got more real enjoyment out of this sport than if we had been hunting or fishing. We got started with the gliders, for as boys we were interested in kites and we usually followed what interested us most. In fact, every thing I have ever done has been done from the viewpoint of interest." Mr. Wright here sounded the keynote of many a successful man's career.

"When still quite young I was attracted by the results of wood engraving and decided to try my luck at it. I did, and enjoyed it so much that I became quite adept with the tools of my own fashioning. Not having the necessary funds to purchase engraving tools I found that the springs out of pocket knives would quite satisfy the purpose and it was with these springs, refashioned of course, that I spent many an hour at wood engraving. Several specimens of the wood engravings were so well done that experts of the art commended them, and you might know that my profession in life was then settled. I was to be a wood engraver." Here Mr. Wright paused with a reminiscent twinkle in his eyes. "Of course it became necessary for me to know the results of my work and I set about getting a means of printing. As I was not able to buy a real printing press I went in search of the materials. I procured an old fragment of a tombstone which due to its plane surface seemed most likely to suit my purpose and after some time had a workable printing press. My father and brother seeing my determination to become a printer managed after a while to get a small printing press for me. This was the apple of my eye for quite a time, but it only whetted my appetite to do larger work and after a short while I was ready to publish my first newspaper. It was not very elaborate but nevertheless it was a newspaper consisting of two sheets and the size was twenty-two by thirty-two inches." These were the ramifications of the earlier pursuits of Orville Wright.

When interest called to greater accomplishments, Mr. Wright found himself taking an active interest in bicycles. Mr. Wright continued: "My brother and I became interested in the sale and finally in the manufacture of bicycles.[2] We did this however because we found the work interesting, we liked it very much and at times perhaps we would not have stayed in the bicycle business had not our fancy commanded us to. Once a year we managed to get away from the usual run of things and we spent that vacation on glider experiments. This was great sport and as such we took the proposition until one time when we came face to face with a problem that aroused our suspicion. We had constructed a glider and based our design on some of the existing aeronautical data of the times. When we tested it out we found that it would not perform as we had anticipated and proved that the data was incorrect. Further tests proved it conclusively and the more experiments we made the greater the number of technical discrepancies we encountered. We were using some of the only existing data on wings and had to go by these characteristics, so when we found them to be wrong we were on the verge of discontinuing our glider building. This was perhaps the only time we were almost thoroughly discouraged, for after finding the data unreliable we were at a loss what figures to incorporate to work out our designs. We knew that it would take considerable time and funds to obtain data of our own but there was some spirit that carried us through, so we set to the task of obtaining reliable information of the forces that played on a wing in flight." Here Mr. Wright paused a moment to bring forth from a cabinet a little pasteboard box from which came, unmistakably, sounds of metal against metal. He set the box on the drawing board and lifted the cover. "Here," said Mr. Wright, "are some of the model wings that we first tested to determine their various characteristics." One by one Mr. Wright explained the various characteristics of each model wing and told just how they obtained the results. Mr. Wright told how by taking first a full size glider and determining the factors such as lift and resistance for the glider wing, then constructing a small scale model of the glider wing for test in the wind tunnel, they established a point of known value from which to work. After this small size model wing was made and tested in the wind tunnel, other model wings were also made and tested being compared with the first one. Mr. Wright said, "We took no absolute measurements on the models for the apparatus would not permit of this, but we compared our various wing models with the first one on which we knew the actual data from full size tests on the gliders." Indeed this was just another way of how genius accomplishes when it starts to work. "This was a simple way of accomplishing our results and they were results that we could go by and guided us in the building of the first power-driven man-carrying flying machine."[3]

Mr. Wright while discussing the various phases of his experiments would frequently refer to his successes as bits of luck. Luck it may have been, but truly the luck of genius, or better, the intuition of a great mind coupled with a tenacity of purpose that admits of no defeat.

"Mr. Wright, were you ever discouraged in your adventures by those near and dear to you?" I ventured.

"No," was the quick response, "on the contrary we were encouraged just so long as we were working on anything, no matter what it was, that remained within the bounds of reason.

"The thing that was the greatest handicap when it came to the realization of the power-driven machine, was the way many of the engine builders responded to our inquiries—there were no responses! Just one, but even in this case the engine was much too heavy and in other respects it would not meet our requirements. So here again we had to do some original work. Finally, however, we succeeded in building an engine that ran nicely and delivered some sixteen horsepower for the first few minutes of operation and then fell off to twelve horsepower. This, however, was ample for our needs and it was with this engine that we finally succeeded in accomplishing power flight."

Just pause a moment, gentle reader, and try to picture to your mind the real problems, handicaps and difficulties that were faced, grappled with, and surmounted. How many of us would have been content to say "it can't be done"; and truly how many did say "it can't be done"! But to the genius that was theirs, "it can't be done" was perhaps the spark that enkindled their potential ability with the enthusiasm and forceful effort that "told the world" it could be done!

"Mr. Wright, what do you hold for the future of the airplane," I asked.

"I would perhaps be guilty of a grave error if I were to prophesy or to limit today, what tomorrow will bring forth. No one really knows just what will be the economic force of the airplane of tomorrow. I do not believe, as some seem to think, that airplanes will be used within the city as the automobile of today is. The airplane has come to solve a problem distinctly its own, not to take from the railroad its work of hauling great loads of ponderous material, or to take the place of the automobile or ocean liner. On the contrary it has come to supplement these and to apply its usefulness to world-wide problems that have not yet found a real solution. The usefulness of the airplane lies in its speed and facility of locomotion, and not so much in its great size and capacity to carry tremendous loads, for we know today that the efficiency of the airplane decreases as its size increases. I have the most optimistic views however, that the airplane will find in the near future its real application in the economics of the universe much the same as the steamship and automobile found their value and worthy application."

The evening light of this wintry day was casting long shadows and the merry glow of the street lamps stood out against the dark background of closed shops as I left Mr. Wright's office with him. The day was done.

Wending my way home I could not help but marvel at the genius of man, yet still more at the designs of the Creator. Indeed there must be a most intricate law by which the Almighty favors man in his earthly endeavors. There must be a law of many variables by which the Creator lets man work out his destiny. It is true that we cannot all be great to the degree of world recognition. There are many who are big of soul and mind who are not men of great renown; just as true that there are men of great renown who are lacking the true qualities of heart and soul that typify genuine nobility. To credit Mr. Orville Wright with merely intellectual genius would be an injustice, for indeed, there exists in his personality that modesty of demeanor, nobility of heart and soul together with the intellectual genius, that all combine to mould out the true greatness that is his—Orville Wright. Many years ago the genius of Tennyson prompted him to write—

"For I dipt into the future, far as human eye could see,
Saw the vision of the world, and all the wonders that would be;
Saw the heavens fill with commerce, argosies of magic sails,
Pilots of the purple twilight, dropping down with costly bales."

Orville and Wilbur Wright realized the dreams of this poet.

---

1. *University of Dayton Exponent,* April 1924, 7–9. Reprinted with the permission of Archives Collection, Roesch Library, University of Dayton, Dayton, Ohio.
2. The Wrights opened their first bicycle shop in 1892. For further details on the Wrights'

bicycle business, see Fred C. Fisk and Marlin W. Todd, *The Wright Brothers: From Bicycle to Biplane* (Dayton, Ohio: Toddfisk, 1995).

3. See document 5, note 15.

16 • OUR EARLY FLYING MACHINE DEVELOPMENTS[1]

Orville Wright

Our first interest in aeronautics dates back as far as 1899,[2] at which time my brother, Wilbur, and I started work on the development of a heavier-than-air machine which would be sufficiently mobile to permit of practical flying. Some of our first experiments were carried out in Dayton and others in Kitty Hawk, North Carolina. The first actual heavier-than-air machine was a glider, flown in the year 1900, at Kitty Hawk. The span of this plane was eighteen feet[3] with a chord of five feet. Most of the experiments with this glider were made as a kite, operating the levers by cords from the ground.[4]

In 1903, we developed a power machine having a span of forty-one feet[5] and a chord of six and one-half feet. Inasmuch as we had previously been unable to secure a satisfactory motor for this plane, we developed and made one which met the requirements and which developed from ten to twelve horse power. The motor was of the horizontal type. The weight of the machine complete with the operator was 750 pounds. This machine made the first flight in the history of the world at Kitty Hawk, North Carolina, on December 17, 1903.

The flights of the 1902 glider had demonstrated the efficiency of our system of maintaining equilibrium, and also the accuracy of the laboratory work upon which the design of the glider was based. We then felt that we were prepared to calculate in advance the performance of machines with a degree of accuracy that had never been possible with the data and tables possessed by our predecessors. Before leaving camp in 1902, we were already at work on the general design of a new machine which we proposed to propel with a motor.

When the motor was completed and tested, we found that it would develop sixteen horse power for a few seconds, but that the power rapidly dropped till, at the end of a minute, it was only twelve horse power. Ignorant of what a motor of this size ought to develop, we were greatly pleased with the performance. More experience showed us that we did not get one-half of the power we should have had.

We left Dayton, September 23, and arrived at our camp at Kill Devil Hill on Friday, the 25th.

On November 28, while giving the motor a run indoors, we thought we again saw something wrong with one of the propeller shafts. On stopping the motor we discovered that one of the tubular shafts had cracked. Immediate preparation was made for returning to Dayton to build another set of shafts.

Wilbur remained in camp while I went to get the new shafts. I did not get back to camp again till Friday the 11th of December. Saturday afternoon the machine was again ready for trial, but the wind was so light a start could not have been made from level ground with the run of only sixty feet permitted by our mono-rail track. Nor was there enough time before dark to take the machine to one of the hills where, by placing the track on a steep incline, sufficient speed could be secured for starting in calm air.

Monday, December 14, was a beautiful day, but there was not enough wind to enable a start to be made from the level ground about camp. We therefore decided to attempt a flight from the side of the Kill Devil Hill. We had arranged with the members of the Kill Devil Hill life-saving station, which was located a little over a mile from our camp, to inform them when we were ready to make the first trial of the machine.

During the night of December 16, 1903, a strong, cold wind blew from the north. When we arose on the morning of the 17th, the puddles of water which had been standing about camp since the recent rains, were covered with ice. The wind had a velocity of ten to twelve meters per second (twenty-two to twenty-seven miles an hour). We thought it would die down before long and so remained indoors the early part of the morning. But when ten o'clock arrived, and the wind was as brisk as ever, we decided that we had better get the machine out and attempt a flight. We hung out the signal for the men of the life-saving station. We thought that by facing the machine into a strong wind there ought to be no trouble in launching it from the level ground about camp. We realized the difficulties of flying in so high a wind, but estimated that the added dangers in flight would be partly compensated for by the slower speed in landing.

After running the motor a few minutes to heat it up, I released the wire that held the machine to the track, and the machine started forward into the wind. Wilbur ran at the side of the machine, holding the wing to balance it on the track. Unlike the start on the 14th, made in a calm, the machine, facing a twenty-seven-mile wind, started very slowly. Wilbur was able to stay with it until it lifted from the track after a forty-foot run. One of the life-saving men snapped the camera for us,[6] taking a picture just as the machine had reached the end of the track and had risen to a height of about two feet.[7]

The course of the flight up and down was exceedingly erratic, partly due to the irregularity of the air, and partly to lack of experience in handling this machine. The control of the front rudder was difficult on account of its being balanced too near the center. This gave it a tendency to turn itself when started, so that it turned too far on one side and then too far on the other. As a result, the machine would rise suddenly to about ten feet and then as suddenly dart for the ground. A sudden dart when a little over a hundred feet from the end of the track, or a little over 120 feet from the point at which it rose into the air, ended the flight. As the velocity of the wind was over thirty-five feet per second and the speed of the machine over the ground against this wind ten feet per second, the speed of the machine relative to the air was over forty-five feet per second, and the length of the flight was equivalent to a flight of 540 feet made in calm air.[8] This flight lasted only twelve seconds, but it was nevertheless the first in the history of the world in which a machine carrying a man had raised itself by its own power into the air in full flight, had sailed forward without reduction of speed, and had finally landed at a point as high as that from which it started.

At twenty minutes after eleven Wilbur started on the second flight. The course of this flight was much like that of the first, very much up and down. The speed over the ground was somewhat faster than that of the first flight, due to the lesser wind. The duration of the flight was less than a second longer than the first, but the distance covered was about seventy-five feet greater.

Twenty minutes later the third flight started. This one was steadier than the first one an hour before. I was proceeding along pretty well when a sudden gust from the right lifted the machine up twelve to fifteen feet and turned it up sidewise in an alarming manner. It began a lively sliding off to the left. I warped the wings to try to recover the lateral balance, and at the same time pointed the machine down to reach the ground as quickly as possible. The lateral control, was more effective than I had imagined, and before I reached the ground the right wing was lower than the left and struck first. The time of this flight was fifteen seconds and the distance over the ground was a little over two hundred feet.

Wilbur started the fourth and last flight at just twelve o'clock. The first few hundred feet were up and down as before, but by the time three hundred feet had been covered, the machine was under much better control. The course for the next four or five hundred feet had but little undulation. However, when out about eight hundred feet the machine began pitching again, and in one of its starts downward struck the ground. The distance over the ground was measured and found to be 852 feet; the time of the flight, fifty-nine seconds. The frame supporting the front rudder was badly broken, but the main part of the machine was not injured at all. We estimated that the machine could be put in condition for flight again in a day or two.[9]

I believe that this brief account of some of our early experiences, problems, and perplexities will indicate something of the difficulties involved and the discouragements surmounted in the early days of our work to produce a heavier-than-air machine which would actually fly.

---

1. *Slipstream,* January 1925, 11–15. Reprinted with the permission of Simmons-Boardman Books, Inc., Omaha, Nebraska.

2. The Wrights built their first aircraft in 1899, a 5-foot-span biplane kite to test their wing-warping lateral control system. Their first full-size piloted glider was built in 1900. Their general interest and research in aeronautics began a few years earlier.
3. The 1900 glider was actually 17½ feet in span.
4. This aircraft was followed by two additional refined gliders, in 1901 and 1902 respectively.
5. The 1903 Wright Flyer was actually 40 feet, 4 inches, in span.
6. This was John T. Daniels. His published reminiscence of the day of the first flight appears in document 70: "Then We Quit Laughing."
7. See photo 23.
8. See document 10, note 9.
9. See document 10, note 11.

17 • THE WRIGHT-LANGLEY CONTROVERSY: BOTH SIDES PRESENTED BY ORVILLE WRIGHT AND DR. WALCOTT[1]

Orville Wright and Charles D. Walcott[2]

***Aviation* gives below both sides of the dispute over the priority of The Wrights or Dr. Langley. First Orville Wright states his version and Dr. Walcott replies.**

Several days ago I was asked by a New York newspaper, Orville Wright is reported to have said, whether the rumor was true that our first plane, of 1903, was about to go to a museum in England.

I stated at that time that I was sending the machine to the Science Museum at South Kensington, London, because I did not dare to intrust it to the only suitable national museum in America in view of the fact that that institution has allowed the historic relics of the Langley machine of 1903[3] to go out of the institution into the hands of private parties to be mutilated for private purposes; that the machine now hanging in the institution is, much of it, new material and some of it of different construction from the original, and that the card attached to the machine is not true of the original machine or of the restored one.

Dr. Walcott, Secretary of the Smithsonian Institution, has made a reply to my statement which does not clearly deny any of my assertions. In order to give the public a clear understanding of the issues I will make the following positive statements:

Patent Decision

On the 13th of January, 1914, the United States Circuit Court of Appeals for the 2d District[4] handed down a decision in which it was held that the machines being built by the Curtiss Company were infringements of the Wright patents and that "the patentees may fairly be considered pioneers in the practical art of flying with heavier-than-air machines and that the claims should have a liberal interpretation."

The Curtiss Company was enjoined from building airplanes such as it had been building. The company then modified its machine and, in anticipation of another suit on claims of the patent not involved in the first, began preparations for a new defense. Now began an active campaign to establish some one else as the pioneer.

Langley was chosen.

On Jan. 26, 1914, less than two weeks after the decision of the Court of Appeals, it was reported in the press that Lincoln Beachy, a stockholder of the Curtiss Company,[5] asked Dr. Walcott's permission to try to fly the original Langley machine, saying: "You can fly a kitchen table if your engine is strong enough."

Dr. Walcott at that time replied "that it would be inadvisable to take out the wrecked machine from its place in the museum." (See daily papers Jan. 26, 1914.) However, Dr. Walcott soon changed his mind, for in the annual report of the Smithsonian Institution of 1924,[6] page 218, this statement appears:

"When in March, 1914, Mr. Glenn H. Curtiss was invited to send a flying boat to Washington to participate in celebrating Langley Day[7] he replied he 'would like to put the Langley plane itself in the air.' Learning of this remark Secretary Walcott of the Smithsonian Institution soon authorized Mr. Curtiss to recanvas the original Langley airplane and to launch it either under its own propulsive power or with a more recent engine and propeller."

These were the circumstances under which Dr. Walcott through "sheer interest in aviation" allowed this historic relic to be taken out of the institution.

Now for the manner in which the tests of the airplane were made; Mr. A. F. Zahm, was appointed by Dr. Walcott as the "official observer" of the Smithsonian Institution in these tests. "Not one penny," Dr. Walcott told me, was paid by the Smithsonian for Mr. Zahm's services in this capacity.[8]

In fact, he told me that the institution did not pay any of the expenses of the test except some transportation charges. I have proof that the following changes were incorporated into the airplane in the trials which Dr. Walcott says he witnessed.

The wings had a different camber, different aspect ratio and different area. (Every aeronautical engineer knows that these are the features which determine the dynamic efficiency of the wings.)

The wings also were of different mechanical construction.

The trussing used by Langley was modified, strengthened and was moved thirty inches backward nearer the center of pressure. (The misplacing of the trussing was the primary cause of the wrecks of the airplane in 1903.)

A new system of control was adopted.

The Penaud tail,[9] fixed, on the Langley machine was made movable.

The fixed vertical keel used in 1903 was entirely omitted. The rudder designed by Langley in 1903 for steering was enlarged and used for maintaining lateral balance.

An entirely new system of launching was used.

The forward corners of the original propellers were cut off after the manner of the early Wright propellers.

The radiator employed by Langley was changed to a radiator of modern type.

The Langley engine was changed by the installation of a new carburetor, new intake manifold and a magneto.

Many other changes of minor importance were made.

And yet in Dr. Walcott's report of the United States National Museum[10] for that year, 1914, appears the statement that the Langley machine was flown "in June last, without modification."

As to the card now hanging on the machine in the museum. This card reads:

"Original Langley flying machine, 1903, the first man-carrying airplane in the history of the world capable of sustained free flight. Invented, built and tested over the Potomac River by Samuel Pierpont Langley in 1903. Successfully flown at Hammondsport, N.Y., June 2, 1914."

The machine as it hangs in the museum today has the appearance of the Langley machine of 1903, but much of the original material, which was mutilated or destroyed at Hammondsport in 1914, has been replaced with new material; and some of these parts are of different mechanical construction. The airplane tested at Hammondsport was not like the original or like the machine hanging in the museum.

It certainly was not the airplane "invented, built and tested over the Potomac River by Samuel Pierpont Langley in 1903." The machine now hanging in the museum (or one like it) was not tried at Hammondsport in 1914. No attempt since 1903 has ever been made to fly the airplane (or one like it) "invented, built and tested over the Potomac River by Samuel Pierpont Langley in 1903."

Statement on Card

The statement, then, on the card in the museum that this is, "The first man-carrying airplane in the history of the world capable of sustained free flight" must be merely an expression of Dr. Walcott's opinion, since it is not based on any actual tests. Dr. Walcott is reported to have said that I do not like the statement on the card. It is not important whether I do or do not like this statement, but it is important whether this statement on the card is true.

Dr. Langley is not responsible for any of the circumstances which led me to refuse to let our machine go into the Smithsonian Institution. Our machine is now wholly in its original form and almost wholly of its original material.

I would not wish to leave to the discretion of the management of any museum the right to make any change in the design of it for any purpose whatever. If one-half of the changes made in the Langley machine were to be made on our machine it could easily be proved not "capable of sustained free flight."

No one could possibly regret more than I do that our machine must go into a foreign museum. It is not safe where it is. It suffered in one flood and has always been liable to fire. Excepting the National Museum or the Smithsonian, I know of none in this country so suitable for such an exhibit as the Science Museum at South Kensington, London.

DR. WALCOTT'S VERSION

I do not know that the American public is interested in the details of opinion of Mr. Wright and myself in relation to the trials of the Langley airplane, but I feel assured that it is deeply interested in any attempt to remove from America, the home of the successful airplane, the original machine that first carried a man in flight.

The Langley machine, after its crash in the Potomac River in 1903, was returned to the Smithsonian shops, where it was cleaned, the wings being stored in their mutilated condition, together with the frame and engine, in the carpenter shop ......[11]

After the final tests in 1903 the War Department turned the Langley plane over to the Smithsonian. As stated on page 279, "Langley memoir on mechanical flight," it was left in Dr. Langley's possession and available for any future tests that he (Langley) might be able to carry on in connection with the problem of mechanical flight.

Dr. Langley, discouraged and without funds, and his health failing, left the airplane untouched, and it remained in the shops in its dismantled condition until 1914 ......

It seemed worth while to give it another tryout, and especially on account of the desirability of testing the tandem wing principle, which was then thought valuable for large aircraft. I talked the matter over with Dr. Albert F. Zahm, who was then not in the employ of the Curtiss Aeroplane Company, but who held the honorary position of recorder of the Langley Aerodynamical Laboratories, which was the forerunner of the present National Advisory Committee for Aeronautics, of which I have been a member since its organization and chairman since 1919.

Dr. Zahm agreeing, I then talked with Dr. Alexander Graham Bell, who was most enthusiastic, and said that the Langley airplane should certainly be given tests, if it was possible to do so. I asked Glenn Curtiss if he would not undertake the tests and submit an estimate of the approximate cost of restoring and testing the machine over the waters of Lake Keuka. The estimate was submitted, approved and the airplane was taken out of the Smithsonian shops and shipped to Hammondsport in April, 1914. It was not an historical relic belonging to the National Museum, but an airplane left with the Smithsonian Institution by the War Department for experimental purposes ......

Mr. Wright is mistaken with reference to my having told that the institution bore no expense of these tests except the transportation charges on the machine to Hammondsport. Not only were these transportation charges paid, but Mr. Curtiss was paid $2,000 for making the tests.

"May 21, 1914, I went to Hammondsport to see the tests and the following day the machine was taken to the aviation field on Lake Keuka and assembled with the floats and their framework that attached the floats to the main frame of the machine, which added over 300 lb. dead weight. I examined the machine carefully and found it with the original engine and driving mechanism, driver's seat, main frame and double tail, and wings inferior in workmanship but of Langley design.

At the test on May 28, 1914, I went out in a boat on Lake Keuka and saw the Langley airplane as just described rise from the water and make short flights with Mr. Curtiss in the cockpit or pilot's seat, as originally provided for by Dr. Langley. Being fully satisfied that the machine was capable of flight, I requested Mr. Curtiss to install a more recent engine and propeller to determine more fully the advantages of the tandem type of airplane.

After the completion of all tests the Langley airplane was returned to the Smithsonian shops, where R. Luther Reed, who was in charge of the construction work of the original machine, carefully restored the parts that had been broken or marred in the crashes of 1903 and the tests of at Hammondsport. Every one who ever knew Mr. Reed will be prepared to take his oath that no power in heaven or earth could have persuaded him to alter, even by so much as a flyspeck, any detail of the original design.

After the machine was restored it was turned over to the National Museum where it has since been on exhibition.

Mr. Wright objects to the label, which reads: "Original Langley flying machine, 1903. The first man-carrying aeroplane in the history of the world capable of sustained free flight. Invented, built and tested over the Potomac River by Samuel Pierpont Langley in 1903. Successfully flown at Hammondsport, N.Y., June 2, 1914. Dimensions: 55 feet long, 48 feet wide; sustaining wing surface, 1,040 square feet."

I believe this label to be correct.

Dr. Walcott quoted a letter from the Wright brothers dated March 26, 1910, replying to a request for an example of the Wright machines, as saying:

"We can reconstruct the 1903 machine, with which the first flights were made at Kitty Hawk. Most of the parts are still in existence."

In the Langley label, Dr. Walcott added, the word "original" is used "in the same sense that it would be applied to the Kitty Hawk Wright machine of 1903, when restored as described by the Wright brothers' letter."

---

1. Aviation, May 18, 1925, 550–51. Reprinted with the permission of *Aviation Week & Space Technology,* Washington, D.C. On the subject of this controversy, see also documents 19, 20, and 24.
2. Charles D. Walcott succeeded Samuel P. Langley as secretary of the Smithsonian Institution after Langley's death in 1906.
3. Langley's piloted *Great Aerodrome,* also known as *Aerodrome A,* failed to fly and crashed on two attempts in the fall of 1903, the second crash occurring just nine days before the

Wrights' success at Kitty Hawk on December 17. For a detailed description of all of Langley's experimental aircraft, see Samuel P. Langley, *Langley Memoir on Mechanical Flight* (Washington, D.C.: Smithsonian Institution, 1911).

4. This was actually the U.S. Circuit Court of Appeals for the Second Circuit, not the Second "District." The Second Circuit included New York, Connecticut, and Vermont.
5. Beachy was also a well-known exhibition pilot.
6. *Annual Report of the Board of Regents of the Smithsonian Institution, 1924* (Washington, D.C.: U.S. Government Printing Office, 1925).
7. "Langley Day" was established by the Aero Club of Washington, D.C., to commemorate Langley's achievement of the first successful flight of a large, unpiloted, powered, heavier-than-air model aircraft. On May 6, 1896, Langley's steam-powered, fourteen-foot-span, tandem-wing Aerodrome No. 5 made a flight of 3,300 feet. For several years beginning in 1911, May 6 was observed with exhibition flights near Washington, D.C., the presentation of the Langley medal, and other ceremonies and events. Curtiss was in Washington on Langley Day in 1913 to receive the second Langley medal (the first was awarded to the Wrights in 1910, see document 7) and to make demonstration flights. He was invited to return to Washington for the 1914 Langley Day celebration. It is unclear how long the formal observance of Langley Day continued.
8. Dr. Albert F. Zahm was a longtime aeronautical experimenter with a particular interest in aerodynamics. He earned a Ph.D. in physics from Johns Hopkins University in 1898 and was an early associate of Octave Chanute. In 1910 Zahm extended an offer to the Wrights to testify, for a fee, as an expert witness on their behalf in the brothers' patent-infringement litigation against Curtiss. The Wrights politely declined, feeling that they should not have to pay anyone to tell the truth. Affronted, Zahm immediately joined the Curtiss defense team and became a bitter opponent of the Wrights. For the rest of his life (he died in 1954), he took every opportunity to discredit Wilbur and Orville and belittle their achievement. In 1914 Zahm was in charge of the Smithsonian Institution's Langley Laboratory and was authorized by Secretary Walcott to turn over to Curtiss the surviving parts of the 1903 piloted Langley Aerodrome for rebuilding and further trials. Zahm was hardly an impartial player in the arrangement.
9. In the 1870s Alphonse Pénaud performed significant pioneering aerodynamic research in the area of inherent stability, using small, rubber-band-powered models. Equilibrium in pitch (climb and descent) occurs when the center of lifting pressure under the wings is kept exactly coincident with the center of gravity of the aircraft. The center of pressure is the point between the leading and the trailing edges of a wing surface at which the lifting force acting on the wing is focused. The center of pressure naturally moves back and forth along the wing with a changing angle of attack. The center of gravity is a fixed point. Thus, maintaining stability requires a means of keeping the moving center of pressure in line with the fixed center of gravity. Pénaud was concerned with making an aircraft *inherently* stable, that is, with maintaining this condition of equilibrium without any external control input. He achieved this by mounting the horizontal stabilizing surfaces, or tail, behind the wings at a slight negative angle. This automatically regulated the movement of the center of pressure under the wings to keep it in line with the center of gravity. This kept the wings at a relatively constant angle of attack or, in other words, in equilibrium in pitch. The arrangement was known as the Pénaud tail. After their success, the Wrights credited Pénaud as one of their most important predecessors.

10. The component of the Smithsonian Institution that housed museum specimens and historical collections in Orville Wright's lifetime was called the United States National Museum. The name was formally abolished in 1967.
11. The ellipsis points in this document appear in the original copy.

18 • WINGED PIONEERS: A THUMBNAIL HISTORY OF AVIATION BY THE MEN WHO HAVE MADE IT[1]

Orville Wright (and others)[2]

FIRST FLIGHT

There was a strong, cold wind from the North when my brother Wilbur and I went to bed at Kitty Hawk, N.C., on the night of December 16, 1903. We arose next morning to find that the puddles of water left by the recent rain were covered with ice, and that the wind was still blowing at a velocity of around twenty-five miles an hour.

Hoping that it would die down, we stayed indoors the early part of the morning. The wind, however, was as brisk as ever at ten o'clock, and as it showed no likelihood of abating we decided to make our experiment anyway. Since we could face the machine into the strong wind, it should be a relatively simple business to launch it from level ground.

The necessary track was laid, though not without difficulty, since the biting cold compelled us frequently to retire to a shed where a wood fire was burning in an old carbide can.

Eventually all was ready. Seven of us were on hand—my brother and I, J. T. Daniels, A. D. Etheridge, and W. S. Dough, members of the Kill Devil Life Saving Station; W. C. Brinkley, of Manteo, and a boy, Johnny Moore, of Nags Head.

A hand anemometer showed the velocity of the wind to be between twenty-four and twenty-seven miles an hour, which is not far off from what Government Weather Bureau records indicated. I mention this because today, with a generation of aerial development and research to profit by, nobody—not myself at least—would dream of going up in a strange machine in a twenty-seven mile wind, even if he knew that the machine had previously flown and was apparently sound.

My brother had made an unsuccessful attempt to fly on December 14th. It was therefore my turn to try. I ran the motor a few minutes to heat it up, and then released the wire that held the machine to a wooden track. The machine started forward, Wilbur helping to balance it by running alongside. With the wind against it, the machine got under way so slowly that Wilbur was able to stay alongside until it lifted from the track after a run of forty feet.

One of the men from the Life Saving station clicked a camera[3] at that instant and caught a historic picture.[4] The machine was at the time about two feet off the ground.

The flight lasted twelve seconds. Its course was rather erratic, owing in part to air conditions, in part to the pilot's inexperience. The front rudder was balanced too near the center, so that it had a tendency to turn by itself, with the result that at times the machine would rise to about ten feet and then as suddenly aim toward the ground. One of these darts ended the flight one hundred and twenty feet from the point where the machine had first risen from the wooden track.

It may be interesting to note that while the machine was making only ten feet a second against a wind that was blowing thirty-five feet a second, the speed of the machine relative to the air was forty-five feet a second, so that the length of the flight was equivalent to five hundred and forty feet in still air.[5] This was the first time in history that a machine carrying a man raised itself by its own power into the air in full flight, went ahead without reduction of speed, and landed at a point as high as that from which it started.

---

1. *American Legion Monthly,* September 1926, 15–17, 84–86. Reprinted with the permission of *The American Legion Magazine,* Indianapolis, Ind., copyright September 1926.
2. Also in this article were statements from thirteen other noted aviators and engineers of the day, including Frank P. Lahm, Benjamin D. Foulois, Eddie Rickenbacker, and Albert C. Read.
3. This was John T. Daniels. His published reminiscence of the day of the first flight appears in document 70: "Then We Quit Laughing."
4. See photo 23.
5. See document 10, note 9.

19 • WHY THE 1903 WRIGHT AIRPLANE IS SENT TO A BRITISH MUSEUM[1]

Orville Wright

I have sent our original 1903 machine to the British National Museum[2] because of the hostile and unfair attitude shown towards us by the officials of the Smithsonian Institution.

While Professor Langley was secretary of the Smithsonian all of the relations between that Institution and ourselves were friendly. At that time Wilbur and I were universally given credit not only for having made the first flight, but for having produced the first machine capable of flight, and for the scientific research from which this first machine sprang. Our 1903 machine was based entirely on our own scientific tables and none other. Langley's published work in aerodynamics consisted of measurements of air pressures on flat surfaces only.[3] By an entirely different method we had made measurements of a great number of cambered surfaces, as well as of flat surfaces. Our measurements of flat surfaces did not agree with those made by Professor Langley. Although we were not able to use any of Professor

Langley's measurements, because we had found them far from accurate, yet on every occasion where opportunity was offered we expressed our sincere appreciation for the inspiration and confidence Professor Langley's standing in the scientific world had given us when we were starting.

After Professor Langley's death the attitude of the Smithsonian began to change. The Institution began a subtle campaign to take from us much of the credit then universally accorded us and to bring this credit to its former secretary, Professor Langley. Through some clever and some absolutely false statements it succeeded in doing this with people who were not acquainted with the facts.

To illustrate the kind of thing to which I object in the attitude of the Smithsonian, I will cite out of many a few specific cases:

It misrepresented in the Annual Report of the Secretary for the year 1910 (page 23) the statement made by my brother Wilbur at the time of the presentation of the Langley Medal to us by inserting a quotation not used by him on that occasion, but used in a different connection at another time. The improper use of this quotation created a false impression over the world that we had acknowledged indebtedness to Langley's scientific work; that it was Langley's scientific work and our mechanical ingenuity that produced the first flying machine. This was not true. In a private letter to Octave Chanute[4] at the time of Professor Langley's death we had used the words in acknowledging an indebtedness to Langley for the inspiration he had been to us. We had previously told Mr. Chanute of our entire lack of confidence in Langley's scientific work in aerodynamics.[5]

Our original 1903 machine was offered in 1910 to the Smithsonian for exhibition in the National Museum.[6] The officials did not want it, but preferred a much later model of less historic interest.

After the United States Circuit Court of Appeals[7] had given a decision pronouncing Glenn H. Curtiss[8] an infringer of the Wright invention and recognizing the Wrights as "pioneers" in the practical art of flying with heavier-than-air machines, Curtiss was permitted to take the original 1903 Langley machine[9] from the Smithsonian to make tests in an attempt to invalidate this title of "pioneer," for purposes of another law suit.[10] The Smithsonian appointed as its official representative at these tests the man who had been Curtiss' technical expert in the former suits and who was to serve again in that capacity in a new one.[11] It paid Curtiss $2,000 towards the expense of the tests.

It published false and misleading reports of Curtiss' tests of the machine at Hammondsport, leading people to believe that the original Langley machine, which had failed to fly in 1903, had been flown successfully at Hammondsport in 1914, without material change. (See *Report of the National Museum, 1914*, pp. 46, 47. *Smithsonian Report, 1914*, pp. 4, 9, 217–222.)[12] These reports were published in spite of the fact that many changes, several of them of fundamental importance, had been made at Hammondsport; among which were the following: Wings of different camber, different area, different aspect; trussing of a different type, placed in a different location; Langley's fixed keel omitted; motor changed by substituting different carburetor, different manifold and different ignition; propeller blades altered; hydroplane floats added; wing spars, which collapsed in 1903, reinforced; tail rudder made operable about a vertical axis, and connected to a regular Curtiss steering post; small vane rudder replaced by a larger rudder of different design.

This machine restored back to its original form with much new material, the old having been mutilated or destroyed at Hammondsport, was placed in the National Museum with a false label, saying that it was the first man-carrying aeroplane in the history of the world capable of sustained free flight, and that it had been successfully flown at Hammondsport, June 2, 1914.

Following the controversy on this subject three years ago the old label was removed and a new one still containing false and misleading statements was put in its stead.

In spite of this long continued campaign of detraction, for years I kept silent, with the thought that any one investigating would find the facts and would expose them. I had thought that truth eventually must prevail, but I have found silent truth can not withstand error aided by continued propaganda. I have endeavored to have these matters investigated within the Smithsonian itself. I wrote to the Chancellor of the Institution asking for an investigation of the acts of its Secretary in this matter, and received an answer that while the Chancellor nominally was the head of the Board of the Smithsonian Institution, his other duties were such as to make it impossible for him to give any real attention to the questions which have to be settled by the Secretary. I have publicly expressed the wish that some national scientific society or other disinterested body make an impartial investigation of my charges against the Smithsonian. To this there has been no response.

In sending our original 1903 machine to the Science Museum, London, I do so with the belief it will be impartially judged and will receive whatever credit it is entitled to. I regret more than any one else that this course was necessary.

---

1. *U.S. Air Services,* March 1928, 30–31. On this controversy, see also documents 17, 20, and 24.
2. Orville meant the Science Museum in London. He mistakenly referred to it as the British National Museum.
3. See document 14, note 3.
4. Wilbur Wright to Octave Chanute, March 2, 1906, in Marvin W. McFarland, ed., *The Papers of Wilbur and Orville Wright,* 2 vols. (New York: McGraw-Hill, 1953), 2:697–98.
5. The words attributed to Wilbur Wright on page 23 of the 1910 Smithsonian annual report (referred to here) were not a direct quote from the March 2, 1906, letter to Chanute, as Orville indicates in the text, but were paraphrased. Nevertheless, the statement attributed to Wilbur in the Smithsonian annual report was not part of his remarks at the presentation of the Langley medal on February 10, 1910, as the Smithsonian implied, and it did have the misleading result that Orville complained about here. For the precise text of the inaccurate statement attributed to Wilbur, see document 7: "Presentation of Langley Medal to Messrs. Wilbur and Orville Wright," note 4.
6. See document 17, note 10.

7. This was the U.S. Circuit Court of Appeals for the Second Circuit, which included New York, Connecticut, and Vermont.
8. See document 8, note 2.
9. See document 17, note 3.
10. The U.S. Circuit Court of Appeals for the Second Circuit handed down its decision upholding the Wright patent on January 13, 1914. However, Curtiss's counsel found another loophole in the case, and Curtiss continued to manufacture aircraft. Orville Wright subsequently filed suit again, resulting in another few years of litigation.
11. The Smithsonian's "official representative" was Albert F. Zahm. See document 17, note 8.
12. *Report on the Progress and Condition of the United States National Museum, 1914* (Washington, D.C.: U.S. Government Printing Office, 1915); and *Annual Report of the Board of Regents of the Smithsonian Institution, 1914* (Washington, D.C.: U.S. Government Printing Office, 1915).

20 • ORVILLE WRIGHT DECLINES—NATURALLY: WITH THE SMITHSONIAN THESE DAYS LIFE IS JUST ONE STATEMENT—AND LABEL—AFTER ANOTHER[1]

C. G. Abbot[2] and Orville Wright

BOARD OF REGENTS "RESOLVES," 25 YEARS AFTER EVENT, THAT WRIGHT BROTHERS MADE FIRST FLIGHT—EVEN SO, THIS FACT REMAINS UNDISPUTED

On March 4, 1928, Secretary C. G. Abbot, of the Smithsonian Institution, issued the following statement to the newspapers:

Elected in January to be Secretary of the Smithsonian Institution, I inherited a knotty problem, for February brought me face to face with the Wright controversy. On February 13th I wrote to Mr. Orville Wright: "It would be a matter of great gratification to me and to all our countrymen if now, or even at a later time, you should see your way to depositing it (the Kitty Hawk machine) here."

On his part Mr. Wright has said that both he and his late brother wished to deposit the plane in the United States National Museum,[3] but that it is now sent "to the British National Museum[4] because of the hostile and unfair attitude shown towards us by the officials of the Smithsonian Institution." [See pages 30 and 31, March, 1928, issue *U.S. Air Services* for Mr. Wright's statement.—Editor.][5] It is stated that the plane is still subject to recall. Since both Mr. Wright and the Smithsonian desire it, there remains only to come to just terms.

The people of the United States, who support the National Museum, are vitally interested. They ardently desire that an object of such pride to all Americans as the Wright machine of 1903 should join the national Valhalla of aeronautics where rest so many planes that have made aviation history.

I will not again present from the other point of view the questions recently raised by Mr. Orville Wright and his friends, for fixed opinions would remain unchanged. Braving warnings that whatever I now say will be misconstrued, I ask a fair hearing for the following offer.

To make understood what I now propose, I must explain that the Langley machine of 1903[6] is now on exhibition in the National Museum, with a label attached which was prepared in 1925, according to the advice of a committee. Two gentlemen from outside the Smithsonian, namely, Dr. Joseph S. Ames, of Johns Hopkins University, Baltimore, and Admiral David W. Taylor, United States Navy, who are now Chairman and Vice-Chairman, respectively, of the U.S. National Advisory Committee for Aeronautics[7] (of which body Mr. Orville Wright is also a member) formed the committee. At the late Secretary Walcott's request they examined the records of the Langley machine, including much unpublished correspondence, took testimony of experts, and presented a report which was given to the press on June 9, 1925. The label as revised to accord therewith now stands as follows:

LANGLEY AERODROME
The Original Langley Flying Machine of 1903, Restored
In the opinion of many competent to judge, this was the first heavier-than-air craft in the history of the world capable of sustained free flight under its own power, carrying a man.

This aircraft slightly antedated the machine designed and built by Wilbur and Orville Wright, which, on December 17, 1903, was the first in the history of the world to accomplish sustained free flight under its own power, carrying a man.

(There follows in small type accounts of the investigations of Langley and of his machines, too long to quote here.)[8]

I believe that label to be just, as do my colleagues, and cannot think anybody would wish us to recant falsely. For the sake of the public, I make the following offer:

If Mr. Wright will openly state in a friendly way that he appreciates that the Smithsonian Institution honestly believes that the Langley machine of 1903 was capable of sustained free flight under its own power, carrying a man, and that it now removes that public statement, not in confession of error, but in a gesture of good will for the honor of America; then I am willing to let Langley's fame stand on its own merits and to reduce the Langley label to this simple statement: "Langley Aerodrome—The Original Langley Flying Machine of 1903, Restored."

"THERE CAN BE NO DODGING OF THE ISSUES"

Mr. Orville Wright replies as follows to the "offer" of the Smithsonian Institution, which was issued to the newspaper of March 4th:

I have had a good opinion of Dr. Abbot, and have never thought that he had any part in the insidious propaganda put out by the Smithsonian Institution before he became Secretary. When he became Secretary I hoped he would ascertain the true state of affairs in the Institution and would try to correct the errors made by a former administration.

Dr. Abbot's proposal to change the label on the Langley machine in the Smithsonian Institution does not correct the more serious things to which I have been raising objections. It does not propose to correct the false propaganda put forth in the reports and other Smithsonian publications in an attempt to take credit from my brother and me and to give this credit to a former secretary of the Institution.

Dr. Abbot's statement gives the impression that the present label is an impartial one. The committee of two gentlemen which prepared the label was appointed by the late Secretary Walcott. I knew nothing of the appointment of such a committee until their report was published in the daily press, and I was never asked by them for any testimony or evidence.

Differences of the kind existing between the Smithsonian and myself can not be settled through discussion in the press. The two sides must be brought together where there can be no dodging of the issues. I have asked for an investigation of my charges against the Smithsonian by some competent and impartial body. If the charges I have made are not true, it should be known. If they are true, that also should be known, so that credit may go where it belongs.

[Mr. Wright's original statement appeared in *U.S. Air Services* for March, pages 30 and 31.— Editor.]

---

1. *U.S. Air Services,* April 1928, 27–28. On this same subject, see also documents 17, 19, and 24.
2. Smithsonian Secretary Charles D. Walcott, with whom the Wright/Smithsonian feud began, died in 1927. He was succeeded by the astrophysicist Charles G. Abbot in 1928. During his tenure Abbot exerted great effort to resolve the controversy to Orville Wright's satisfaction without embarrassing the Smithsonian. Finally, with much reluctance, Abbot approved the publication in the 1942 Smithsonian annual report, under his name, of a full accounting of the modifications made to the Langley airplane in 1914 and an unequivocal acknowledgment that the Wrights were the first to fly. See C. G. Abbot, "The 1914 Tests of the Langley 'Aerodrome,'" *Annual Report of the Board of Regents of the Smithsonian Institution, 1942* (Washington, D.C.: U.S. Government Printing Office, 1943), 111–18. Even though the publication finally satisfied Orville's long-standing demands, he surprisingly remained silent on the issue. From the Smithsonian point of view, the situation remained at an impasse for several years beyond Abbot's retirement in 1944. Only after Orville's death in January 1948 did his private negotiations, begun in 1943, with the Science Museum in London for the return of the Wright Flyer to the United States become public. Arrangements were made to transport the historic airplane to the Smithsonian. The Flyer was formally accepted by Smithsonian Secretary Alexander Wetmore in an elaborate ceremony in Washington, D.C., on December 17, 1948, the forty-fifth

anniversary of the first flight. See also document 24: "Orville Wright Ordered Return to America of Original Airplane."
3. See document 17, note 10.
4. Orville meant the Science Museum in London. He mistakenly referred to it as the British National Museum.
5. See document 19: "Why the 1903 Wright Airplane Is Sent to a British Museum."
6. See document 17, note 3.
7. The National Advisory Committee for Aeronautics (NACA) was created by an act of Congress in 1915 to conduct basic aeronautical research and development, primarily as a service to the emerging U.S. aircraft industry and to various government aeronautical programs. Smithsonian Secretary Walcott, who had earlier founded the Langley Aeronautical Laboratory at the Smithsonian, was a key player in the establishment of NACA. His proposal for a national aeronautical research organization was the basis for the legislation signed into law by President Woodrow Wilson on March 3, 1915. NACA did not manufacture aircraft or conduct business of its own. Its principal contributions were defining key research areas, gathering and disseminating data, and providing overall leadership to the field of aeronautics. Orville Wright served as a NACA committee member for twenty-eight years, although his influence on NACA programs was minimal. NACA was the predecessor organization to NASA, the National Aeronautics and Space Administration, created in 1958. For a history of NACA, see Alex Roland, *Model Research: The National Advisory Committee for Aeronautics, 1915–1958* (Washington, D.C.: National Aeronautics and Space Administration, 1985).
8. This parenthetical comment is in the original document.

21 • WILBUR WRIGHT[1]

Orville Wright

WRIGHT, WILBUR (1867–1912), American inventor, son of Milton and Susan Catharine (Koerner) Wright, was born near Millville, Ind., on April 16, 1867. When Wilbur Wright was one month old his father was elected editor of the official organ of the Church of the United Brethren in Christ, necessitating moving his family to Dayton, O.; and eight years later he was elected a bishop of that denomination requiring other changes of residence. As a result Wilbur Wright received his education in the public schools of Dayton, Ohio, Richmond, Indiana, and Cedar Rapids, Iowa. Just when he was expecting to enter college, an accident while playing in a game of ice hockey, disabled him for some six or eight years for active work. These years of poor health he devoted to the care of his invalid mother and to assisting his father in legal matters connected with the church. In 1890 he joined his brother, Orville, who was publishing a small weekly newspaper.

Experiments in Gliding. Reading of the experiments of Otto Lilienthal in Germany, Wilbur and his brother became intensely interested in gliding as a sport. Lilienthal's experiments were suddenly ended in 1896 by his death, resulting from an accident due to insufficient control of the equilibrium of his glider. Lilienthal had balanced his machine by shifting the weight of his body. The brothers, believing this method incapable of expansion to meet the requirements of flight, set about to develop a more effective system. They developed a system in which the centre of gravity remained constant and the equilibrium was maintained by varying the air pressures on different parts of the machine through adjustments of the angles of the wings and auxiliary surfaces. This system, patented by them, is now generally known as aileron control.

Although Wilbur and his brother had taken up aeronautics merely as a sport, their chief interest soon turned to its more scientific aspects. Having found in their experiments that the existing scientific data was almost altogether untrustworthy, they cast it all aside and began investigations of their own, using methods which avoided many of the errors in the work of their predecessors. In 1901 they set up a small wind tunnel in their work-shop at Dayton in which they made measurements of the lift and drag of a great number of different-shaped aerofoils at angles from zero to 45 degrees. The results derived from this tunnel so stimulated their interest that often they worked into the early hours of the morning. Measurements also were made to determine the position of the centre of pressure on cambered surfaces and to determine the effect on the lift and drag when one surface was placed above another or when one surface followed another.[2]

The First Motor-driven Aeroplane. With this mass of data in their possession they thought it now possible to predict from calculation the performance of a flying machine; they thought they could design a machine which would require not over one-half to one-fourth of the power that would have been necessary for any of the earlier proposed machines. Accordingly in Oct. 1902, they began the design of a motor-driven aeroplane. When completed the machine including the pilot weighed 750 lb. and was propelled by a four cylinder petrol motor of 12 horse power. Tested at Kitty Hawk, N.C., on Dec. 17, 1903, the machine carrying a man made four sustained free flights. The longest of these had a duration of 59 seconds and a speed of 30 m. an hour. This machine is now exhibited in the Science museum at South Kensington, London.

Experiments were continued in 1904, but it was not until Sept. 1905, that they learned to avoid the "tail-spin" in making short turns. The flights then rapidly increased in length, and on Oct. 5 Wilbur Wright flew for 38 min. over a small circular course covering a distance of 24 miles. Believing the machine now to be developed to a stage of practical usefulness, the Wrights spent several years in finding a market for the invention. Wilbur Wright went to Europe in 1908 to make the tests required in the sale of the French rights to a syndicate. While there, his flights at Le Mans and Pau, France and at Rome, attracted world-wide attention and the kings of England, Spain and Italy went to see them. In recognition of his pioneer work he received many honours and medals in European countries and in America.

During the last three years of his life he served as president of the Wright Company, which had taken over the patent rights for America. Much of this time he devoted to upholding the Wright aeroplane patents in law courts of America and Europe. He died of typhoid fever at Dayton, O., on May 30, 1912. (O. W.)

1. *Encyclopaedia Britannica,* 14th ed., vol. 23 (1929): 808–9. Reprinted with the permission of *Encyclopaedia Britannica,* 14th edition, copyright 1929 by Encyclopaedia Britannica, Inc.
2. See document 5, note 15.

22 • WHAT'S GOING ON HERE? AN ANSWER BY OUR TRAVELING REPORTER, FRED C. KELLY[1]

Interview with Orville Wright by Fred C. Kelly

Last week I decided to go hunting. Or maybe I should say fishing. I wasn't after squirrels or bass, but information. I said to myself: "If I start out and roam over these United States and keep at it long enough, and ask enough questions of all manner of men and women, perhaps I'll find out something of interest. Sooner or later I may even hear something the newspapers have overlooked. As in hunting, or fishing, I may bag the best catch when I'm least expecting it. The only way to succeed is to try every pool or tree that seems to offer any possibilities."

I put into my suitcase a few shirts and collars, my Sunday suit for use when discussing affairs with the elite, and a more threadbare suit to wear when trying to place the proletariat at its ease, got into my once luxurious 1928 model coupé, and set out on a journey, without knowing exactly where I was going.

One of the first persons I met was Orville Wright. I had a long talk with him in Dayton, Ohio. Besides being co-inventor of the airplane, he is at heart a social philosopher. Slightly more gray than when I last saw him, but apparently in excellent health, he motioned me to a chair in front of the fireplace in his homelike mansion.

"What do you think we're headed for in this country?" I asked him.

"I think we're in for some form of socialism," he replied. "I used to think we would probably have socialism in about fifty years; but now it looks to me as if it might come in less than ten years."

"Do you say that in fear or in hope?"

"Neither," he said. "I simply think it's going to come. The only thing I hope about it is that *if* it comes, it arrives within my lifetime." Smilingly, he added: "It would be such an interesting thing to observe, in this country, I do hope I'm still here to see how it works."

"But you're a capitalist," I suggested. "You doubtless have investments."

"Yes, every penny I receive is from capital—interest on money invested. I have no paying job, do not receive any money whatever as salary or wages."

"Then, of course, you believe in capitalism?"

"I accept the interest," he replied, again smiling, "but for thirty years I have had grave doubts about the justice of getting interest for the use of money. Money, of course, doesn't produce anything of itself. Probably it's wrong to pay interest."

"But isn't present money worth more than future money?" I asked. "The old economists have always told us that is enough justification for interest—that if you postpone enjoyment of your present wealth, then you're entitled to more money back from the man you permit to take it and use it now."

"Yes, but you can look at that in two ways," declared Orville Wright. "If I am saving money now to use in old age—when I no longer have earning power, the most important thing to me is assurance that I really shall have the money in old age—that it won't be lost. If one knew a place where it would be completely safe, then one might be willing to pay a fee to the man, or to the government, that preserved it, just as we now pay fees for safe storage of other kinds of goods. As it is now, one can't well store up automobiles, machinery, or buildings, because they soon become obsolete. If you lend money to different people, hoping they will pay it back, part of the money usually gets lost. Even if you lend it to the government, and the government is still intact, you may still lose through decreased buying power of money. If you put it in a safe deposit box, you must pay the banker for the use of the box and, moreover, if you had now your money in gold you discover you are a lawbreaker. So you see the most important thing would be to get back exactly the same purchasing power as the money you saved. If you could be sure of this, you should be willing to pay interest, or a fee, for the protection."

"Without capitalism and the profit motive, would there be as many inventions as now?" I asked the inventor.

At this, Orville Wright began to chuckle.

"All I can say is that if a profit motive were necessary for an invention, most certainly my brother Will and I would not have invented the airplane," he said. "Instead of thinking about getting money out of an airplane, our chief concern was always to get money to put into it. We were at it for the sport. It was something to spend money on, because it interested us, just as a man spends money on golf if that interests him, with no thought of making it pay."

"Didn't it ever occur to you that if you *should* be the first to fly, the patents would have immense value?"

"No, because we never expected to get as far as we did in flying. We didn't expect it to go beyond the realm of sport. Commercial planes were beyond our dreams. If we had been thinking of making money, we would have tried to invent something where chances for success were brighter."

"You didn't expect to see planes costing $50,000 or more, and the government appropriating millions for the air service?"

"No, when we first talked of building a plane for the government for $5,000, the government thought the cost was too great and we couldn't much blame them. It did seem like a lot of money."

"Well, if you didn't have a profit motive when you first thought of an airplane, you must have been spurred on by the profit motive at other times," I suggested. "You had a printing business and later a bicycle repair business and you must have been in it as a means of making a living."

Still showing quiet amusement, the inventor shook his head. "We got into the printing business, Will and I, when we were children," he said. "I had got interested in some woodcuts I saw in a magazine, and tried to make some tools for carving wood blocks. I made my first tool out of the spring of a pocket knife and Will fashioned a wooden handle for it. Then we rigged up a crude press, mostly of wood. Finally we got a few fonts of brevier type. It was no fun having a press and type without printing something, and we began to get out a little neighborhood paper, as boys often do. That was the beginning of our printing business. Making it pay came as an after-thought."

"The same thing was true of your bicycle business?" I queried.

"Yes, our first interest in bicycles was racing. Then we took an agency and began to do repairing.[2] I doubt if we ever would have been in the business except for our primary interest in bicycling as a sport."

Taking another tack, I remarked: "You and your brother are often mentioned as examples of the free working of rugged individualism—where two humble boys, with no money, no influence, and no special advantage, could start at the bottom and come up. Isn't that an argument for capitalism, *laissez faire,* and all that goes with it?"

"But it isn't true to say we had no special advantages. We did have unusual advantages in childhood, without which I doubt if we could have accomplished much."

"Those advantages weren't from wealth?"

"No, wealth might have been a disadvantage. The greatest thing in our favor was growing up in a family where there was always much encouragement to intellectual curiosity. If my father had not been the kind who encouraged his children to pursue intellectual interests without any thought of profit, our early curiosity about flying would have been nipped too early to bear fruit."

As I walked down the drive from the Wright home, I recalled that Alexander Graham Bell once told me he had no thought of profit when he invented the telephone. Maybe the profit motive in human affairs isn't so important after all.

1. *Today,* March 31, 1934, 8, 22.
2. The Wrights opened their first bicycle shop in 1892. See document 15, note 2.

23 • OUR LIFE IN CAMP AT KITTY HAWK[1]

Orville Wright

The following is a story of camp life at Kitty Hawk made up entirely of excerpts from letters written at Kitty Hawk by Wilbur and me to our sister Katharine. It is edited, but slightly, to correct the more glaring mistakes in grammar and spelling, but in a few places where the excerpts would not have been clear, slight rearrangement of words has been made. The story of the first flight is not included, since it already has been told many times and is well known.

1900

Kitty Hawk is a fishing village [really a hamlet]. The people make what little living they have by fishing. They ship tons and tons of fish away every year to Baltimore and other northern cities; yet, as might be expected, we never can buy any fish!

The Kitty Hawker's house is a one or two story frame with unplaned siding, not painted, and no plaster on the walls. He has no carpets, very little furniture, and no books or pictures. There may be one or two better homes here, but this is the average. You will see that there is little wealth and luxurious living. A few men have saved up a thousand dollars, but this is the savings of a long life. Their yearly income is small. They are friendly and neighborly and I think there is rarely any real suffering among them. They are satisfied in keeping soul and body together.

Mr. Tate[2] is probably the one exception. He gets interested in anything we have; wants to put acetylene gas in his house, because he saw my bicycle gas lamp; and has decided to buy our gasoline stove when we leave. Gasoline stoves are a curiosity in this neighborhood. Mr. Tate also would like to spend his remaining days—which might be few—in experimenting with flying machines. He is already postmaster, farmer, fisherman, and political boss of Kitty Hawk. Doc. Cogswell, his brother-in-law, says Tate will be dead before Christmas from excitement, if we don't get out.

I suspect you sometimes wonder what we eat, and how we get it. There is no store in Kitty Hawk; that is, not anything that you would call a store. Our pantry at home in its most depleted state, would be a mammoth affair compared with our Kitty Hawk stores. Our camp alone exhausts the output of all the henneries within a mile. What little canned goods, such as corn, etc., is of such a nature that only a Kitty Hawker could down it. Mr. Calhoun, the groceryman, says he is "striving to raise the tastes of the community to better goods," but in vain. They never had anything good in their lives, and consequently are satisfied with what they have. Calhoun is one of the most interesting characters I have found here. He is an old man, broken in health, who came here to seek recovery. "It was the greatest mistake of my life," he always tells you, "and I will die here before I am able to get away."

I am sitting on our chicken coop writing this letter. The coop has never had a chicken in it yet, but we hope to have two tomorrow morning. Trying to camp down here reminds me of those poor arctic explorers. We are living nearly the whole time on reduced rations. We are expecting to have a big blowout tomorrow when we get those two chickens.

We have just appointed the Kitty Hawk storekeeper our agent to buy us anything he can get hold of, in any quantities he can get. We have had biscuits, molasses, coffee and rice today. Tomorrow morning we will have biscuits (made without either eggs or milk), coffee and rice. The economics of this place were so nicely balanced before our arrival that everybody here could live and yet nothing be wasted. Our presence brought disaster to the whole arrangement. We, having more money than the natives, have been able to buy up the whole egg product of the hamlet and about all the canned goods in the store.

I believe I started to tell what we eat. Well, part of the time we eat hot biscuits and eggs and tomatoes; part of the time eggs, and part, tomatoes. Just now we are out of gasoline and coffee, therefore, no hot drink or bread or crackers. The order sent off Tuesday has been delayed by the winds. Will is 'most starved. But he kept crying that, when we were rolling in luxuries such as butter, bacon, cornbread and coffee. I think he will survive. We still have half a can of condensed milk. No one down here has any regular milk. The poor cows have such a hard time scraping up a living that they don't have any time for making milk. You never saw such pitiable looking creatures as the horses, hogs and cows down here are. The only things that thrive and grow fat are the bedbugs, mosquitoes, and woodticks.

1901

Mr. Huffaker[3] arrived Thursday afternoon, and with him a swarm of mosquitoes which came in a mighty cloud, almost darkening the sun. This was the beginning of the most miserable existence I have ever passed through. The agonies of typhoid fever with its attending starvation are as nothing in comparison. The sand and grass and trees and hills and everything were fairly covered with them. They chewed us clear through our underwear and socks. Lumps began swelling up all over my body like hen-eggs.

We attempted to escape by going to bed a little after six. We put our cots out under the awnings and wrapped up in our blankets with only our noses protruding from the folds, thus exposing the least surface to attack. The wind, which until now had been blowing over twenty miles an hour, dropped off entirely. Our blankets then became unbearable, the perspiration rolled off of us in torrents. We would partly uncover and the mosquitoes would swoop down upon us in vast multitudes. We would make a few desperate and vain slaps, and again retire behind our blankets.

The half can never be told! We passed the next ten hours in a state of hopeless desperation. Morning brought a little better condition, and we attempted on several occasions to begin work on our glider, but all attempts had to be abandoned.

The next night we constructed mosquito frames and nets over our cots. We put the cots out on the sand twenty or thirty feet from the tent and house, and we lay there on our backs smiling at the way in which we had got the best of the mosquitoes. The top of the canopies became covered with them till there was hardly standing room for another one. But what was our astonishment, when in a few minutes we heard a terrific slap, and a cry from Mr. Huffaker announcing that the enemy had gained the outer works, and he was engaged in a hand-to-hand conflict. All our forces were put to complete rout. In our desperate attacks on the advancing foe our fortifications were almost entirely torn down. In desperation, we fled, rushing all about for several hundred feet trying to find some place of safety. But it was of no use. We again took refuge in our blankets with the same results as in the previous night. Affairs had now become so desperate that it began to look as if camp would have to be abandoned.

"Hope springs eternal," that is, it does the next morning when we begin to recover from the attack of the night before. Remembering the dictum of the U.S. Army that safety is in "a superior fire," we proceeded to build big fires about camp, and kept up such a smoke that the enemy could not find us. Mr. Spratt, after getting in bed with the smoke blowing over him, before long announced that he could no longer stand the smoke, and dragged his cot out into the clear air.

A few minutes later he returned, saying the mosquitoes were worse than the smoke. He spent the balance of the night in retreat from mosquito to smoke and from smoke to mosquito. Mr. Huffaker, Will and I passed the night in comparative comfort, but Mr. Spratt, in the morning, announced that that was the most miserable night he had ever been through.

1902

I suppose Will has told you how we got along like "greased lightning" till we got aboard ship (at 3 o'clock in the morning) and then got into a calm, and floated about on the water for two days before reaching Kitty Hawk. As the cabin of the *Lou Willis*[4] is not a very spacious or commodious quarter (about six feet square) and there being a lady passenger aboard, Will and I decided to allow the whole cabin to the crew and lady passenger. Taking our blankets we made beds on deck. The only trouble was to find smooth spots on deck two by six on which to stretch out. I finally settled down on the top of a lumber pile, and but for several contrary "two by fours" which wouldn't lie down, would have passed a comfortable night. We would have been in a sweet mess, had a rain set in!

The economics practiced aboard ship are even ahead of those in camp. After the mate had drawn us each a bucket of water with which to wash off the wrinkles from our faces the next morning, he proceeded to wash the dishes from the night before in cold water, without soap, in the same bucket; and then carrying it below, he made up the dough for bread in it, I suspected. However, as I had had hardly anything to eat for a couple of days, I didn't follow it below deck to see just what it was used for there, for I found the more I saw the less I ate.

We resumed our sailing with a nice strong breeze, but dead ahead, so that we had to sail about double distance, by zigzagging, in order to get to Kitty Hawk. The strong east wind blew the water out of the bay, so that the water was some eighteen inches lower than usual, and as the boat is too deep for the bay at the best, we got aground, but were fortunate in getting free in a short time.

We cast anchor some distance from the Perry wharf and put some goods ashore with a bateau, after Orville and I had come to the rescue in getting a barrel of sugar out of the hold through a hole several inches smaller than the barrel itself.

About the only exciting experiences we have had so far have been in pursuit of a little mouse which has a habit of coming out every night, prowling around in the kitchen, running over the stove, rattling through the tin oven, and overturning a tin can or two in trying to peep into them for something to eat.

He met with a rather warm reception the other night when he undertook to promenade on Will's bed. He got tossed like Sancho Panza in the blanket, until he finally escaped. We found him snugly wrapped up in our carpet this afternoon. We had a merry chase all about the building, inside and out, the large cracks in the floor making it easy for him to get in or out in a hurry when necessary. But as there were two of us, one with a stick and one with a gun, one above and one below the floor, his chances of escape were beginning to look rather shaky.

Finally he nestled up in a corner below the floor to take time to get a breath, when I blazed away at him with the gun. The mark of the bullet is in the corner right back of where he stood; nevertheless the little beastie turned around and calmly walked away, and I, in my astonishment, just stood there and watched him go. I have sworn vengeance on the "wee beastie thing" (quoted from Burns and Carrie).

Will nearly shakes the house down laughing up there in bed, when in the early hours of morning I crawl up to examine the "death trap," which I have spent whole days in preparing, only to find the pit empty and the corn bread gone. My respect for the intelligence of that wee beastie has grown wonderfully the last week. When I fix things so that it is impossible for him to get on the shelf except over the "death trap" and then get up to find all the corn bread bait I have placed on the shelf gone, I can't help thinking his ways past finding out.

He sometimes, just for fun, tosses the bread down on the tin oven to wake me up, and then disappears—where, I don't know; how, I can't imagine. The other morning, failing to awaken me in this way, he had the impudence to come onto my bed and promenade on my head, to tell me to get up and put another piece on the shelf. Will had admonished me the first night I placed the trap to take warning from the fate of Guillaume Mona, who had his head chewed off by the bear he was hunting—hunting with stratagems equal to mine—and have my head well protected.

The little mousie is truly a case of the survival of the fittest. There was a whole raft of them when we first arrived, but we soon disposed of all, with the aid of the gun and sticks, excepting this one little beast, whose cunning has defeated every stratagem our ingenuity could devise.

The pigs—they have shown some sense, too. They have learned that they are perfectly safe when Will rushes out after them with the fusseldy ammunition *(fusil de munition)*, tentpegs, if they stand still. It is only when they try to run that they get in front of his sticks. But I—that terror to burglars, mice and hogs—I sailed out with a whole armload of fusseldy ammunition on a poor razor-back that had overturned our chicken coop and laid himself down on its former site to sun himself. I placed the first with terrific force squarely in the pit of his stomach, the second the full length of his side, and the third on the back of his head. This was a victory equal to Dewey's at Manila; but when the old fellow ran off a few steps, stood dazed for some seconds, and then dropped down on his knees, I decided to sneak off. I have been afraid to go out to look for him since.

Our only other domestic creatures are our chickens, and they are now reduced to two—a pretty good-sized young pullet that limps about on one foot as a result of having scratched too much among the sand burrs; and a little bit of a fat rooster, who has had all his tail feathers pulled out by the pigs, but who feels pretty smart, just the same. However, I can't say that he always displays as much sense as the mouse. He gets out in front of one of the ponds on a day when the wind blows twenty-five miles an hour, turns his back to the wind and allows the wind to get under his wings and spread them out like two big sails.

He then is gradually and steadily pushed down to the water's edge, where, with a heroic effort, he generally succeeds in making a stand, but is kept for whole minutes at a time in a desperate struggle to keep from being blown into the water. When the wind lets down for a few seconds, he turns around and goes off twenty-five or thirty feet, only to repeat the performance at the next gust. Well, if I attempt to tell all the smart and all the fool things these birds and beasts perform to our amusement, I would be busy the rest of the night.

The mosquitoes put in their first appearance a week ago Friday, but gave us little trouble until two or three days ago. Since that time we have been building a little fire in our "brazier," and have been giving the building a good smoking early in the evening.

If my ideas seem a little clouded you will understand the reason. I can hardly see across the room tonight. This brazier is a grand thing. It was first a dishpan—a mighty poor one—so we punched holes in the bottom of it and sank it into the sand for a well, before we got the pipe down. It served much better for a well, but when Bill Tate came with his horse to visit us, we needed a manger for the horse to eat out of, so we pulled it up and fed the horse his corn out of it. We next used it for a sieve, the holes in the bottom serving this purpose very well. Finally, when the mosquitoes came, we built a small fire in it, and carried it into the building. When the mosquitoes are all smoked out, we carry it out again, and close the doors.

Orville says tell Sterchens[5] that we are going to have wild fowl for supper. He went over to the beach to shoot sea chickens and shot three. That will make one mouthful for me, and a half mouthful for him. This is an exact-size drawing of a dressed sea chicken. After a bullet has gone through one of them there is just a little meat left around the edges. Our meat, you see, is costing us about 60 cents per pound in cartridges, so you understand what epicures we are in our eating.

If we only had some butter and some lard instead of the cottonseed oil which we are using at present, and which has the effect of making the crust of our muffins resemble the shell of a terrapin in hardness, we would be living in the sixth story instead of the basement, speaking in W. H. Clay style. I hope you will interpret correctly.

1903

We reached camp Friday noon, having come over from Manteo in a small gasoline launch. We found everything in pretty good shape. The building, however, is several feet nearer the ocean than when we left last year, and about a foot lower, in places. Every year adds to our comprehension of the wonders of this place.

Two years ago, when the wind, at a speed of 107 miles per hour, took the anemometer cups away, and the mosquitoes were so thick as to dim the very brightness of the sun, and last year, when lightning burned down every telegraph pole between here and Kitty Hawk, we had supposed that nature had reached her limit; but far from it!

Dan[6] says this year has been one continuous succession of storms of unprecedented severity; the rain has descended in such torrents as to make a lake for miles about our camp; the mosquitoes were so thick they turned day into night, and the lightning so terrible it turned night into day. Really it nearly paralyzes the mind to try to think of all these things at once. Nevertheless, these sturdy Kitty Hawkers have survived it all, and are still here to welcome us among them.

But worse trouble came from my beginning on Sunday to predict a north wind for Thursday. When Thursday appeared with a mere breath of air from the south my reputation as a prophet went down below that of people who set up in this business "in their own country."

However, about two o'clock in the afternoon, a storm hove to view that made the storm that followed the prayers of Elijah look small in comparison. The wind suddenly whirled round to the north and increased to something like forty miles an hour, and was accompanied by a regular cloudburst.

In this country the winds usually blow from the north, then from the east, next from the south, and then from the west, and on to the north again. But when the wind begins to "back up," that is, veer from south to east and north, etc., then look out, for it means a cyclone is coming. Well, the wind backed up in such a hurry that it became dizzy or something. Maybe it got so in love with backing up that it went forward a little sometimes just to have the fun of "backing up" again.

It repeated this process seven times in four days, and as it reared up every time it backed, you can imagine that there was something doing. The first night the wind was probably about fifty miles and Orville and I lost much sleep. I suspect that in our early days we had a habit of contrariness which made us determined that the more they rocked us, the more we would not go to sleep. I cannot otherwise account for having such a habit now. It is really an unfortunate habit in this climate. As the new building was not quite complete as to bracing, etc., we expected it to go first, so we lay there waiting to hear it crash.

The second day opened with the gale still continuing with a steady drizzling rain. The wind veered from the northwest to the north during the morning and dropped to about thirty miles, but after dinner it began to back up again. We set to work tooth and nail (using a hammer instead of our teeth, however) putting braces inside our new building.

The climax came about four o'clock when the wind reached seventy-five miles an hour. Suddenly a corner of our tar-paper roof gave way under the pressure and we saw that if the trouble were not stopped the whole roof would probably go.

Orville put on my heavy overcoat, and grabbing the ladder sallied forth from the south end of the building. At first it appeared that he was going down to repair some of the rents in the Big Hill, which was being badly torn to pieces, for he began by walking backwards about fifty feet. After a while, I saw him come back past the side opening in our partially raised awning door. (The annexed wood cut shows the situation at this time. The wings on his back are the tails of my overcoat. The big mosquito-like images just above him are imaginary trees being bent over by the force of the wind.) Thereupon I sallied out to help him and after a tussle with the wind found him at the north end ready to set up the ladder. He quickly mounted to the edge of the roof, when the wind caught under his coat and folded it back over his head.

As the hammer and nails were in his pockets and up over his head he was unable to get his hands on them or to pull his coat tails down, so he was compelled to descend again. The next time he put the nails in his mouth and took the hammer in his hand and I followed him up the ladder hanging on to his coat tails. He swatted around a good little while trying to get a few nails in, and I became almost impatient, for I had only my common coat on and was getting well soaked.

He explained afterward that the wind kept blowing the hammer around so that three licks out of four hit the roof or his fingers instead of the nail. Finally, the job was done and we rushed for cover. He took off the overcoat and felt his other coat and found it nice and dry; but after half an hour or so, finding that he was feeling wetter and wetter, he began a second investigation and found the inside of his coat sopping wet, while the outside was nice and dry. He had forgotten when he first felt of his coat, that it, as well as the overcoat, was practically inside out while he was working on the roof.

We went to bed and both slept soundly. In the morning we found the larger part of our floor under water; but the kitchen and dining room were all right, the water being merely even with the under side of the floorboards. The storm continued through Saturday and Sunday, but by Monday it had reared up so much that it finally fell over on its back and lay quiet.

Saturday afternoon while the wind was blowing only twenty-five to thirty-five miles an hour we took the 1902 glider out and were going to soar; but we soon found that it was only too anxious to soar, and we had great difficulty in keeping it from going up too high. On Orville's second glide he shot straight up into the air and in bringing it down struck me on the head and broke one end of the machine. The wind was getting up pretty well towards forty miles again, so we had to beat a hasty retreat to camp. While trying to get the machine into the house a wind gust raised one end of the door off the props and broke the door in two.

We have been loafing most of the time for the past two weeks, though we have put in a few hours at the "unreasonable work" that caused the strike a few weeks ago. As a result we now have a good supply of hard wood well seasoned. The pine we bought of Mr. Baum was hardly worth putting in the stove, it burned up so quickly. We get fourfold value from the live oak. I warms us once to chop it down, second to carry it to camp, third to split it up, and last, but not least, when we burn it in our patent carbide stove.

We can hold fire all night easily. The weather is warm most of the time and we go about in our shirt sleeves, but after each Norther it is rather cold. However, we are entirely comfortable, and have no trouble keeping warm at nights. In addition to the classifications of last year, to-wit: 1, 2, 3 and 4-blanket nights, we now have 5 blanket nights, and 5 blanket and 2 quilt. Next come 5-blanket, 2-quilt and fire; then

5-2-fire and hot water jug. This is as far as we have got so far. Next come the addition of sleeping without undressing; then shoes and hats, and finally overcoats. We intend to be comfortable while we are here.

Mr. Chanute says that no one before ever has tried to build a machine so close to calculation. He says that nevertheless he has hope of our machine going. He seems to think we have luck, and that we are pursued by blind fate from which we are unable to escape. We do not think it is luck.

When we mounted the power machine on rollers to measure the thrust, after getting the engine running all right, we obtained a thrust of 132 pounds. As we estimate that 95 pounds will be sufficient to drive the machine, stock in flying soared tremendously and is now over 500, speaking figuratively.[7]

---

1. *U.S. Air Services,* December 1943, 12–18.
2. William J. Tate was the Wright brothers' host and assistant at Kitty Hawk. Two articles of Tate's reminiscences of the Wrights appear in the appendix. See document 71: "With the Wrights at Kitty Hawk: Anniversary of First Flight Twenty-five Years Ago," and document 72: "I Was Host to Wright Brothers at Kitty Hawk."
3. Edward C. Huffaker was a member of the late-nineteenth-century community of aeronautical experimenters working on the problem of heavier-than-air flight. He had been in the employ of Samuel P. Langley, and in 1901, when he visited the Wright brothers at Kitty Hawk, he was working for Octave Chanute. Chanute had asked the Wrights if they would welcome Huffaker into their camp, ostensibly to test a new glider he had built to Chanute's specifications. The craft was a hopeless design made of paper tubes that fell apart before even a single attempt to fly it could be made. Huffaker's abrasive personality and general incompetence sorely tried the Wrights' patience. Chanute later felt more than a little regret over imposing his tedious associate on the brothers.
4. This was the ferry boat that the Wrights took to cross Albemarle Sound to get to Kitty Hawk on the Outer Banks of North Carolina. At this time, there were no road bridges linking the Outer Banks to the Carolina mainland.
5. "Sterchens" was Katharine's nickname within the family.
6. Dan Tate, William Tate's half-brother, provided frequent assistance to the Wrights in handling the aircraft during their flying seasons at Kitty Hawk.
7. In communications sent home to Dayton, the Wrights used the reference to the stock market as a joking metaphor to chart their progress and attitude as they worked to prepare the powered airplane for its flight tests at Kitty Hawk in late 1903.

24 • ORVILLE WRIGHT ORDERED RETURN TO AMERICA OF ORIGINAL AIRPLANE[1]

The world has been advised, since the death of Orville Wright, that he ordered the return of the original Kitty Hawk airplane to America in a letter dated December 8, 1943, addressed to Colonel E. E. B. Mackintosh, Director and Secretary, The Science Museum, London, England. His letter was acknowl-

edged by Colonel Mackintosh under date January 15, 1944. Through the courtesy of Miss Mabel Beck, Secretary to Orville Wright for many years, we herewith reproduce the contents of this correspondence, as follows:

Dayton, Ohio
December 8, 1943

Dear Colonel Mackintosh:

I have decided to have the Kitty Hawk plane returned to America when transportation is less hazardous than at present. Later I will let you know the time for its return. I think you will not be surprised in learning of this decision, but I wish to let you know of it before a public announcement is made. President Roosevelt has asked that the announcement be made at a dinner to be held in Washington on the 17th of this month celebrating the fortieth anniversary of flight.

I appreciate the great trouble the plane has been to the Museum under war conditions, and I am grateful for the unusual care the Museum has taken for the plane's safety.[2]

It has been suggested that I permit the plane to be retained and again to be exhibited in the Museum for six months after the war is over, while a copy of it is being made. I think this will be agreeable to me. But before the construction of a copy is started I would suggest that another set of the drawings made by the Museum in 1928 be sent to me for correction. I have found in your drawings a number of structural details that need correction, especially in places where details could not be seen by the draftsman without a complete tearing down of the machine. However, one error, easily found, was made by your draftsman in assuming the machine is symmetrical from side to side. The right side actually is four inches longer than the left. A draftsman for the United States Army some years ago made this same mistake.

I have complete and accurate drawings of the engine. I shall be glad to furnish them, if you decide to make a replica. I also have the patterns from which the engine body was cast and would be pleased to have an aluminum casting made from them without expense to you. I shall do whatever I can in helping you to get an accurate copy of the plane and motor.

Sincerely yours,
(signed) Orville Wright

Colonel E. E. B. Mackintosh,
The Director and Secretary,
The Science Museum,
London, S.W.7, England

Follows the reply by Colonel Mackintosh.

The Science Museum,
South Kensington,
London. S.W.7

15th January 1944

Dear Mr. Orville Wright:

I must write and thank you at once for your letter of December 8th—it took just over a month to reach me, so I expect that this reply will spend the same time en route.

In your letter you tell me of your decision to have the Kitty Hawk plane returned to America as soon as the danger in transportation is eliminated. As you rightly surmise, I am not surprised to learn of your decision. The full recantation by the Smithsonian[3] at long last was so whole-hearted and satisfactory, and the recent extracts in our papers from the American press have been so explicit, that I naturally began to feel that the precious plane would have to recross the Atlantic again, and I was indeed expecting a letter from you.

Now it has come, and, if I may say so, nothing could have been more charming and courteous and helpful than its tenor.

I do earnestly wish to make an exact replica of the plane before it leaves England, for its place in our history of aviation at this Museum is of course unique. I am cursed (or blessed) with a tidy mind, and am insistent—as you yourself would be—that all details of the replica should be accurate; and, personal whims apart, accuracy is essential for historical reasons.[4]

I note your suggestion that another set of drawings made by us some years ago should be sent to you for correction. I quite agree, and much appreciate the kind thought which prompted you. At the moment I shall be held up over this; as the Museum was to be closed to the public during the war, I released the maximum possible number of staff for more imperative work elsewhere—I let all my draughtsmen go and closed the drawing office; they'll come back in time.

It is extremely good of you to offer us the complete drawings of the engine, and also an aluminum casting of the patterns for the engine body. I am most grateful for such welcome help and consideration on your part, and gladly accept your kind offer; it will be invaluable in assuring accuracy in the replica.

You say you will let me know later as to the time for the return of the machine; I shall be content to wait until in your judgment the time is opportune.

If I may presume to offer advice, as the temporary custodian of the Kitty Hawk, I feel very strongly that she should not be exposed above ground until all possibility of aerial attack on this country has ceased (except perhaps once, for a technical inspection, and then for a minimum of time), nor should she cross the Atlantic until all menace from attack by sea and air has finished.

This may sound over cautious, but I am prompted solely by my veneration for the plane and in no way, as I am sure you will realize, by any desire to retain the plane longer than is necessary for purely practical purposes. In the history of aviation Kitty Hawk is the plane for all time and all generations, and for this she must be preserved.

Perhaps 1945 will see the end of the conflict in the European theatre; no one of course can prophesy, but I have hope that the Germans will then cry halt, from a shortage of oil and man-power (breeding stock for their next war!).

Meanwhile, I send you my kindest regards and remain
Sincerely yours.
(signed) Ernest Mackintosh
The Director and Secretary

Mr. Orville Wright
Dayton
Ohio
U.S.A.

Terms of Will Regarding Return of Plane

It is known that Orville Wright was writing a new will, which was not executed before his death. The old will is eleven years old, dated in June, 1937, and in it he stated that "unless prior to my decease I personally in writing have requested its withdrawal from the museum," the plane should remain abroad.

A copy of the will, along with the original of Colonel Mackintosh's letter of acknowledgment, dated January 15, 1944, of Orville's letter of December 8, 1943, was taken to the Probate Court in Dayton, Ohio, by Miss Mabel Beck, Mr. Wright's secretary, and Harold S. Miller, nominated as co-executor in the will. Probate Judge Rodney M. Love stated on February 6:

"It is my opinion at this time that the letter meets the conditional terms expressed in Mr. Wright's will, and passes title to the plane to the executors of the estate."[5]

Birdseye View of Previous Events

On page 14 in this issue is reproduced the article written by Orville Wright, exclusively for *U.S. Air Services,* which appeared in its issue for March, 1928, giving specifically the reasons prompting him to send the original Kitty Hawk airplane to the Science Museum in South Kensington, London, England.[6] The reader is referred to it, that he may understand why Orville Wright felt that sending the Kitty Hawk machine to a foreign museum would be the only way of correcting the history of the flying machine, which by false and misleading statements had been perverted by the Smithsonian Institution.

In reply to letters deploring this decision, he said, in part, as follows:

> With this machine in any American museum the national pride will be satisfied; nothing further would be done and the Smithsonian will continue its propaganda. In a foreign museum this machine will be a constant reminder of the reason of its being there, and after the people and petty jealousies of this day are gone, the historians of the future may examine impartially the evidence and make history accord with it.
>
> Your regret that this old machine must leave our country can hardly be so great as my own.

Dr. Charles G. Abbot became the Secretary and Director of the Smithsonian Institution in 1928, the year the machine was sent abroad, succeeding Dr. Charles D. Walcott, who had died in 1927. Dr. Abbot had not been responsible for the disgraceful situation he inherited. He was in an uncomfortable, unenviable position. In *The Wright Brothers* by Fred C. Kelly (Harcourt, Brace & Company, New York) it is stated (p. 319):

> Soon after he became head of the Institution Dr. Abbot invited Orville Wright to go to lunch with him at the Carlton Hotel in Washington. In the course of their talk Dr. Abbot expressed the wish that they might come to an agreement by which the Kitty Hawk plane would be returned to America, and placed under the care of the Smithsonian in the National Museum. Orville Wright said that this could easily be done. All that he asked for, he said, was a correction in the Smithsonian publications of the false and misleading statements previously made in those publications. Dr. Abbot expressed a willingness to do so, provided this could be accomplished without injuring the reputation of his predecessor or the prestige of the Institution.
>
> But the painful fact was that the Smithsonian, however spotless its previous reputation, had committed a reprehensible act, and its reputation and prestige were bound to suffer when its guilt became known. Having committed a serious offense, one or the other of two courses were open to it: (1) to confess its guilt and make a full, frank correction or (2) to try to keep the misdeed concealed. Unfortunately, the Institution adopted, at the beginning, the latter course, evidently in the belief that its great prestige, acquired through an honorable past, could crush any imputation against it. Indeed, that course did prove successful up to the time Orville Wright sent the Kitty Hawk plane abroad.

Dr. Abbot continued to fail to publish the changes.

It was not until October, 1942, that he published them, and the statement then made is part of the annual report of the Smithsonian Institution for that year.[7]

Plane Goes to Smithsonian

The executors of the Orville Wright estate announced on February 18 at Dayton, Ohio, that the original Wright airplane will be placed on permanent exhibition in the National Museum, a section of the Smithsonian Institution, Washington, D.C. In their statement the executors, Harold S. Miller, of Dayton, and Harold W. Steeper, of Lawrence, Kans., said: "We have definitely determined that it was Orville Wright's intention to return the Kitty Hank plane to the United States and place it in the custody of the National Museum in Washington, D.C."

It can he seen there by more persons than anywhere else, a good thing in itself.

---

1. *U.S. Air Services*, February 1948, 15–16. For additional information on this subject, see also documents 17, 19, and 20.
2. With war clouds building in Europe, Science Museum Director Mackintosh first removed the Wright Flyer from display on September 28, 1938, in response to the Munich Crisis. The airplane was disassembled, crated, and stored in the basement of the museum. Following the signing of the Munich Agreement on September 30, Mackintosh informed Orville that the airplane had been reassembled and placed back on display in the central hall of the museum. After the fall of France in June 1940, the Flyer was returned to the Science Museum basement for safekeeping. In April 1942, Mackintosh informed Orville that the Flyer had been removed from the museum entirely, to protect it from potential bomb damage, and placed in an underground storage facility near the country village of Corsham, approximately one hundred miles west of London. This was the site of an ancient stone quarry that had been used by the Romans to build the nearby city of Bath. Tunnels cut into the walls of the quarry were used during World War II to store national treasures and other material of vital importance. After the war, in the spring of 1946, the Flyer was put on display in the Science Museum once again.
3. See C. G. Abbot, "The 1914 Tests of the Langley 'Aerodrome,'" *Annual Report of the Board of Regents of the Smithsonian Institution, 1942* (Washington, D.C.: U.S. Government Printing Office, 1943), 111–18.
4. The reproduction Wright Flyer was constructed by Mackintosh's staff and is still on display in the Science Museum.
5. The amendment regarding the disposition of the Wright Flyer in Orville Wright's second, unsigned will, which he was working on at the time of his death, read as follows: "I give and bequeath to the United States National Museum of Washington, D.C., for exhibition in the National Capital only, the original Wright aeroplane (now in the Science Museum, London, England), which flew at Kitty Hawk, North Carolina, on the 17th of December, 1903" (memo quoting item 5 of Orville Wright's will, Box 107, Office of the Secretary, 1925–49 [Charles D. Walcott, Charles G. Abbot, Alexander Wetmore], Record Unit 46, Smithsonian Institution Archives, Washington, D.C.).
6. See document 19: "Why the 1903 Wright Airplane Is Sent to a British Museum."
7. See Abbot, "The 1914 Tests of the Langley 'Aerodrome.'"

25 • ORVILLE WRIGHT—"FIRST MAN TO FLY"[1]

Interview with Orville Wright by Leland D. Case

On January 30, Orville Wright died in Dayton, Ohio, where he and his brother, Wilbur, invented the machine which within a generation has changed the way men and nations live and think. His last press interview—only a few weeks before his death—is recounted herewith.—The Editors

Every airplane that flies—from beetle-size models fed from an eye-dropper to that six-engined monster in California—is a mechanical grandson of the fragile contraption of sticks, wire, and canvas that lifted itself for 12 seconds from the North Carolina sand dunes only 45 years ago. It flew 120 feet—which is three feet less than the wing span of the Constellation[2] that took me to Dayton, Ohio, to talk with the man who made that first of all flights in a powered, heavier-than-air machine: Orville Wright.

Now 77,[3] he continues a lifetime habit. Each weekday from 8:30 to 6, with an hour for lunch, he works in a modest brick building on a side street. No sign is on the door or window and none is needed.

"Oh, that's Mr. Wright's office and shop," the taxi driver told me when I had given the address. "Everybody here knows that."

But local as well as global fame came unbidden to the cordial little man in a blue pin-striped double-breasted suit who greeted me. His grip was firm, but his is a sensitive, thoughtful face with questing blue eyes. Smile grooves that cut the corners of his clipped gray mustache deepened as he motioned me to a sturdy chair.

How like Paul Harris, I thought, both in manner and appearance. I mentioned the resemblance and that Rotary's Founder, always avid for new experiences, had first flown when planes were "flying crates" and cockpit passengers wore glass goggles and linen dusters.

"Perhaps you are like him in another way," I suggested. "Paul wrote in *The Rotarian* a few months before he died that he had never worn the prophet's mantle—that he didn't dream the Rotary Club he was starting in Chicago—about the time you were pioneering the airplane—would ever become a world-wide movement. Did you expect your brain child to grow into aviation as we know it today?"

"Not at all," chuckled Mr. Wright. "We—my brother Wilbur and I—did it for fun. We got interested in the problem of whether it was possible to fly and we kept at it because we wanted to see if we could work it out."

"Not to make money?"

Mr. Wright's amused glance was answer enough. "No," he said, "at one time we would have sold out for very little—*very* little. If our first interest had been money, we would have tried something in which chances for success were brighter!"

Hopes for flying *were* at low ebb in 1903. Any schoolboy could get laughs with a recitation of the poem about "Darius Green and his flying machine." After spending $100,000 on experiments, Sir Hiram Maxim had given up.[4] Efforts in Europe and America to produce even a safe glider had failed. Rear Admiral George W. Melville, chief engineer of the U.S. Navy, wrote in the *North American Review* that flying in a heavier-than-air device was an absurdity. And Professor Simon Newcom, distinguished astronomer and physicist, set forth profoundly logical reasons why it was scientifically impossible.[5]

In the face of such erudite discouragement, Wilbur and Orville Wright, two bicycle repair men who had never gone to college, went to work on the problem—for fun.

It was a toy helicopter spun by a rubber band, Orville Wright recalled, that first piqued their curiosity about flying. Alphonse Pénaud, a Frenchman, had invented it in 1871, and their father gave them one while Wilbur and Orville were lads.[6] Though they wore it out, as well as others they themselves made, their concern with flying was sidetracked several years by school and other interests.

But encouraged by their father and a mother whose clever hands "could mend anything," their inventive bent soon asserted itself. They devised gadgets for home use, then built a printing press, made a calculating machine that would multiply as well as add, and developed a simplified typewriter. Bicycles were zooming into popularity among belles and gentlemen of the gay '90s, so Wilbur and Orville opened a repair shop.[7]

In 1895 came the spark that lighted the slow fuse of their enthusiasm for flying. Over in Germany, newspapers reported, one Otto Lilienthal was having great sport in a glider.[8] The Wright brothers would go soaring too. They read everything on flying they could find in Dayton. From the Smithsonian Institution and other sources they got reports on efforts of man to fly, from Leonardo da Vinci down to Professor Langley and others still working and theorizing—the latter, chiefly, with the problem. He who thinks the Wrights were to fly because they luckily hit on a successful device is guided by a faulty assumption rather than by facts. They stood on the shoulders of all who had worked on the problem before them.

Old Leonardo had dreamed of flapping wings, like those of a bird, to carry man aloft. But it was soon obvious to Wilbur and Orville that not imitation of Nature, but a different principle, was needed. A sheet of paper sliding from a table doesn't drop directly to the floor; if shoved, it sweeps through the air at some distance, and if caught in a draft, it may float about some distance before alighting. This was the principle used in Lilienthal's glider. *A successful glider plus power would equal a flying machine!*

So in time they could spare from their thriving bicycle business, the Wright brothers poured their enthusiasm into gliders. They studied mathematical tables of air resistance. They built gliding models galore.[9] Later they developed a wind tunnel, keeping meticulous figures on behavior of various planes in air currents.[10] To try out their gliders they went to Kitty Hawk, North Carolina, where terrain was suitable and wind velocities, judging from Weather Bureau reports, would be favorable. Orville Wright's records show that more than 1,000 glider flights, several for more than 600 feet, were made there in 1902.

Now, to put power into the glider. No manufacturer of gasoline engines was interested in supplying what they needed, so they made it themselves—a not-too-smoothly operating four-cylindered device which weighed 170 pounds and delivered 12 horsepower. Ship propellers gave them their cue for a propulsive device, but many a futile experiment preceded installation of two on the machine they proposed to fly.[11]

Who should take it up first? Both were eager to do it so they flipped a coin. Wilbur won, but his trial was a failure. Two days later repairs had been made and it was Orville's turn.

The date was December 17, 1903. Water from recent rains stood in ice-skimmed puddles. A chilling 27-mile wind was blowing, but the plane's nose was thrust into it. When the motor was warmed, Orville took his place—lying flat on the lower wing. He slipped the restraining wire and the plane skidded down a monorail track with Wilbur trotting at its side.

"Here's a picture of it." Mr. Wright pointed to it on the wall. "We had set the camera on a tripod and pointed it toward where we hoped to go. John Daniels,[12] a lifesaving guardsman, took it."[13]

It was a rare experience to hear a firsthand account of man's first flight in a power-driven, heavier-than-air machine. It was a privilege to hold—and later to possess—a print made from the original 5 x 7 glass negative. There is Orville, prone, holding the rudder cords. Wilbur has just let go the wing he was steadying.

"What a moment—when your plane left the ground!" I exclaimed.

Mr Wright's response was simple, and perhaps reveals, more than any other words during the two hours we talked, the sort of man he is.

"Of course—but we expected it to."

My memory flashed back to 1927 to Lindbergh and Paris. "Lucky Lindy" we had headlined him over there in the *Herald.* But he had demurred. Hadn't he the best plane he could get? Hadn't he taken every precaution? Hadn't he flown the Atlantic, therefore, as naturally as two plus two equals four!

"Were you scared?" I asked Mr. Wright.

"Scared?" He smiled. "There wasn't time."

"Thrilled? You must have been—up there above the ground supported by wings, the first man ever to fly!"

"Well," allowed Mr. Wright, his eyes atwinkle, "I remember that at times—say, lying in bed before the event—I used to be thrilled to think of it as a possibility. But when I was actually in the air that day, I had my hands full!"

Having fun!

We didn't talk about the long years that intervened before an incredulous American press and public would believe the story told by the picture on the wall. That strange commentary on human nature has been reported in Fred C. Kelly's admirable biography *The Wright Brothers.*[14] It is corroborated by several framed photographs, hanging in Mr. Wright's office, of half-remembered figures once prominent in French and English aviation. Half covering the large golden-oak table is an extraordinary 3-foot bronze figure with batlike wings spread in flight. Seemingly trying to hold it to earth are tiny mortals.

"It's the Michelin Prize," Mr. Wright explained. "Wilbur got it in 1908 for the longest flight of the year, at Auvours, France. It was expected that Henri Farman, a Frenchman, would win it. Everyone thought Wilbur wouldn't enter the competition because our plane was being launched by pylons, with weights. But Wilbur put on wheels—and he stayed up two hours and 20 minutes."

That *was* a record in 1908—and there was an accent of pride, a nostalgic hint of high adventure in Mr. Wright's voice as he told of his brother's achievement.

A small ivory trowel, lying beside the Michelin Award, elicited another reminiscence. It was used in laying the first stone of the Wright memorial at Pau, France, in 1932, recalling the eventful months there in 1908 when Wilbur Wright demonstrated his plane to thousands of sight-seers. King Alphonso, of Spain, came with his formal entourage, but was like a boy in his enthusiasm. He wanted to fly! His Queen and his cabinet forbade it, so he clambered aboard the machine and listened as long as Wilbur would explain its structure and operation.

In those days of personal journalism, Pau was on the "black list" of the New York *Herald* and its little brother, the Paris *Herald,* both owned by James Gordon Bennett.[15] Because one of his guests at a tallyho party there years before had received attention from the police, he had issued orders that Pau was to be boycotted for news.

"But Mr. Bennett was so interested in our flying," Mr. Wright recalled with a puckish grin, "that he had to let his *Heralds* publish the news from Pau—and so Pau was put back on the map!"

While in France, Wilbur unwittingly was the cause of the "new look" of 1908. He had taken Mrs. Hart O. Berg[16] for a flight—the first made by a woman—and when she landed she walked with difficulty because her husband had tied rope around her skirt to keep it from blowing. A fashion designer was present, reports biographer Fred C. Kelly, and sensed that an outlandish skirt impeding locomotion would appeal to "customers who happened to be both stupid and rich." Thus was started the "hobble skirt."

Europe's interest in and enthusiasm for the Wright brothers' invention had no counterpart in the United States. Though they had repeatedly made planes available to the Army, the largest potential customer in America, it was not until after a brilliant demonstration in 1908 at Fort Myer, Virginia, just outside Washington, that "the brass" capitulated and placed an order.[17]

Orville Wright has reason to remember that exhibition. A cracked propeller forced a crash landing in the final flight, and the passenger, Lieutenant Thomas Selfridge, was fatally injured.[18] Mr. Wright was cut over his left eye and his left leg and four ribs were broken. Twelve years later X rays discovered overlooked hip injuries that had started sacroiliac trouble. To this day it causes great discomfort when he sits on an unpadded chair, which reduces his pleasure of and attendance at public functions. Though he became a member of the Rotary Club of Dayton in 1912, shortly after it started, he relinquished active membership in 1913 and accepted honorary status.

Extreme sensitivity to low vibration, caused by his 1908 injuries, has further limited his social orbit. Most automobiles and all trains set up a throbbing pain. It is so with ships; he hasn't been out of the United States since 1913.

"And planes?"

"They don't have a plane I can ride in comfort. Probably I shall never fly again."[19]

He told how in 1939 he went up in the then new DC-4 and was painfully uncomfortable until he stood on his toes. The Constellation, out in 1944, was smoother—and that improvement suggests more to come.[20] Future developments may enable Orville Wright to consort with the clouds again. He would like that, but he concedes that his piloting days are over.

"The last time I took up a plane was in May, 1918. I flew one of our 1911 models starting out alongside a DH-4, a French de Haviland model copied here.[21] George Creel, who directed the U.S. wartime Committee on Public Information, arranged the event to show the progress of aviation."

"Progress from 1903 to 1918 has been dwarfed by developments since," I observed.

"Especially during the last war," he agreed. "When Wilbur and I started, we never dreamed of the wealth this country would have nor what would be spent on aviation. I am told it was the biggest industry in the world during the war."

"Did you and Wilbur ever think the machine you invented would be used for bombing?"

The smile that characteristically flitted over his face as he talked disappeared as he picked his words. They had conceived it principally for civil use, he said—for sports and exhibitions, as balloons were used at county fairs—also for exploration. Back in the nineteen noughts interest in polar regions ran high, and the Wrights thought their plane might carry Peary[22] or some other explorer to the North Pole.

"Yes, we thought it might have military use—but in reverse," Mr. Wright went on. "Because the men who start wars aren't the ones who do the fighting, we hoped that the possibility of dropping bombs on capital cities would deter them."

"That was idealism somewhat akin to Nobel's," I suggested. He believed the dynamite he manufactured would make war so catastrophic men would give it up. "The day when two army corps will be able to destroy each other in a second," he had said in 1892, "all civilized nations will recoil in horror and disband their armies." That day is here with push-button planes carrying atomic bombs, yet even at this hour men talk of World War III: What of that?

"We talked and we thought that way too," Mr. Wright replied with great soberness. "We dared to hope we had invented something that would bring lasting peace to the earth. But we were wrong. We underestimated man's capacity to hate and to corrupt good means for an evil end. It is a deep disappointment that through the airplane one country can go around threatening others with a new instrument of destruction."

There are better ways, he believes, to create durable peace than through use of force, even in its sophisticated form known as "dollar diplomacy." He deeply feels that the best technique to "contain" communism is through having a better life to offer; if democracy and communism are permitted to live side by side, the better system will win out.

Definitely, Orville Wright is not a herd thinker. The originality that made him an inventor he applies to all questions of the day—social, political, economic. Sometimes he comes up with answers not shared by closest friends. But always his conclusions are colored by an idealism which recalls his boyhood in a parsonage: his father was the Reverend Milton Wright, bishop of the United Brethren Church. "All the money anyone needs," he used to tell his children, "is just enough to prevent one from being a burden on others."

Those words echo in Orville Wright's comment that "I believe in taking care of one's own, but one should have concern for others." He accepts Rotary's motto, "He Profits Most Who Serves Best," with the proviso that "serves best" must mean "serves unselfishly." He is pleased that "commercial backscratching," which he observed in Rotary's earliest days, has disappeared.

"I suppose you would say I am well-to-do," he continued, "but I am not wealthy." And those words brought up a problem he has pondered deeply: the sharing of fruits of production. As for inventors, he feels they should be compensated on the basis of the usefulness to society of their creations, wherefore he believes that he profits unduly.

"Are you inventing now?" I asked.

He motioned across the hall where his efficient secretary, Miss Mabel Beck, who started with Wilbur in 1910, was at work before the old-fashioned roll-top desk that backed his own.

"I work there," he said, "and I have a drafting board and a shop."

"Do you tackle aviation problems?"

"Anything that interests me. When I was a boy, collecting tobacco tags was a hobby. Now it's work—but it's still for fun. I've always made my work my play."

When asked to be specific, he spoke of the split flap on the rear surface of wings. He had offered it to the Navy as early as 1922, but was rebuffed. Ten years later it was accepted with avidity for it enables a plane to dive sharply or land slowly.

"Did you patent it?"

"The Dayton-Wright Company—in which I am not financially interested—took one out for myself and an assistant. But the papers carried a clause that assigned it to the company for 'one dollar and other valuable considerations'—and, really, I don't believe I ever got the dollar!"

A sly chuckle confirmed my suspicion that Mr. Wright considered this a good joke—yet not without an overload of meaning. This became clearer as he told of the 1907 Wright patent on the extension of the fuselage beyond the wings to prevent tail spins. An association of manufacturers wanted Orville Wright to sue Henry Ford for infringement, but he declined because Ford's entry into aviation gave it prestige and advanced the industry.

"What mechanical problems interest you now?"

His answer mentioned hydraulic drives, cipher machines—oh, yes, and automatic record players.

"I like music—that is, some music: it's restful to have your favorite pieces played over and over. So I developed a machine to play both sides of a dozen or more records and to repeat indicated ones as many times as I desire."

That, I declared, was a machine I wanted. I'd look for an announcement in advertisements.

A mischievous look spread over his face. "I don't think you'll find it."

"Why?"

"It's not patented. It's not on the market. It's just something I worked out—for fun."[23]

1. *The Rotarian,* April 1948, 8–10, 50–53. Reprinted with the permission of *The Rotarian,* Rotary International, Evanston, Ill.
2. This was the Lockheed Constellation transport aircraft.
3. Born on August 19, 1871, Orville was actually seventy-six years old.
4. See document 5, note 7.
5. George W. Melville, "The Engineer and the Problem of Aerial Navigation," *North American Review,* December 1901, 820–21. The full quotation from the article is: "A calm survey of certain natural phenomena leads the engineer to pronounce all confidant prophecies for future success as wholly unwarranted, if not absurd." In the years just preceding the Wrights' success, Professor Newcomb (correct spelling), a leading astronomer and scientist of his day, made numerous statements proclaiming the impossibility of heavier-than-air flight. In the October 22, 1903, issue of *The Independent,* just fifty-six days before the brothers' triumph at Kitty Hawk on December 17, Newcomb

published an article entitled "The Outlook for the Flying Machine," in which he yet again argued that humans would never fly.

6. This occurred in 1878, when Wilbur was eleven years old and Orville, seven.
7. The opened their shop in 1892. See document 15, note 2.
8. Lilienthal began his experiments with full-size gliders in 1891. By the time of his death in a glider accident in August 1896, Lilienthal had made close to two thousand flights in sixteen different glider designs. His best efforts covered more than one thousand feet and were twelve to fifteen seconds in duration.
9. This statement is untrue. The Wrights built only three piloted gliders, in 1900, 1901, and 1902, before building the first powered aircraft, flown at Kitty Hawk in 1903.
10. See document 5, note 15.
11. See document 5, note 16.
12. John T. Daniels's published reminiscence of the day of the first flight appears in document 70: "Then We Quit Laughing."
13. See photo 23.
14. Kelly's book was published in 1943.
15. The American publisher James Gordon Bennett was a strong supporter of early aviation. He contributed a number of significant monetary prizes to major flying competitions. Before turning to aviation, Bennett had established similar prestigious awards for automobile-, yacht-, and balloon-racing events.
16. Hart O. Berg was the Wrights' friend and business agent in Europe. Berg oversaw the European operations of Flint & Company, the investment firm the Wrights engaged to sell their invention in foreign markets. Mrs. Berg's flight on October 7, 1908, was the first *true* flight made with a female passenger. Madame Thérèse Peltier was the first woman actually to ride in an airplane. Three months earlier, on July 4, 1908, she flew in a Voisin biplane piloted by Léon Delagrange. But unlike the sustained flight of Mrs. Berg, this flight was merely a short, straight-line hop.
17. The U.S. Army did not actually purchase the Wright airplane until 1909, after the Wrights returned to Fort Myer with a new airplane and completed the trials interrupted in 1908 by Orville's crash with Lieutenant Thomas E. Selfridge on board. For the first airplane sold to the U.S. Army, the Wrights were paid $30,000.
18. See document 11, note 3, and document 43, note 5.
19. See document 53, note 9.
20. On April 26, 1944, Orville Wright was taken up in the new four-engine Lockheed Constellation transport aircraft on a U.S. Army demonstration flight over Dayton, Ohio. During the flight, Orville handled the controls for a brief period. This and the 1939 flight marked the only two times he had been up in an airplane, even as a passenger, in the previous twenty years.
21. The DH-4 was actually a British design also built in the United States during World War I. The firm's name is properly spelled "De Havilland."
22. Robert E. Peary reached the North Pole on April 6, 1909.
23. Ivonette Wright Miller, the brothers' favorite niece, later shared a humorous recollection of Orville's automatic record changer: "I don't remember whether he ever got it working right, but I do remember he came to our house asking us if we had any old records—he was breaking so many he was running out of supplies!" (quoted in Crouch, *The Bishop's Boys: A Life of Wilbur and Orville Wright* [New York: W. W. Norton and Co., 1989], 514).

1. Wilbur Wright (1867–1912), age twelve

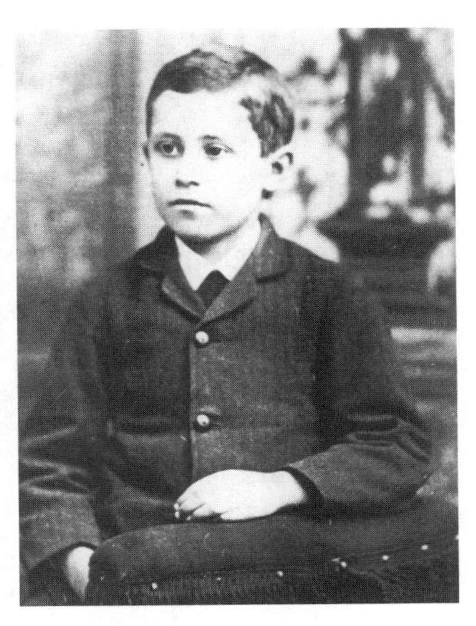

2. Orville Wright (1871–1948), age eight

3. Wilbur (left) and Orville Wright, posing for the camera on the back porch of their Dayton, Ohio, home in June 1909

4. *Above:* The Wright brothers' bicycle shop at 1127 West Third Street in Dayton. The historic structure was purchased by Henry Ford in 1936 and was moved to Ford's museum complex, called Greenfield Village, in Dearborn, Michigan, in 1937.

5. *Left:* Octave Chanute (1832–1910), the elder statesman of aeronautics and the Wrights' faithful correspondent

6. *Above:* Chanute's influential "double-decker" glider, designed in 1896, with Augustus Herring in the pilot's position

7. *Below:* Otto Lilienthal, the famed German aeronautical experimenter and glider pioneer, making a flight in one of his successful monoplane glider designs in 1895. Lilienthal was the most important pre-Wright aeronautical figure, and he strongly influenced the brothers. Wilbur later referred to him as "the greatest of the precursors."

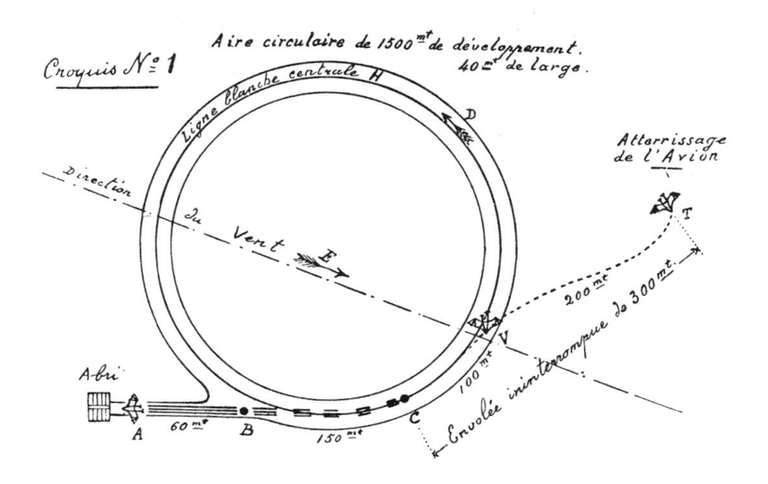

8. *Top:* Sketch of the alleged flight path of Clément Ader's aircraft on October 14, 1897, which was included with the French government's original report on the event. Wilbur Wright transcribed this report for his article "What Clement Ader Did" (document 39).

9. *Above:* The Wrights' 1900 glider, the brothers' first full-size aircraft, being flown as a kite at Kitty Hawk. The Wrights' methodical program of flight testing always began with kiting the gliders before attempting free glides.

10. *Top:* William J. Tate, the Wrights' enthusiastic host and assistant at Kitty Hawk, with his family

11. *Above:* The Wrights' 1901 glider being flown as a kite. The Wrights' original glass-plate negative of this image, along with many others, was severely damaged in a Dayton flood in 1913. This version was restored and retouched for the publication in 1953 of *The Papers of Wilbur and Orville Wright,* ed. Marvin W. McFarland. Numerous photographs in *The Papers* were restored in this way. The retouched prints are located in the McFarland boxes (86–87) in the Wright Papers collection in the Manuscript Division of the Library of Congress.

12. *Top:* Wilbur Wright on board the 1901 glider, illustrating the manner of launching the aircraft for free glides

13. *Above:* Wilbur soaring in 1901. Note the levers to actuate the forward elevator and control the glider in pitch.

14. *Top:* Wilbur making a free glide in 1901. Although this glider was successful by the standards of the day, the brothers were dissatisfied with both its lift and its control performance.

15. *Above:* The 1901 glider on landing. Chanute cautioned the Wrights about the dangers of flying the gliders with the pilot lying prone; he favored an upright pilot's position. Wilbur expressed his views on the matter in his 1901 article "The Horizontal Position during Gliding Flight" (document 27).

16. *Above left:* A reproduction of the Wrights' wind tunnel, photographed at Wright Field in 1939. In the fall of 1901 the Wrights began a series of pivotal wind tunnel tests to answer questions raised by their 1900 and 1901 gliding experiments at Kitty Hawk. The original wind tunnel was disposed of some time after the successful powered flights in 1903 (although the air pressure measuring instruments placed inside the tunnel do survive). No photographs of the original tunnel exist, but a number of accurate reproductions have been constructed over the years.

17. *Below left:* The 1902 glider. The Wrights designed their new glider in 1902 using the aerodynamic data they had gathered in their wind tunnel. The low angle of attack and the near-vertical lines while kiting the machine indicate a much superior lift-to-drag ratio of this aircraft over that of the earlier gliders. Unlike the lift of the 1900 and 1901 gliders, the actual lift of the 1902 glider was in accordance with the Wrights' calculations.

18. Wilbur gliding in 1902. The Wrights added a vertical tail to their third glider to deal with the lateral control problems experienced in 1901. The 1902 glider had a more graceful appearance than the previous gliders, as evidenced in this picture.

19. A view of the coordinated wing warping and rudder movement. The Wrights further refined their lateral control system by making the vertical tail movable.

20. The 1902 glider as it takes wing in 1903. When the Wrights returned to Kitty Hawk in 1903 to test their first powered airplane, they began by practicing with the old 1902 glider to sharpen their piloting skills. The hangar housing the powered airplane can be seen in the distance.

21. *Top:* The four-cylinder, twelve-horsepower gasoline engine that powered the 1903 Wright Flyer at Kitty Hawk. The engine was built by Charlie Taylor.

22. *Above:* The completed 1903 powered Flyer sitting outside its hangar at Kitty Hawk, ready for a trial, with Wilbur Wright looking on

23. *Top:* The moment of invention. Three days after Wilbur's abortive first trial on December 14, the Wright Flyer lifts off the launching rail at 10:35 A.M. on December 17, 1903, with Orville as pilot and Wilbur trailing behind. John Daniels, a crew member at the nearby lifesaving station, snapped the shutter of Orville's camera just as the airplane left the rail, resulting in one of the most famous photographs ever taken.

24. *Above:* The Wright Flyer at the end of its third flight, with Orville at the controls. This is the only other picture of the Flyer in the air.

Form No. 168.

THE WESTERN UNION TELEGRAPH COMPANY.

INCORPORATED

23,000 OFFICES IN AMERICA. CABLE SERVICE TO ALL THE WORLD.

This Company TRANSMITS and DELIVERS messages only on conditions limiting its liability, which have been assented to by the sender of the following message. Errors can be guarded against only by repeating a message back to the sending station for comparison, and the Company will not hold itself liable for errors or delays in transmission or delivery of Unrepeated Messages, beyond the amount of tolls paid thereon, nor in any case where the claim is not presented in writing within sixty days after the message is filed with the Company for transmission.
This is an UNREPEATED MESSAGE, and is delivered by request of the sender, under the conditions named above.

ROBERT C. CLOWRY, President and General Manager.

RECEIVED at

176 C KA CS 33 Paid. Via Norfolk Va

Kitty Hawk N C Dec 17

Bishop M Wright

7 Hawthorne St

Success four flights thursday morning all against twenty one mile wind started from Level with engine power alone average speed through air thirty one miles longest 57 seconds inform Press home [illegible] Christmas . Orevelle Wright 525P

25. *Top:* The Wright Flyer comes to rest 852 feet from the launching rail after its fourth and final flight. This 59-second effort clearly demonstrated that the Wrights had flown.

26. *Above:* The brief telegram that the Wrights sent home on December 17, 1903, announcing their success

27. *Top:* Orville (left) and Wilbur standing before their second powered airplane, in 1904. Following their triumph at Kitty Hawk, the brothers continued their experiments closer to home at a cow pasture a few miles outside Dayton known as Huffman Prairie.

28. *Above:* The Wrights' third powered airplane, built in 1905, the world's first truly practical flying machine. Wilbur stayed aloft in this airplane for thirty-nine minutes on October 5, 1905.

29. Wilbur Wright flying before cheering crowds at Le Mans, France, in August 1908. This was the Wrights' first official public demonstration of their airplane. All doubts about their accomplishment were put to rest.

30. Wilbur (center) engaged in discussion at Le Mans in 1908

TECHNICAL ARTICLES BY THE WRIGHTS

THE WRIGHT BROTHERS' "EUREKA MOMENT" came at 10:35 A.M. on December 17, 1903, when for the first time Orville lifted their Flyer off the chilly, wind-swept beach at Kitty Hawk, North Carolina. But the Wrights are not the central figures in the birth of powered flight merely because of the singular act of getting an airplane off the ground. That first flight represented four years of systematic research, and their flying machine embodied each of the critical elements of all subsequent successful aircraft. In every meaningful sense, their airplane operated in the same manner as does a modern airliner or jet fighter. The Wright brothers established the fundamental principles of aircraft design that are still in place today. They not only created the technology of flight but, of equal significance, invented the practice of aeronautical engineering.

Aerospace engineers today are aided by sophisticated wind tunnels and complex computer-design and computer-simulation programs. Modern aerodynamic theory and formulas encompass a broad range of interrelated variables. Current-day flight-testing capabilities provide an incredible array of performance data on which to refine the structures, aerodynamics, controls, and propulsion systems of new aircraft. Yet for all these advances in the tools of aircraft design, the fundamental problems to be solved and the basic practices for addressing them have changed little since Wilbur and Orville pioneered the field at the turn of the century. The performance elements they identified as critical, the way in which they used the wind tunnel to gather data and to design an aircraft, the integration of flight test data from actual field trials of their aircraft, and the process of feeding information back into a continually evolving basic design are all examples of the aeronautical engineering technique that was developed by the Wrights and that became standard practice for the engineers who followed. The talent and genius of the Wright brothers lies as much in this aspect of their work as in the assemblage of wood, wire, and fabric that rose off the sand on that momentous December day in 1903. For a thorough treatment and analysis of the Wrights' creative process and engineering method, see Peter L. Jakab's *Visions of a Flying Machine: The Wright Brothers and the Process of Invention.*

The Wright brothers' approach to aeronautical research and engineering is reflected in the technical papers gathered here in part 2. Some of the pieces present the status of the Wrights' progress as their research and findings moved toward the resolution of the basic problems of mechanical flight. Others offer the brothers' commentary on various technical issues. All demonstrate that Wilbur and Orville were clearly no mere tinkerers. Although they possessed little formal technical training, they were talented and insightful engineers. They were successful not only because of the skill in their hands but also because of the way they conceptualized problems and thought through solutions.

"Angle of Incidence" (document 26) and "The Horizontal Position during Gliding Flight" (document 27), both published in July 1901, showed the early sophistication of the brothers' approach to aeronautics. Two months later, Wilbur presented a paper before a meeting of the Western Society of Engineers in Chicago. Modestly entitled "Some Aeronautical Experiments" (document 28), the paper indicated how quickly the brothers had moved ahead of the rest of the aeronautical community. After barely more than two years of serious research, Wilbur offered the clearest and most useful statement of the basic technical requirements of mechanical flight and of what he and Orville had so far achieved toward mastering them. After a transcript of the paper appeared in the society's proceedings, it quickly became one of the most sought-after pieces of aeronautical thinking yet published. It was reprinted or abstracted in numerous scientific and engineering journals in the United States and Europe. The paper literally set the new starting point from which any successful flight research would begin.

Moreover, their work has stood the test of time. Almost all of the aerodynamic data they generated, within the limitations of their test equipment and working assumptions, is still viable when compared with data collected with today's advanced instrumentation and more thorough knowledge of aerodynamics. This collection of technical papers provides a revealing entrée to the brothers as engineers and technical thinkers. Their impressive articulation of the state of the problems and of their proposed answers speaks for itself. These two were not only creative inventors: they were engineers of the highest order.

26 • ANGLE OF INCIDENCE[1]

Wilbur Wright

If the term "angle of incidence," so frequently used in aeronautical discussions, could be confined to a single definite meaning, *viz.*, the angle at which aeroplane and wind actually meet, much error and confusion would be averted. But many of the best writers use this term loosely and inexactly, with the result that their calculations and explanations of phenomena are thereby often rendered of little value, and students are misled.

If a plane be held stationary in a horizontal wind (Fig. 1), the angle of incidence ACD will be equal to the angle with the horizon. But if the wind have an upward trend, the angle of incidence will be increased to ACD^2. A calculation based on the assumption that ACD still remained the true angle would, of course, be seriously in error.

If it be assumed (Fig. 2) that the wind moves from D^2 to C, while the plane moves from E to C, the angle of incidence will become ACD^3. The wind having an apparent horizontal speed of FC + EC, which is equal to F^2C, as compared with a vertical speed of D^2F, the wind will appear to strike the plane from the direction D^3C, thus making its angle of incidence ACD^3 instead of ACD^2.

Taking still another case (Fig. 3), in which the wind moves from D^2 to C, while the plane is rising from C to C^2 the angle of incidence will be ACX. The horizontal speed of the wind will be FC, and its apparent vertical speed

$$D^2F - CC^2 = XF,$$

so that the wind will appear to strike the plane from the direction XC. If the plane had fallen from C to C^3 the angle of incidence would have been ACX^2, since the vertical motion would now have been

$$D^2F + CC^3 = X^2F.$$

A study of the foregoing will lead to the conclusion that in order to obtain the angle of incidence, it is first necessary to know correctly (1) the angle of the plane with the horizon; (2) the horizontal speed of the wind; (3) the vertical speed of the wind;

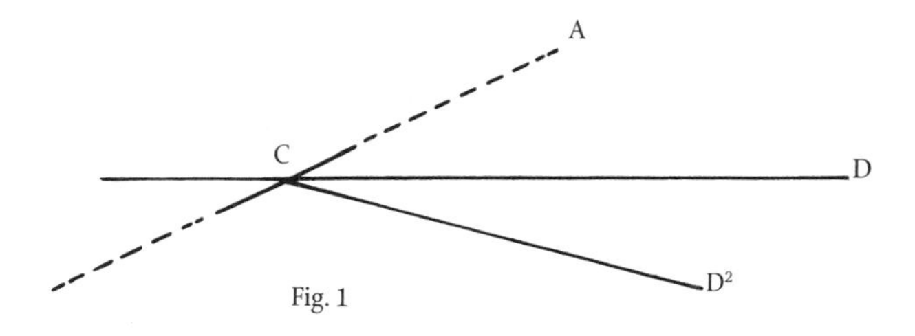

Fig. 1

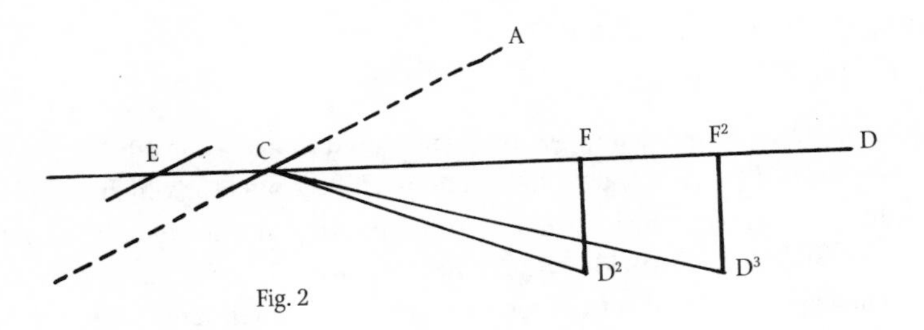

Fig. 2

(4) the horizontal speed of the plane; (5) the vertical speed of the plane. Now, since the probability of obtaining five correct simultaneous measurements is very slight when the observation is taken in the open air, and since the soaring angle is not supposed to exceed three degrees, it is evident that calculations based upon observations of soaring birds are of exceedingly doubtful value.

But though direct attempts to calculate the angle of incidence promise little of accuracy, another method remains by which approximately correct results may be obtained. The tables of Langley, Lilienthal, Chanute, and others give with a good degree of accuracy, the vertical component of the normal pressure at all angles and speeds, both for planes and curved surfaces.[2] Now, since the elements of these tables are four, *viz.*, area, speed, angle, and lift, it follows that three factors being known the fourth may readily be obtained. The angle of incidence may be calculated in any case where speed, lift and area are commensurable. Of these, area may be obtained by actual measurement. Lift is equal to weight supported, and can also be exactly measured. Speed alone requires to be calculated at the instant the observation is made. Thus the opportunity for error is reduced to a single item, and this the one which affects the result least seriously in case of a slight error. It is easier to measure speeds than angles, and errors are less costly. There is, of course, a possibility of error in the tables, but the results have been confirmed by the experiments of independent observers, and are believed to be substantially correct. Calculations of the angle of incidence based upon this plan would scarcely be so seriously in error as that of a well-known writer based upon observations of soaring gulls, in which he obtained from his measurements of angles and speeds an angle of incidence which called for an upward lift of nearly three pounds upon a two-pound bird. It was his idea that the excess of lift was expended in raising the bird above its original level. This, however, is scarcely a satisfactory explanation of how a lift of three pounds could be applied to a two-pound bird in contradiction of the law that action and reaction are always equal. It would be more reasonable to assume that the excessive lift never existed, but that the upward motion of the bird kept the angle of incidence (Fig. 3) reduced to a point where the lift was just equal to the bird's weight all of the time.

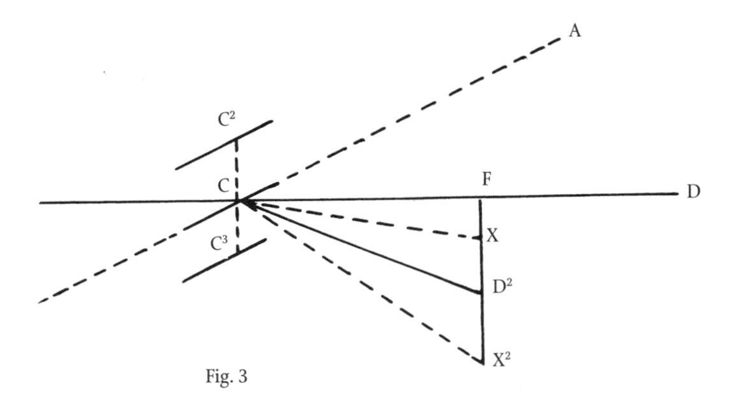

Fig. 3

If students of aeronautical problems will constantly bear in mind that (1) area of surface; (2) weight or lift; (3) relative speed are the only factors concerned in determining the angle of incidence, many errors will be detected and much trouble saved. It is clear that a bird, instead of possessing full control of its angle of incidence (as writers sometimes assume), is in fact almost powerless to change it. The bird is really itself controlled by a kind of automatic governor, for a gust of wind which tends to increase the lift is balked by the fact that the weight of the bird is not sufficient to furnish the required reaction, and the bird must either float back horizontally with a speed equal to the increase in the velocity of the wind, or it will involuntarily be raised at a speed sufficient to keep its angle of incidence at a point where the increased lifting pressure naturally due to the increased speed will be exactly counterbalanced. Nevertheless the bird can, to a limited extent, affect its area, its weight, and its speed, and thus indirectly its angle of incidence also. Its area may be reduced (and its angle increased) by partly folding its wings but as, in actual practice, a folding of the wings always accompanies an increase of relative velocity (which produces a decrease in angle), the real effect is to preserve the original angle instead of changing it. The apparent weight may be momentarily increased by a sudden curve in the direction of motion, in which case the momentum of its body acts to produce a centrifugal force which increases the downward pressure on its wings, and thus requires an increase in the angle of incidence to furnish the required extra support. Speed may be controlled by increasing or decreasing the elevation of the bird or its rate of fall. But none of these changes in speed, area or weight, quickly and permanently affect its angle of incidence. The bird can at will vary its angle with the horizon, even to the extent of three hundred and sixty degrees in less than a second, as when it turns a complete somersault in the air; but its angle of incidence probably does not vary as much as one twentieth of that amount in the same case. It is very important to distinguish carefully between the angle of incidence, and the angle with the horizon, as the latter has nothing at all *per se* to do with the former. By keeping the distinction carefully in mind, the student will quickly obtain new ideas of the correct explanation of the action of the Pénaud tail[3] used by Lilienthal, Pilcher,[4] and Chanute; and correct the sequence of cause and effect in many explanations of phenomena which occur in aeronautical writings.

Since the formulation of a principle into a rule often serves to fix it more prominently in the mind, the writer ventures to offer the following—

Rule. The angle of incidence is fixed by area, weight, and speed alone. It varies directly as the weight, and inversely as the area and speed, though not in exact ratio.

---

1. *Aeronautical Journal,* July 1901, 47–49.
2. Langley's principal aerodynamic research and data were published in Samuel P. Langley, *Experiments in Aerodynamics* (Washington, D.C.: Smithsonian Institution, 1891), and Samuel P. Langley, *The Internal Work of the Wind* (Washington, D.C.: Smithsonian Institution, 1893). Lilienthal's principal aerodynamic research and data were published in Otto Lilienthal, *Birdflight as the Basis of Aviation,* trans. A. W. Isenthal (New York: Longmans Green, 1911), originally published as *Der Vogelflug als Grundlage der Fliegekunst* in 1889; and in Hermann W. L. Moedebeck, *Pocket-Book of Aeronautics,* trans. W. Mansergh Varley (London: Whittaker and Co., 1907), pp. 287–94, originally published as *Taschenbuch zum praktischen Gebrauch für Flugtechniker und Luftschiffer* in 1895. Chanute published the data of various experimenters in Octave Chanute, *Progress in Flying Machines* (New York: M. N. Forney, 1894). He also published the Lilienthal table in his article "Sailing Flight," in James Means, ed., *The Aeronautical Annual, 1897* (Boston: W. B. Clarke and Co., 1897).
3. See document 17, note 9.
4. See document 5, note 11.

27 • THE HORIZONTAL POSITION DURING GLIDING FLIGHT[1]

Wilbur Wright

All who are practically concerned with aerial navigation agree that the safety of the operator is more important to successful experimentation than any other point. The history of past investigations demonstrates that greater prudence is needed rather than greater skill. Only a madman would propose taking greater risks than the great constructors of earlier times. Nevertheless, it may be permissible to ask whether they had entirely correct views of what was necessary for their safety. The late Herr Lilienthal was convinced that the upright position of the operator constituted the essential factor of safety in flight, and Chanute, Pilcher, and others have agreed with him. His thought was that this position made landing easier; but if the probability exists that this position results in less control of the machine in the air, it may be that more is lost by it than is gained. It is more important to prevent disastrous crashes than to mitigate somewhat their violence.

The principal advantages of the upright position are obviously in starting and landing. Once in the air, many disadvantages become evident. The body, suspended only by the arms, does not act quite as a part of the machine. Should a fall occur, if the man is lying securely prone rather than hanging like a pendulum, the strength required to alter the angle of the machine has only to overcome the slight inertia of the wing, instead of the much greater weight of man and machine together. Only the strength of his arms prevents a sudden change of the angle with the horizon, without a corresponding movement of the operator's body. This strength often does not suffice in such alterations to prevent fatal falls from resulting. Moreover, the great muscular exertion to which the operator's arms are subjected soon brings on a fatigue which seriously depletes his energy.

The horizontal position requires assistance for the launching, but once the machine is in the air, it travels more steadily and its turning motions are slower, the operator's body now being a part of the machine, and its inertia accordingly greater. It is still necessary, however, to take precautions to bring the center of pressure and center of gravity into harmony, but sudden wind gusts, which almost wrench the machine from the operator's control, lose part of their terror. Landings—as this writer knows from his own experience—are less difficult and less dangerous than one might naturally suppose. The experiments which my brother and I conducted were carried out at the seashore where sand hills rise on the sloping plain.[2] Under these conditions we made repeated landings in wind velocities exceeding 20 miles per hour (9 meters per second), without incurring any accident to us or the machine. It might not be possible to apply this system where landings have to be made on uneven or rocky ground, but on soft sand or turf it is in any case less dangerous—if indeed there is any risk—than to try to land on one's feet.

The fact that the head resistance of a flying machine is reduced by a good third if the operator adopts the horizontal position is a further argument of great consequence to the practicability of this scheme.[3] However, the fact remains that we have probably reached the limits of preserving equilibrium by shifting the operator's upright body. If other methods of preserving equilibrium are used, new ways of securing the safety of the operator must also be tested. Nevertheless, in preliminary experiments, the greatest prudence must not be neglected.

---

1. First published as "Die wagerechte Lage während des Gleitfluges" in *Illustrierte Aeronautische Mitteilungen,* July 1901, 108–9. Wilbur Wright's original unpublished English manuscript did not survive. This translation is taken from Marvin W. McFarland, ed., *The Papers of Wilbur and Orville Wright,* 2 vols. (New York: McGraw-Hill, 1953), 1:61–63.
2. This "seashore" was Kitty Hawk, North Carolina.
3. Although the Wrights calculated a one-third reduction in head resistance from using the horizontal position rather than the vertical position, they believed the reduction to be possibly as much as one-half. For the Wrights' calculation of head resistance of the pilot,

see Wilbur Wright's letter to Octave Chanute of December 3, 1900, in McFarland, *The Papers of Wilbur and Orville Wright,* 1:49–50.

28 • SOME AERONAUTICAL EXPERIMENTS[1]

Wilbur Wright

Introduction by President Chanute[2]

"Engineers have, until recent years, fought shy of anything relating to aerial navigation. Those who ventured, in spite of the odium attached to that study, to look into it at all became very soon satisfied that the great obstacle in the way was the lack of a motor sufficiently light to sustain its weight and that of an aeroplane upon the air. Fifteen years ago the lightest steam motor was the marine engine, weighing 60 pounds to the horsepower, while the gas engine weighed very much more; the locomotive weighed 200 pounds per horse power. During the past fifteen years a great change has taken place. Steam motors have been produced weighing only 10 pounds per horsepower, and gas engines have been lightened down to 12½ to 15 pounds per horsepower, so that the status, so far as engineers are concerned, is very greatly changed, and there is some hope that, for some limited purposes at least, man will eventually be able to fly through the air. There is, however, before that can be carried out—before a motor can be applied to a flying machine—an important problem to solve—that of safety or that of stability.

"I had the honor of telling you, some four or five years ago, something about the progress that had been made up to that time. Since then further advances have been made by two gentlemen from Dayton, Ohio—Mr. Wilbur Wright and Mr. Orville Wright—who tried some very interesting experiments in October, 1900. These experiments were conducted on the seashore of North Carolina, and were again resumed last July. These gentlemen have been bold enough to attempt some things which neither Lilienthal, nor Pilcher, nor myself dared to do. They have used surfaces very much greater in extent than those which hitherto have been deemed safe, and they have accomplished very remarkable results, part of which was my privilege to see on a visit which I made to their camp about a month ago.

"I thought it would be interesting to the members of this society to be the first to learn of the results accomplished, and therefore I have the honor of presenting to you Mr. Wilbur Wright."

The difficulties which obstruct the pathway to success in flying machine construction are of three general classes: (1) Those which relate to the construction of the sustaining wings; (2) those which relate to the generation and application of the power required to drive the machine through the air; (3) those relating to the balancing and steering of the machine after it is actually in flight. Of these difficulties two are already to a certain extent solved. Men already know how to construct wings or aeroplanes which, when driven through the air at sufficient speed, will not only sustain the weight of the wings themselves, but also that of the engine and of the engineer as well. Men also know how to build engines and screws of sufficient lightness and power to drive these planes at sustaining speed. As long ago as 1894 a machine weighing 8,000 pounds demonstrated its power both to lift itself from the ground and to maintain a speed of from 30 to 40 miles per hour, but failed of success owing to the inability of the operators to balance and steer it properly.[3] This inability to balance and steer still confronts students of the flying problem, although nearly eight years have passed. When this one feature has been worked out, the age of flying machines will have arrived, for all other difficulties are of minor importance.[4]

The person who merely watches the flight of a bird gathers the impression that the bird has nothing to think of but the flapping of its wings. As a matter of fact this is a very small part of its mental labor. To even mention all the things the bird must constantly keep in mind in order to fly securely through the air would take a considerable part of the evening. If I take this piece of paper, and after placing in parallel with the ground, quickly let it fall, it will not settle steadily down as a staid, sensible piece of paper ought to do, but it insists on contravening every recognized rule of decorum, turning over and darting hither and thither in the most erratic manner, much after the style of an untrained horse. Yet this is the style of steed that men must learn to manage before flying can become an everyday sport. The bird has learned this art of equilibrium, and learned it so thoroughly that its skill is not apparent to our sight. We only learn to appreciate it when we try to imitate it. Now, there are two ways of learning how to ride a fractious horse: One is to get on him and learn by actual practice how each motion and trick may be best met; the other is to sit on a fence and watch the beast a while, and then retire to the house and at leisure figure out the best way of overcoming his jumps and kicks. The latter system is the safest, but the former, on the whole, turns out the larger proportion of good riders. It is very much the same in learning to ride a flying machine; if you are looking for perfect safety, you will do well to sit on a fence and watch the birds; but if you really wish to learn, you must mount a machine and become acquainted with its tricks by actual trial.

Herr Otto Lilienthal seems to have been the first man who really comprehended that balancing was the first instead of the last of the great problems in connection with human flight. He began where others left off, and thus saved the many thousands of dollars that it had theretofore been customary to spend in building and fitting expensive engines to machines which were uncontrollable when tried. He built a pair of wings of a size suitable to sustain his own weight, and made use of gravity as his motor. This motor not only cost him nothing to begin with, but it required no expensive fuel while in operation, and never had to be sent to the shop for repairs. It had one serious drawback, however, in that it always insisted on fixing the conditions under which it would work. These were, that the man should first betake himself and machine to the top of a hill and fly with a downward as well as a forward motion. Unless these conditions were complied with, gravity served no better than a balky horse—it would not work at all. Although Lilienthal must have thought the conditions were rather hard, he nevertheless accepted them till something better should turn up; and in this manner he made some two thousand flights, in a few cases landing at a point more than 1,000 feet distant from his place of starting.[5] Other men, no doubt, long before had thought of trying such a plan. Lilienthal not only thought, but acted; and in so doing probably made the greatest contribution to the solution of the flying problem that has ever been made by any one man. He demonstrated the feasibility of actual practice in the air, without which success is impossible. Herr Lilienthal was followed by Mr. Pilcher, a young English[6] engineer, and by Mr. Chanute, a distinguished member of the society I now address. A few others have built gliding machines, but nearly all that is of real value is due to the experiments conducted under the direction of the three men just mentioned.

The balancing of a gliding or flying machine is very simple in theory. It consists in causing the center of gravity to coincide with the center of pressure.[7] But in actual practice there seems to be an almost boundless incompatibility of temper which prevents their remaining peaceably together for a single instant, so that the operator, who in this case acts as peacemaker, often suffers injury to himself while attempting to bring them together. If a wind strikes a vertical plane, the pressure on that part to one side of the center will exactly balance that on the other side, and the part above the center will balance that below. But if the plane be slightly inclined, the pressure on the part nearest the wind is increased and the pressure on the other part decreased, so that the center of pressure is now located, not in the center of the surface, but a little toward the side which is in advance. If the plane be still further inclined the center of pressure will move still farther forward, and if the wind blow a little to one side it will also move over as if to meet it. Now, since neither the wind nor the machine for even an instant maintains exactly the same direction and velocity, it is evident that the man who would trace the course of the center of pressure must be very quick of mind; and he who would attempt to move his body to that spot at every change must be very active indeed. Yet this is what Herr Lilienthal attempted to do, and did do with most remarkable skill, as his two thousand glides sufficiently attest. However, he did not escape being over turned by wind gusts several times, and finally lost his life as the result of an accidental fall.[8] The Pilcher machine was similar to that of Lilienthal. On one occasion, while exhibiting the flight of his machine to several members of the Aeronautical Society of Great Britain, it suddenly collapsed and fell to the ground, causing injuries to the operator which proved sadly fatal.[9] The method of management of this machine differed in no important respect from that of Lilienthal, the operator shifting his body to make the centers of pressure and gravity coincide. Although the fatalities which befell the designers of these machines may have been due to the lack of structural strength rather than to lack of control, nevertheless it had become clear to the students of the problem that a more prefect method of control must be evolved. The Chanute machines marked a great advance in both respects.[10] In the multiple wing machines the tips folded slightly backward under the pressure of wind gusts, so that the travel of the center of pressure was thus largely counterbalanced. The guiding of the machine was done by a slight movement of the operator's body toward the direction in which it was desired that the machine should go. The double-deck machine, built and tried at the same time, marked a very great structural advance, as it was the first in which the principles of the modern truss bridges were fully applied to flying machine construction. This machine, in addition to its greatly improved construction and general design of parts, also differed from the machine of Lilienthal in the operation of its tail. In the Lilienthal machine the tail, instead of being fixed in one position, was prevented by a stop from folding downward beyond a certain point, but was free to fold upward without any hindrance. In the Chanute machine the tail was at first rigid, but afterwards, at the suggestion of Mr. Herring,[11] it was held in place by a spring that allowed it to move slightly either upward or downward with reference to its normal position, thus modifying the action of the wind gusts upon it, very much to its advantage. The guiding of the machine was effected by slight movements of the operator's body, as in the multiple-wing machines. Both these machines were much more manageable than the Lilienthal type, and their structural strength, notwithstanding their extreme lightness, was such that no fatalities or even accidents marked the glides made with them, although winds were successfully encountered much greater in violence than any which previous experimenters had dared to attempt.

My own active interest in aeronautical problems dates back to the death of Lilienthal in 1896. The brief notice of his death which appeared in the telegraphic news at that time aroused a passive interest which had existed from my childhood and led me to take down from the shelves of our home library a book on Animal Mechanism, by Professor Marey,[12] which I had already read several times. From this I was led to read more modern works, and as my brother soon became equally interested with myself we soon passed from the reading to the thinking, and finally to the working stage. It seemed to us that the main reason why the problem had remained so long unsolved was that no one had been able to obtain any adequate practice. We figured that Lilienthal in five years of time had spent only about five hours in actual gliding through the air. The wonder was not that he had done so little, but that he had accomplished so much. It would not be considered at all safe for a bicycle rider to attempt to ride through a crowded city street after only five hours' practice, spread out in bits of ten seconds each over a period of five years; yet Lilienthal with this brief practice was remarkably successful in meeting the fluctuations and eddies of wind gusts. We thought that if some method could be found by which it would be possible to practice by the hour instead of by the second there would be hope of advancing the solution of a very difficult problem. It seemed feasible to do this by building a machine which would be sustained at a speed of 18 miles per hour, and then finding a locality where winds of this velocity were common. With these conditions, a rope attached to the machine to keep it from floating backward would answer very nearly the same purpose as a propeller driven by a motor, and it would be possible to practice by the hour, and without any serious danger, as it would not be necessary to rise far from the ground, and the machine would not have any forward motion at all. We found, according to the accepted tables of air pressures on curved surfaces that a machine spreading 200 square feet of wing surface would be sufficient for our purpose, and that places could easily be found along the Atlantic coast where winds of 16 to 25 miles were not at all uncommon. When the winds were low it was our plan to glide from the tops of sand hills, and when they were sufficiently strong to use a rope for our motor and fly over one spot. Our next work was to draw up the plans for a suitable machine. After much study we finally concluded that tails were a source of trouble rather than of assistance; and therefore we decided to dispense with them altogether. It seemed reasonable that if the body of the operator could be placed in a horizontal position instead of the upright, as in the machines of Lilienthal, Pilcher, and Chanute, the wind resistance could be very materially reduced, since only 1 square foot instead of 5 would be exposed. As a full half horsepower could be saved by this change, we arranged to try at least the horizontal position. Then the method of control used by Lilienthal, which consisted in shifting the body, did not seem quite as quick or effective as the case required; so, after long study, we contrived a system consisting of two large surfaces on the Chanute double-deck plan,[13] and a smaller surface placed a short distance in front of the main surfaces in such a position that the action of the wind upon it would counterbalance the effect of the travel of the center pressure on the main surfaces. Thus changes in the direction and velocity of the wind would have little disturbing effect, and the operator would be required to attend only to the steering of the machine, which was to be affected by curving the forward surface up or down. The lateral equilibrium and the steering to right or left was to be attained by a peculiar torsion of the main surfaces, which was equivalent to presenting one end of the wings at a greater angle than the other.[14] In the main frame a few changes were also made in the details of construction and trussing employed by Mr. Chanute. The most important of these were (1) the moving of the forward main crosspiece of the frame to the extreme front edge; (2) the encasing in the cloth of all crosspieces and ribs of the surfaces; (3) a rearrangement of the wires used in trussing the two surfaces together, which rendered it possible to tighten all the wires by simply shortening two of them.

With these plans we proceeded in the summer of 1900 to Kitty Hawk, N.C., a little settlement located on the strip of land that separates Albemarle Sound from the Atlantic Ocean. Owing to the impossibility of obtaining suitable material for a 200 square foot machine, we were compelled to make it only 165 square feet in area, which according to the Lilienthal tables[15] would be supported at an angle of 3° in a wind of about 21 miles per hour. On the very day that the machine was completed the wind blew from 25 to 30 miles per hour, and we took it out for a trial as a kite. We found that, while it was supported with a man on it in a wind of about 25 miles, its angle was much nearer 20° than 3°. Even in gusts of 30 miles the angle of incidence did not get as low as 3°, although the wind at this speed has more than twice the lifting power of a 21-mile wind. As winds of 30 miles per hour are not plentiful on clear days, it was at once evident that our plan of practicing by the hour, day after day, would have to be postponed. Our system of twisting the surfaces to regulate the lateral balance was tried and found to be much more effective than shifting the operator's body.[16] On subsequent days, when the wind was too light to support the machine with a man on it, we tested it as a kite, working the rudders by cords reaching to the ground.[17] The results were very satisfactory; yet we were well aware that this method of testing is never wholly convincing until the results are confirmed by actual gliding experience.

We then turned our attention to making a series of actual measurements of the lift and drift[18] of the machine under various loads. So far as we were aware this had never previously been done with any full-size machine. The results obtained were most astonishing, for it appeared that the total horizontal pull of the machine, while sustaining a weight of 52 pounds, was only 8.5 pounds, which was less than had previously been estimated for head resistance of the framing alone. Making allowance for the weight carried, it appeared that the head resistance of the framing was but little more than 50 per cent of the amount which Mr. Chanute had estimated as the head resistance of the framing of his machine. On the other hand, it appeared sadly deficient in lifting power as compared with the calculated lift of curved surfaces of its size.[19] This deficiency we supposed might be due to one or more of the following causes: (1) That the depth of the curvature of our surfaces was insufficient, being only about 1 in 22 instead of 1 in 12.[20] (2) That the cloth used in our wings was not sufficiently air tight. (3) That the Lilienthal tables might themselves be somewhat in error. We decided to arrange our machine for the following year so that the depth of curvature of its surfaces could be varied at will and its covering air-proofed.

Our attention was next turned to gliding, but no hill suitable for the purpose could be found near our camp at Kitty Hawk. This compelled us to take the machine to a point 4 miles south, where the Kill Devil sand hill rises from the flat sand to a height of more than 100 feet. Its main slope is toward the northeast and has an inclination of about 10°. On the day of our arrival the wind blew about 25 miles an hour, and as we had had no experience at all in gliding we deemed it unsafe to attempt to leave the ground. But on the day following, the wind having subsided to 14 miles per hour, we made about a dozen glides. It had been the original intention that the operator should run with the machine to obtain initial velocity and assume the horizontal position only after the machine was in free flight. When it came time to land he was to resume the upright position and light on his feet, after the style of previous gliding experimenters. But on actual trial we found it much better to employ the help of two assistants in starting, which the peculiar form of our machine enabled us readily to do, and in landing we found that it was entirely practicable to land while still reclining in a horizontal position upon the machine. Although the landings were made while moving at speeds of more than 20 miles an hour, neither machine nor operator suffered any injury. The slope of the hill was 9.5°, or a drop of 1 foot in 6. We found that after attaining a speed of about 25 or 30 miles with reference to the wind, or 10 to 15 miles over the ground, the machine not only glided parallel to the slope of the hill, but greatly increased its speed, thus indicating its ability to glide on a somewhat less angle than 9.5°, when we should feel it safe to rise higher from the surface. The control of the machine proved even better than we had dared to expect, responding quickly to the slightest motion of the rudder.[21] With these glides our experiments for the year 1900 closed. Although the hours and hours of practice we had hoped to obtain finally dwindled down to about two minutes, we were very much pleased with the general results of the trip, for, setting out as we did, with almost revolutionary theories on many points and an entirely untried form of machine, we considered it quite a point to be able to return without having our pet theories completely knocked in the head by the hard logic of experience, and our own brains dashed out in the bargain. Everything seemed to us to confirm the correctness of our original opinions, (1) that practice is the key to the secret of flying; (2) that it is practicable to assume the horizontal position; (3) that a smaller surface set at a negative angle in front of the main bearing surfaces, or wings, will largely counteract the effect of the fore and aft travel of the center of pressure; (4) that steering up and down can be attained with a rudder without moving the position of the operator's body; (5) that twisting the wings so as to present their ends to the wind at different angles is a more prompt and efficient way of maintaining lateral equilibrium than shifting the body of the operator.

When the time came to design our new machine for 1901, we decided to make it exactly like the previous machine in theory and method of operation. But as the former machine was not able to support the weight of the operator when flown as a kite, except in very high winds and at very large angles of incidence, we decided to increase its lifting power. Accordingly, the curvature of the surfaces was increased to 1 in 12, to conform to the shape on which Lilienthal's table was based, and to be on the safe side we decided also to increase the area of the machine from 165 square feet to 308 square feet, although so large a machine had never before been deemed controllable. The Lilienthal machine had an area of 151 square feet, that of Pilcher 165 square feet, and the Chanute double-decker 134 square feet. As our system of control consisted in a manipulation of the surfaces themselves instead of a shifting of the operator's body, we hoped that the new machine would be controllable, notwithstanding its great size. According to calculations, it would obtain support in a wind of 17 miles per hour with an angle of incidence of only 3°.

Our experience of the previous year having shown the necessity of a suitable building for housing the machine, we erected a cheap frame building, 16 feet wide, 25 feet long, and 7 feet high at the eaves. As our machine was 22 feet wide, 14 feet long (including the rudder), and about 6 feet high, it was not necessary to take the machine apart in any way in order to house it. Both ends of the building, except the gable parts, were made into doors, which hinged above, so that when opened they formed an awning at each end and left an entrance the full width of the building. We went into camp about the middle of July, and were soon joined by Mr. E. C. Huffaker,[22] of Tennessee, an experienced aeronautical investigator in the employ of Mr. Chanute, by whom his services were kindly loaned, and by Dr. G. A. Spratt,[23] of Pennsylvania, a young man who has made some valuable investigations of the properties of variously curved surfaces and the travel of the center of pressure thereon. Early in August Mr. Chanute came down from Chicago to witness our experiments and spent a week in camp with us. These gentlemen, with my brother and myself, formed our camping party, but in addition we had in many of our experiments the valuable assistance of Mr. W. J. Tate[24] and Mr. Dan Tate,[25] of Kitty Hawk.

The machine was completed and tried for the first time on the 27th of July, in a wind blowing about 13 miles an hour. The operator having taken a position where the center of pressure was supposed to be, an attempt at gliding was made, but the machine turned downward and landed after going only a few yards. This indicated that the center of gravity was too far in front of the center of pressure. In the second attempt the operator took a position several inches farther back, but the result was much the same. He kept moving farther and farther back with each trial, till finally he occupied a position nearly a foot back of that at which we had expected to find the center of pressure. The machine then sailed off and made an undulating flight of a little more than 300 feet. To the onlookers this flight seemed very successful, but to the operator it was known that the full power of the rudder had been required to keep the machine from either running into the ground or rising so high as to lose all headway. In the 1900 machine one-fourth as much rudder action had been sufficient to give much better control. It was apparent that something was radically wrong, though we were for some time unable to locate the trouble. In one glide the machine rose higher and higher till it lost all headway. This was the position from which Lilienthal had always found difficulty to extricate himself, as his machine then, in spite of his greatest exertions, manifested a tendency to dive downward almost vertically and strike the ground head on with frightful velocity. In this case a warning cry from the ground caused the operator to turn the rudder to its full extent and also to move his body slightly forward. The machine then settled slowly to the ground, maintaining its horizontal position almost perfectly, and landed without any injury at all. This was very encouraging, as it showed that one of the very greatest dangers in machines with horizontal tails had been overcome by the use of a front rudder.[26] Several glides later the same experience was repeated with the same result. In the latter case the machine had even commenced to move backward, but was nevertheless brought safely to the ground in a horizontal position. On the whole, this day's experiments were encouraging, for while the action of the rudder did not seem at all like that of our 1900 machine, yet we had escaped without difficulty from positions which had proved very dangerous to preceding experimenters, and after less than one minute's actual practice had made a glide of more than 300 feet, at an angle of descent of 10°, and with a machine nearly twice as large as had previously been considered safe. The trouble with its control, which has been mentioned, we believed could be corrected when we should have located its cause. Several possible explanations occurred to us, but we finally concluded that the trouble was due to a reversal of the direction of the travel of the center of pressure at small angles. In deeply curved surfaces the center of pressure at 90° is near the center of the surface, but moves forward as the angle becomes less, till a certain point is reached, varying with the depth of curvature. After this point is passed, the center of pressure, instead of continuing to move forward, with the decreasing angle, turns and moves rapidly toward the rear. The phenomena are due to the fact that at small angles the wind strikes the forward part of the surface on the upper side instead of the lower, and thus this part altogether ceases to lift, instead of being the most effective part of all, as in the case of the plane. Lilienthal had called attention to the danger of using surfaces with a curvature as great as 1 in 8, on account of this action of the upper side; but he seems never to have investigated the curvature and angle at which the phenomena entirely cease. My brother and I had never made any original investigation of the matter, but assumed that a curvature of one in twelve would be safe, as this was the curvature on which Lilienthal based his tables. However, to be on the safe side, instead of using the arc of a circle,[27] we had made the curve of our machine very abrupt at the front, so as to expose the least possible area to this downward pressure. While the machine was building Messrs.

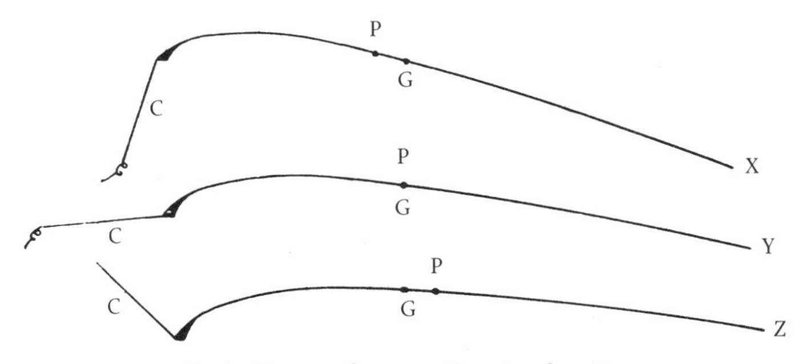

Fig. 1—P, center of pressure; G, center of gravity.

Huffaker and Spratt had suggested that we would find this reversal of the center of pressure, but we believed it sufficiently guarded against. Accordingly, we were not at first disposed to believe that this reversal actually existed in our machine, although it offered a perfect explanation of the action we had noticed in gliding. Our peculiar plan of control by forward surfaces, instead of tails, was based on the assumption that the center of pressure would continue to move farther and farther forward as the angle of incidence became less, and it will be readily perceived that it would make quite a difference if the front surface instead of counteracting this assumed forward travel should in reality be expediting an actual backward movement. For several days we were in a state of indecision, but were finally convinced by observing the following phenomena (fig. 1): We had removed the upper surface from the machine and were flying it in a wind to see at what angles it would be supported in winds of different strengths. We noticed that in light winds it flew in the upper position shown in the figure, with a strong upward pull on the cord *c*. As the wind became stronger the angle of incidence became less, and the surface flew in the position shown in the middle of the figure, with a slight horizontal pull; but when the wind became still stronger it took the lower position shown in the figure, with a strong downward pull. It at once occurred to me that here was the answer to our problem, for it is evident that in the first case the center of pressure was in front of the center of gravity, and thus pushed up the front edge; in the second case they were in coincidence and the surface in equilibrium, while in the third case the center of pressure had reached a point even behind the center of gravity, and there was therefore a downward pull on the cord. This point having been definitely settled, we proceeded to truss down the ribs of the whole machine, so as to reduce the depth of curvature. In fig. 2 line 1 shows the original curvature; line 2, the curvature when supporting the operator's weight, and line 3, the curvature after trussing.

On resuming our gliding, we found that the old conditions of the preceding year had returned, and after a few trials made a glide of 366 feet and soon after one of

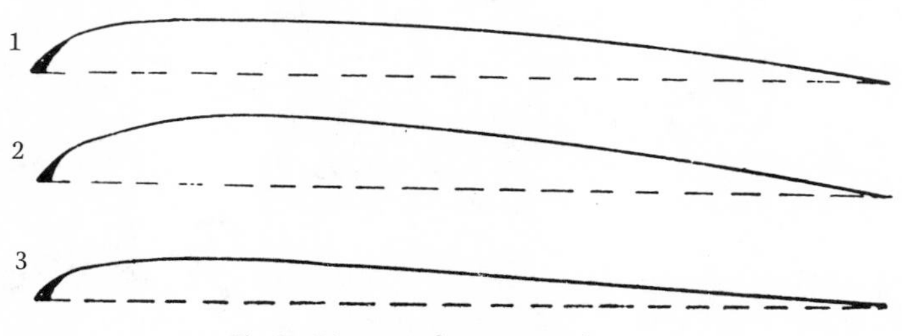

Fig. 2—Diagrams of pressures and curves.

389 feet. The machine with its new curvature never failed to respond promptly to even small movements of the rudder. The operator could cause it to almost skim the ground, following the undulations of its surface, or he could cause it to sail out almost on a level with the starting point, and passing high above the foot of the hill, gradually settle down to the ground. The wind on this day was blowing 11 to 14 miles per hour. The next day, the conditions being favorable, the machine was again taken out for trial. This time the velocity of the wind was 18 to 22 miles per hour. At first we felt some doubt as to the safety of attempting free flight in so strong a wind, with a machine of over 300 square feet, and a practice of less than five minutes spent in actual flight. But after several preliminary experiments we decided to try a glide. The control of the machine seemed so good that we then felt no apprehension in sailing boldly forth. And thereafter we made glide after glide, sometimes following the ground closely and sometimes sailing high in the air. Mr. Chanute had his camera with him and took pictures of some of these glides, several of which are among those shown.[28]

We made glides on subsequent days, whenever the conditions were favorable. The highest wind thus experimented in was a little over 12 meters per second—nearly 27 miles per hour.

It had been our intention when building the machine to do the larger part of the experimenting in the following manner: When the wind blew 17 miles an hour or more we would attach a rope to the machine and let it rise as a kite with the operator upon it. When it should reach a proper height the operator would cast off the rope and glide down to the ground just as from the top of a hill. In this way we would be saved the trouble of carrying the machine up hill after each glide, and could make at least ten glides in the time required for one in the other way. But when we came to try it we found that a wind of 17 miles, as measured by Richard's anemometer,[29] instead of sustaining the machine with its operator, a total weight of 240 pounds, at an angle of incidence of 3°, in reality would not sustain the machine alone—100 pounds—at this angle. Its lifting capacity seemed scarcely one-third of the calculated amount.[30] In order to make sure that this was not due to the porosity of the cloth, we constructed two small experimental surfaces of equal size, one of which was air-proofed and the other left in its natural state; but we could detect no difference in their lifting powers. For a time we were led to suspect that the lift of curved surfaces little exceeded that of planes of the same size, but further investigation and experiment led to the opinion that (1) the anemometer used by us over-recorded the true velocity of the wind by nearly 15 per cent; (2) that the well-known Smeaton coefficient[31] of 0.005 V^2 for the wind pressure at 90° is probably too great by at least 20 per cent; (3) that Lilienthal's estimate that the pressure on a curved surface having an angle of incidence of 3° equals 0.545 of the pressure at 90° is too large, being nearly 50 per cent greater than very recent experiments of our own with a special pressure-testing machine indicate; (4) that the superposition of the surfaces somewhat reduced the lift per square foot, as compared with a single surface of equal area.

In gliding experiments, however, the amount of lift is of less relative importance than the ratio of lift to drift, as this alone decides the angle of gliding descent. In a plane the pressure is always perpendicular to the surface, and the ratio of lift to drift is therefore the same as that of the cosine to the sine of the angle of incidence. But in curved surfaces a very remarkable situation is found. The pressure, instead of being uniformly normal to the chord of the arc, is usually inclined considerably in front of the perpendicular. The result is that the lift is greater and the drift less than if the pressure were normal. Lilienthal was the first to discover this exceedingly important fact, which is fully set forth in his book, *Bird Flight the Basis of the Flying Art,*[32] but owing to some errors in the methods he used in making measurements, question was raised by other investigators not only as to the accuracy of his figures, but even as to the existence of any tangential force at all. Our experiments confirm the existence of this force, though our measurements differ considerably from those of Lilienthal. While at Kitty Hawk we spent much time in measuring the horizontal pressure on our unloaded machine at various angles of incidence. We found that at 13° the horizontal pressure was about 23 pounds. This included not only the drift proper, or horizontal component of the pressure on the side of the surface, but also the head resistance of the framing as well. The weight of the machine at the time of this test was about 108 pounds. Now, if the pressure had been normal to the chord of the surface, the drift proper would have been to the lift (108 pounds) as the sine of 13° is to the cosine of 13°, or

$$(.22 \times 108)/.97 = 24 + \text{pounds};$$

but this slightly exceeds the total pull of 23 pounds on our scales. Therefore it is evident that the average pressure on the surface instead of being normal to the chord was so far inclined toward the front that all the head resistance of framing and wires used in the construction was more than overcome. In a wind of 14 miles per hour resistance is by no means a negligible factor, so that tangential is evidently a force of considerable value. In a higher wind, which sustained the machine at an angle of 10°, the pull on the scales was 18 pounds. With the pressure normal to the chord the drift proper would have been

$$(.17 \times 98^{a})/.98 = 17 \text{ pounds},$$ [33]

so that, although the higher wind velocity must have caused an increase in the head resistance, the tangential force still came within 1 pound of overcoming it. After our return from Kitty Hawk we began a series of experiments to accurately determine the amount and direction of the pressure produced on curved surfaces when acted upon by winds at the various angles from zero to 90°. These experiments are not yet concluded, but in general they support Lilienthal in the claim that the curve gives pressures more favorable in amount and direction than planes; but we find marked differences in the exact values especially below 10°. We were unable to obtain direct measurements of the horizontal pressures of the machine with the operator on board, but by comparing the distance traveled in gliding with the vertical fall it was easily calculated that at a speed of 24 miles per hour the total horizontal resistances of our machine when bearing the operator amounted to 40 pounds, which is equivalent to about 2⅓ horsepower. It must not be supposed, however, that a motor developing this power would be sufficient to drive a man-bearing machine. The extra weight of the motor would require either a larger machine, higher speed, or a greater angle of incidence in order to support it, and therefore more power. It is probable, however, that an engine of 6 horsepower, weighing 100 pounds, would answer the purpose. Such an engine is entirely practicable. Indeed, working motors of one-half this weight per horsepower (9 pounds per horsepower) have been constructed by several different builders. Increasing the speed of our machine from 24 to 33 miles per hour reduced the total horizontal pressure from 40 to about 35 pounds. This was quite an advantage in gliding as it made it possible to sail about 15 per cent farther with a given drop. However, it would be of little or no advantage in reducing the size of the motor in a power-driven machine, because the lessened thrust would be counterbalanced by the increased speed per minute. Some years ago Professor Langley called attention to the great economy which might be obtained by using very high speeds, and from this many were led to suppose that speeds of 50 or 60 miles an hour were essential to success; but the introduction of curved surfaces as substitutes for planes had very greatly reduced the speed of greatest economy. The probability is that the first flying machines will have a relatively low speed, perhaps not much exceeding 20 miles per hour, but the problem of increasing the speed will be much simpler in some respects than that of increasing the speed of a steamboat; for, whereas in the latter case the size of the engine must increase as the cube of the speed, in the flying machine until extremely high speeds are reached the capacity of the motor increases in less than simple ratio; and there is even a decrease in the fuel consumption per mile of travel. In other words, to double the speed of a steamship (and the same is true of the balloon type of air ship) eight times the engine and boiler capacity would be required and four times the fuel consumption per mile of travel. But, looking at the matter conversely, the great disadvantage of the flying machine is apparent; for in the latter no flight at all is possible unless the proportion of horsepower to flying capacity is very high; but, on the other hand, a steamship is a mechanical success if its ratio of horsepower to tonnage is insignificant. A flying machine that would fly at a speed of 50 miles an hour with engines of 1,000 horsepower would not be upheld by its wings at all at a speed of less than 25 miles an hour, and nothing less than 500 horsepower could drive it at this speed. But a boat which could make 40 miles per hour with engines of 1,000 horsepower would still move 4 miles an hour even if the engines were reduced to 1 horsepower. The problems of land and water travel were solved in the nineteenth century, because it was possible to begin with small achievements and gradually work up to our present success. The flying problem was left over to the twentieth century, because in this case the art must be highly developed before any flight of considerable duration can be obtained.

However, there is another way of flying which requires no artificial motor, and many workers believe that success will first come by this road. I refer to the soaring flight, by which the machine is permanently sustained in the air by the same means that are employed by soaring birds. They spread their wings to the wind, and sail by the hour, with no perceptible exertion beyond that required to balance and steer themselves. What sustains them is not definitely known, though it is almost certain that it is a rising current of air. But whether it be a rising current or something else, it is as well able to support a flying machine as a bird, if man once learns the art of utilizing it. In gliding experiments it has long been known that the rate of vertical descent is very much retarded and the duration of the flight greatly prolonged if a strong wind blows up the face of the hill parallel to its surface. Our machine, when gliding in still air, has a rate of vertical descent of nearly 6 feet per second, while in a wind blowing 26 miles per hour up a steep hill we made glides in which the rate of descent was less than 2 feet per second. And during the larger part of this time, while the machine remained exactly in the rising current, there was no descent at all, but even a slight rise. If the operator had had sufficient skill to keep himself from passing beyond the rising current, he would have been sustained indefinitely at a higher point than that from which he started. The illustration shows one of these very slow glides at a time when the machine was practically at a standstill.[34]

The failure to advance more rapidly caused the photographer some trouble in aiming, as you will perceive. In looking at this picture you will readily understand that the excitement of gliding experiments does not entirely cease with the breaking up of camp. In the photographic dark room at home we pass moments of as thrilling interest as any in the field, when the image begins to appear on the plate and it is yet an open question whether we have a picture of a flying machine or merely a patch of open sky. These slow glides in rising currents probably hold out greater hope of extensive practice than any other method within man's reach, but they have the disadvantage of requiring rather strong winds or very large supporting surfaces. However, when gliding operators have attained greater skill, they can, with comparative safety, maintain themselves in the air for hours at a time in this way, and thus by constant practice so increase their knowledge and skill that they can rise into the higher air and search out the currents which enable the soaring birds to transport themselves to any desired point by first rising in a circle to a great height and then sailing off at a descending angle. The last illustration shows the machine, alone, flying in a wind of 35 miles per hour on the face of a steep hill 100 feet high.[35] It will be seen that the machine not only pulls upward, but also pulls forward in the direction from which the wind blows, thus overcoming both gravity and the speed of the wind. We tried the same experiment with a man on it, but found danger that the forward pull would become so strong that the men holding the ropes would be dragged from their insecure foothold on the slope of the hill. So this form of experimenting was discontinued after four or five minutes' trial.

In looking over our experiments of the past two years, with models and full-size machines, the following points stand out with clearness:

1. That the lifting power of a large machine, held stationary in a wind at a small distance from the earth, is much less than the Lilienthal table and our own laboratory experiments would lead us to expect. When the machine is moved through the air, as in gliding, the discrepancy seems much less marked.

2. That the ratio of drift to lift in well-shaped surfaces is less at angles of incidence of 5° to 12° than at an angle of 3°.

3. That in arched surfaces the center of pressure at 90° is near the center of the surface, but moves slowly forward as the angle becomes less, till a critical angle, varying with the shape and depth of the curve, is reached, after which it moves rapidly toward the rear till the angle of no lift is found.

4. That with similar conditions large surfaces may be controlled with not much greater difficulty than small ones, if the control is effected by manipulation of the surfaces themselves, rather than by a movement of the body of the operator.

5. That the head resistances of the framing can be brought to a point much below that usually estimated as necessary.

6. That tails, both vertical and horizontal, may with safety be eliminated in gliding and other flying experiments.

7. That a horizontal position of the operator's body may be assumed without excessive danger, and thus the head resistance reduced to about one-fifth that of the upright position.

8. That a pair of superposed or tandem surfaces has less lift in proportion to drift than either surface separately, even after making allowance for weight and head resistance of the connections.

---

1. *Annual Report of the Board of Regents of the Smithsonian Institution, 1902* (Washington, D.C.: Government Printing Office, 1903), 133–48. An earlier version of this article appeared in *Journal of the Western Society of Engineers,* December 1901, 489–510. Wilbur Wright revised the piece for publication in the Smithsonian annual report in 1902. The article was so influential that it was reprinted or abstracted in dozens of publications for many years after its initial appearance. In addition, an abridged version of the article was combined with an abridged version of the article "Experiments and Observations in Soaring Flight" (document 29) and published as "How to Glide and Soaring Flight," in *Flight,* October 2, 1909, 607–8, 621–22, 647–48, 672–73, 693–94, 721–23, 757–58 (not included in this work).
2. Originally this article was an address presented to the Western Society of Engineers, of which Octave Chanute was president, in Chicago on September 18, 1901. No record of the spoken text of the lecture survives.
3. The reference is to Hiram Maxim's large steam-powered aircraft built in 1893. See document 5, note 7.
4. These views on the status of aeronautics were overly optimistic. The Wrights soon discovered that a great deal more work was required on wing and propulsion system design before a successful powered flying machine could be built. It is unlikely that Wilbur would have made a similar statement even a few months later.
5. Before his death in a glider accident in 1896, Lilienthal did experiment with two powered aircraft designs. Both were fitted with a carbonic-acid gas motor that drove flapping wing tips for propulsion. Neither was successful.
6. Percy Pilcher was a Scottish, not English, glider pioneer who patterned his experiments after the work of Lilienthal. See document 5, note 11.
7. The term "balance" in this context refers to maintaining equilibrium in climb and descent, also known as *pitch.* Equilibrium in the pitch axis occurs when the center of lifting pressure under the wings is kept exactly coincident with the center of gravity of the aircraft. The center of pressure is the point between the leading and trailing edges of a wing surface at which the lifting force acting on the wing is focused. The center of pressure naturally moves back and forth along the wing with changing angle of attack. Thus, maintaining equilibrium requires a means of keeping the moving center of pressure in line with the center of gravity. Lilienthal's method of maintaining equilibrium was to shift his body weight, thereby moving the center of gravity of the aircraft, to follow the roving center of pressure. Although he achieved successful glides with this technique, it required tremendous reflexes and acrobatic ability and would never have been effective with a larger, heavier powered airplane. The Wrights developed a system with

which the pilot controlled the movement of the center of pressure with respect to a fixed center of gravity.

8. On August 9, 1896, Lilienthal stalled his glider at an altitude of approximately fifty feet, crashed, and broke his spine. He died the following day in a Berlin hospital.
9. Pilcher died on October 2, 1899, two days after suffering injuries in a gliding accident that was remarkably similar to the one that took the life of Lilienthal in 1896.
10. For a detailed treatment of Chanute's experimental gliders, see Tom D. Crouch, *A Dream of Wings: Americans and the Airplane, 1875–1905* (New York: W. W. Norton and Co., 1981), 175–202.
11. Augustus M. Herring was a paid assistant to Chanute intermittently during the mid-1890s. He also performed contractual aeronautical work for Chanute when not in his employ. For a detailed discussion of Herring's aeronautical career and his relationships with Chanute and the Wright brothers, see Tom D. Crouch, *A Dream of Wings: Americans and the Airplane, 1875-1905* (New York: W. W. Norton and Co., 1981). Herring later partnered with Glenn H. Curtiss to form the Herring-Curtiss Company in 1909, the firm that would he the initial target of the Wright brothers' famous patent infringement suits. (See document 8, note 3.)
12. *Animal Mechanism,* second edition, 1890, was written by Étienne Jules Marey (1830–1904), a French physician and photographer and a pioneer in the use of graphic instruments for the study of physiological phenomena. The book was not very helpful with regard to the Wrights' aeronautical interests. It contained several photographs of birds in the air, but Marey provided no explanation of the physics of bird flight.
13. The reference is to Chanute's successful biplane glider flown in 1896. The wings were trussed one above the other with struts and cross wires, forming a light, sturdy biplane wing cell. The concept was derived from Chanute's knowledge and experience with trussed bridge designs.
14. The Wrights referred to their method of lateral control as "wing warping." They reasoned that an effective way to maneuver their craft laterally would be to alter independently the angle at which each wing-half attacks the oncoming flow of air. If one wing-half is presented at a greater angle to the wind than the other, it will generate more lift, causing that side of the aircraft to rise, which will result in a banking of the entire machine. If the pilot could mechanically and precisely manipulate the wings in this fashion, he could not only maintain lateral equilibrium but also initiate controlled turns when desired. This principle of twisting, or warping, the wings in opposite directions as a means of lateral control was at the heart of the Wrights' successful control system, and it was a central element of their basic 1906 patent on the airplane.
15. This refers to Lilienthal's table of lift and drag coefficients, according to which the Wrights designed their first glider. Based on Lilienthal's aerodynamic research conducted in the 1870s and 1880s, his table was first published in 1895 in Hermann W. L. Moedebeck's *Taschenbuch zum praktischen Gebrauch für Flugtechniker und Luftschiffer* (Pocket-Book of Aeronautics) and elsewhere subsequently. In light of Lilienthal's well-publicized successful glider flights of the 1890s, the table of coefficients became a standard starting point for all serious aeronautical experimenters who followed the great German pioneer.
16. Lilienthal used weight shifting to balance his aircraft laterally as well as in pitch.
17. So effective was this method of testing the glider that the Wrights subsequently adopted the practice of initially kiting each of their new gliders before making free

glides. They would first kite the glider empty, then with a pilot aboard to enable him to get the feel of the craft. The technique gave them the opportunity to gain vital performance information and data on their aircraft safely and efficiently, before launching into the more perilous free-flight trials. This approach of systematic and gradual flight testing of each refined design was a key element of the Wrights' success. Moreover, it was the origin of modern flight test procedures and was a significant aeronautical engineering innovation in and of itself.

18. "Drift," a term used by the Wrights, is analogous to the modern *drag.* The term *drag* in its modern aerodynamic sense did not come into common usage until after the Wrights' experimental work. They worked in terms of "total resistance," which included not only the parasitic drag of the airframe but also several other components. One of these the Wrights called "drift," which they identified not as a horizontal resistance but as a loss of altitude they expressed as a downward force.
19. The Wrights' first glider, in 1900, generated only one-half of the lift their calculations had predicted.
20. The depth of the curvature of the wing, also known as *camber,* is the ratio of the maximum height of the curve traced out by the wing profile to the width of the wing. Thus, the higher the ratio, the flatter the wing's airfoil cross section. The "1 in 12" referred to was the camber that Lilienthal's table of lift and drag coefficients was based on. His table supplied data for only this one wing curvature. Since the Wrights' wing of 1 in 22 differed significantly from Lilienthal's, this was an obvious design aspect to suspect.
21. By "rudder," Wilbur means the horizontal surface used to control the glider in pitch, now known as the *elevator.* Until the term *rudder* came to be used exclusively for the vertical surface employed for lateral stability and control, the Wrights typically referred to their horizontal pitch control surface mounted ahead of their wings as the forward or front rudder.
22. See document 23, note 3.
23. See document 10, note 6.
24. See document 23, note 2.
25. William Tate's half-brother.
26. Wilbur is describing the phenomenon commonly known today as a stall; however, when the Wrights were first experimenting, they were unaware of what a stall was or why it occurred. They did know, based on the experiences of Lilienthal and others, that when an airplane was in an extreme nose-up attitude or lost too much speed, the general result was a violent, uncontrollable crash. Even though they as yet did not understand why this happened, they were acutely aware of the danger and were ever mindful of avoiding such situations. The Wrights' forward-mounted elevator surface, or "rudder" as they called it, also known as a *canard configuration,* was extremely effective in reducing the violent reaction of a stall. Following a stall at low altitudes, the Wrights' canard design settled to the ground almost parachute style rather than going into the chilling spin common to aircraft with the elevator mounted in the rear. The glider hit with a fairly good jolt on landing, but it was usually not hard enough to damage the aircraft or to injure the pilot. The design saved Wilbur and Orville from serious injury on several occasions. It is of course possible to design a stable aircraft with gentle stall characteristics using a rear-mounted stabilizer, as is the modern convention. But with very unstable aircraft such as the Wrights' experimental machines, the canard offered a much better chance for a safe recovery from a stall. These early experiences gave the

Wrights such confidence in the design that they retained the arrangement long after their improved aircraft and flying skills permitted them to mount the elevator in the rear with safety.

27. Lilienthal's wing curvature was a perfect arc.
28. See photos 13, 14, 15.
29. "Richard's anemometer" was a French-made instrument loaned to the Wrights by Chanute. The anemometer is now in the collection of the National Air and Space Museum, Smithsonian Institution.
30. This lifting capacity was even worse than that of the 1900 glider, which produced one-half of the predicted lift.
31. The Smeaton Coefficient was a term in the basic equations that the Wrights and other contemporary experimenters used for calculating the lift and drag; it accounted for the density of the medium through which the object being studied moved, in this case a wing surface traveling through air. (If the wing was moving through some other fluid, such as water, oil, etc., the value of the term would vary accordingly.) John Smeaton was an eighteenth-century British engineer who, among other things, studied water mills and windmills. In 1759 he published a well-known paper entitled "An Experimental Enquiry Concerning the Natural Powers of Water and Wind to Turn Mills and Other Machines Depending on Circular Motion," *Philosophical Transactions of the Royal Society* 51 (London). Using the information and data in Smeaton's paper, other researchers derived the coefficient named after the author, establishing a value for the constant of 0.005. Too high by nearly 40 percent, the Smeaton Coefficient stood unquestioned until the Wrights' day, when they and other aeronautical researchers began to doubt its accuracy. The Wrights eventually arrived at a value of 0.0033, a figure confirmed by modern aerodynamicists to be accurate to within a few percentage points.
32. *Birdflight as the Basis of Aviation* is a more precise translation of the original German title, *Der Vogelflug als Grundlage der Fliegekunst* (1889). The book did not appear in English until 1911: Otto Lilienthal, *Birdflight as the Basis of Aviation,* trans. A. W. Isenthal (New York: Longmans Green, 1911).
33. [Footnote "a" appeared with the original article:] The travel of the center of pressure made it necessary to put sand on the front rudder to bring the centers of gravity and pressure into coincidence. Consequently the weight of the machine varied from 98 pounds to 108 pounds in the different tests.
34. See photo 13.
35. See photo 11.

29 • EXPERIMENTS AND OBSERVATIONS IN SOARING FLIGHT[1]

Wilbur Wright

In the address which I delivered before this society in September, 1901,[2] some account was given of the gliding experiments made by my brother, Orville Wright, and myself in the years 1900 and 1901. Afterward laboratory experiments were undertaken for the purpose of determining for ourselves the amount and direction of the pressures produced by the wind upon plane and arched surfaces exposed at various angles of incidence.[3] The results having indicated the possibility of a gliding machine capable of much better performance than any previously built by us, we set about designing a new one for the 1902 season, and in August repaired to our old camp at the Kill Devil hills.[4] We found that in our absence the wind had blown the sand from under the ends of our building and let them down fully two feet, so that after a rain the floor was covered with water to a depth of about twenty inches. We, therefore, proceeded to raise the building to its former level, and built a small addition to make it large enough to house the new machine.

The 1902 pattern was a double deck machine having two surfaces each 32 feet from tip to tip, and 5 feet from front to rear. The total area of the main surfaces was about 305 square feet. The front rudder[5] spread 15 square feet additional, and the vertical tail about 12 square feet, which was subsequently reduced to 6 square feet. The weight was 116½ lbs. Including the operator, the total weight was from 250 to 260 lbs. It was built to withstand hard usage, and in nearly a thousand glides was injured but once. It repeatedly withstood without damage the immense strains arising from landing at full speed in a slight hollow where only the tips of the wings touched the earth, the entire weight of machine and operator being suspended between.

The practice ground at the Kill Devil hills consists of a level plain of bare sand, from which rises a group of detached hills or mounds formed of sand heaped up by the winds. These hills are constantly changing in height and slope, according to the direction and force of the prevailing winds. The three which we use for gliding experiments are known as the Big Hill, the Little Hill and the West Hill, and have heights of 100 feet, 30 feet and 60 feet, respectively. In accordance with our custom of beginning operations with the greatest possible caution, we selected the Little Hill as the field of our first experiments, and began by flying the machine as a kite. The object of this was to determine whether or not it would be capable of soaring in a wind having an upward trend of a trifle over 7 degrees, which was the slope of the hill up which the current was flowing. When I speak of soaring, I mean not only that the weight of the machine is fully sustained, but also that the direction of the pressure upon the wings is such that the propelling and the retarding forces are exactly in balance; in other words, the resultant of all the pressures is exactly vertical, and therefore without any unbalanced horizontal component. A kite is soaring when the string stands exactly vertical, this showing that there is no backward pull. The phenomenon is exhibited only when the kite is flown in a rising current of air. In principle soaring is exactly equivalent to gliding, the practical difference being that in one case the wind moves with an upward trend against a motionless surface, while in the other the surface moves with a downward trend against motionless air. The reactions are identical. The soaring of birds consists in gliding downwards through a rising current of air which has a rate of ascent equal to the bird's relative rate of descent. Testing a gliding machine as a kite on a suitable slope, with just enough wind to sustain the machine at its most favorable angle of incidence, is one of the most satisfactory methods of determining its efficiency.[6] In soaring, the kite must fly steadily with the string vertical or a little to the front. Merely darting up to this position for an instant is not soaring. On trial we found that the machine would soar on the side of a hill having a slope of about 7 degrees, whenever the wind was of proper force to keep the angle of incidence between 4 and 8 degrees. If the wind became too strong or too weak the ropes would incline to leeward. The picture was taken when the wind was too weak for real soaring.[7] The surfaces are inclined 4 degrees above the horizon, which is marked by the ocean level in the distance. Since the wind had an upward trend of 7 degrees, the total angle of incidence was 11 degrees, which is outside the limits specified. On steeper slopes the ropes inclined to windward quite strongly. In experimenting on this plan, it is essential that a uniform slope be found which will give the air current a rising trend just sufficient to cause the kite string to stand vertical. Then both gravity and the pull on the string, which together provide the force counteracting the wind pressure on the surfaces, are applied in a single direction. It is therefore not material what proportion of the total counteracting force is due to each of the several components, nor even what is their total amount, because the experiment is exclusively for the purpose of determining the direction of the pressure on the surfaces by observing the direction of the reaction. When the kite string inclines to windward the slope is too steep, if to leeward not steep enough. But it is not advisable to attempt to determine how much the slope varies from the proper amount by observing the angle of the string from the vertical, for when the pull of the string differs in direction from that of gravity it becomes necessary to know not only the angle but also the exact amount of the pull and the proportion which it bears to the weight of the kite. It is therefore advisable to hunt a better slope rather than attempt to make so many observations.

The kite experiments having shown that it ought to be possible to glide on the 7-degree slope, we next proceeded to try it. Although on the first day it was not considered advisable to venture upon any absolutely free flights, the machine soon demonstrated its ability to glide with this angle of descent. At a later period we made more than a hundred flights the full length of this slope and landed a short distance out on the level ground. On the second day the machine was taken to the Big Hill and regular gliding was commenced. The wind was somewhat brisk. In one flight the wind struck the machine from the left and began lifting the left wing in a decidedly alarming manner. Owing to the fact that in the new machine changes had been made in the mechanisms operating the rudders, so that the movements were exactly reversed, it was necessary to think a moment before proceeding to make the proper adjustment. But meanwhile the left wing was rising higher and higher. I therefore decided to bring the machine to the ground as quickly as possible, but in my confusion forgot the change that had been made in the front rudder and instinctively turned it the wrong way. Almost instantly it reared up as though bent on a mad attempt to pierce the heavens. But after a moment it seemed to perceive the folly of such an undertaking and gradually slowed up till it came almost to a stop with the front of the machine still pointing heavenward. By this time I had recovered myself and reversed the rudder to its full extent, at the same time climbing upward toward the front so as to bring my weight to bear on the part that was too high. Under this heroic treatment the machine turned downward and soon began to gather headway again. By the time the ground was reached it was under fair control, but as one wing touched first it swung around in landing and came to rest with the wind blowing in from the rear. There was no unusual shock in landing and no damage at all resulted. In several other glides there were disturbances of the lateral equilibrium more marked than we had been accustomed to experience with former machines, and we were at a loss to know what the cause might be. The new machine had a much greater tip-to-tip dimension than our former machines; it also had a vertical tail while the earlier ones were tailless; and the wing tips were on a line with the center while the old machines had the tips drawn down like a gull's wings. The trouble might be due to either of these differences. We decided to begin alterations at the wing tips, and the next day made the necessary changes in the trussing, thus bringing the tips six inches lower than the center. For several days thereafter the weather was not suitable for gliding on account of rain, but finally the sky cleared and the machine was taken out again. As the anemometer indicated a wind velocity of more than 11 meters a second, it was thought best to make use of the Little Hill in testing the effect of the changes that had been made. But later in the day, when the velocity fell to about nine meters a second, the Big Hill was tried again. On this day my brother Orville did most of the gliding.[8] After a few preliminary flights to accustom himself to the new method of operating the front rudder, he felt himself ready to undertake the management of the lateral control also. Shortly afterward he started on a flight with one wing slightly higher than the other. This caused the machine to veer to the left. He waited a moment to see whether it would right itself, but finding that it did not, then decided to apply the control. At the very instant he did this, however, the right wing most unexpectedly raised much worse than before and led him to think that possibly he had made a mistake. A moment of thought was required to assure himself that he had made the right motion, and another to increase the movement. Meanwhile he had neglected the front rudder by which the fore and aft balance was maintained. The machine turned up in front more and more till it assumed a most dangerous attitude. We who were on the ground noticed this in advance of the aviator, who was thoroughly absorbed in the attempt to restore the lateral balance, but our shouts of alarm were drowned by the howling of the wind. It was only when the machine came to a stop and started backward that he at length realized the true situation. From the height of nearly thirty feet the machine sailed diagonally backward till it struck the ground. The unlucky aeronaut had time for one hasty glance behind him and the next instant found himself the center of a mass of fluttering wreckage. How he escaped injury I do not know, but afterward he was unable to show a scratch or bruise anywhere, though his clothes were torn in one place. This little misadventure which occurred almost at the very beginning of our practice with the new machine was the only thing approaching an accident that happened during these experiments, and was the only occasion on which the machine suffered any injury. The latter was made as good as new by a few days' labor, and was not again broken in any of the many hundred glides which we subsequently made with it. By long practice the management of a flying machine should become as instinctive as the balancing movements a man unconsciously employs with every step in walking, but in the early days it is easy to make blunders. For the purpose of reducing the danger to the lowest possible point we usually kept close to the ground. Often a glide of several hundred feet would be made at a height of a few feet or even a few inches sometimes. It was the aim to avoid unnecessary risk. While the high flights were more spectacular, the low ones were fully as valuable for training purposes. Skill comes by the constant repetition of familiar feats rather than by a few over-bold attempts at feats for which the performer is yet poorly prepared.[9]

It had been noticed during the day that when a side gust struck the machine its effect was at first partly counteracted by the vertical tail, but after a time when the machine had acquired a lateral motion, the tail made matters worse instead of better. Although the change that had been made in the wing tips made some improvement, the lateral control still remained somewhat unsatisfactory. The tail was useful at times and at others was seriously in the way.[10] It was finally concluded that the best way of overcoming the difficulty was by making the tail movable like a rudder.[11] As originally built the fixed vertical tail or vane was double, but in changing to a movable rudder it was made single, as the smaller area was believed to be sufficient. As reconstructed it spread a little less than six square feet. With this improvement our serious troubles ended and thereafter we devoted ourselves to the work of gaining skill by continued practice. When properly applied the means of control proved to possess a mastery over the forces tending to disturb the equilibrium. Since balancing was effected by adjustments of the surfaces, instead of by movements of weight, the controlling forces increased in power in the same ratio as the disturbing forces, when the machine was suddenly struck by a wind gust. For this reason we did not seem to experience the same difficulty in managing the machine in high winds, that Lilienthal who used a different system seems to have met. Fully half of our glides were made in winds of 10 meters a second, over 20 miles an hour. One day we stopped gliding for a moment to take an anemometer reading and found that it indicated 16.7 meters a second, 37 miles an hour. Of course such high winds require much greater readiness on the part of the operator than the low winds, since everything happens much more quickly, but otherwise the difference is not so very marked. In those machines which are controlled by the shifting of weight, the disturbing influences increase as the square of the velocity, while the controlling factor remains a constant quantity. For this reason a limit to the wind velocity which it is possible to safely encounter with such machines is soon reached, regardless of the skill of the operator. With the method we have been using the capacity of control is evidently very great. The machine seems to have reached a higher state of development than the operators. As yet we consider ourselves little more than novices in management. A thousand glides is equivalent to about four hours of steady practice, far too little to give anyone a complete mastery of the art of flying. Progress is very slow in the preliminary stages, but when once it becomes possible to undertake continuous soaring advancement should be rapid. Under special conditions it is possible that this point is not so far away as might be supposed. Since soaring is merely gliding in a rising current it would be easy to soar in front of any hill of suitable slope, whenever the wind blew with sufficient force to furnish support, provided the wind were steady. But by reason of changes in wind velocity there is more support at times than is needed, while at others there is too little, so that a considerable degree of skill, experience and sound judgment is required in order to keep the machine exactly in the rising current. So far our only attempts at soaring have been made on the Little Hill, which has a slope of only seven degrees. In a wind blowing from 11 to 16 meters a second, we frequently made glides of 8 to 15 seconds' duration with very little forward motion. As we kept within five or six feet of the ground, a momentary lessening of the wind speed, or a slight error in management, was sufficient to bring about a landing in a short time. The wind had too little rising trend to make soaring easy. The buzzards themselves were balked when they attempted to soar on this hill, as we observed more than once. It would be well within the power of the machine to soar on the Big Hill, which has steeper slopes, but we have not felt that our few hours of practice is sufficient to justify ambitious attempts too hastily. Before trying to rise to any dangerous height a man ought to know that in an emergency his mind and muscles will work by instinct rather than by conscious effort. There is no time to think.

During a period of five weeks glides were made whenever the weather conditions were favorable. Many days were lost on account of rain. Still more were lost on account of light winds. Whenever the breeze fell below six miles an hour, very hard running was required to get the machine started, and the task of carrying it back up the hill was real labor. A relative speed of at least 18 miles an hour was required for gliding, while to obtain a speed of 12 miles by running required very severe exertion. Consequently unless the wind blew in our faces with a speed of at least six miles we did not usually attempt to practice; but when the wind rose to 20 miles an hour, gliding was real sport, for starting was easy and the labor of carrying the machine back uphill was performed by the wind. On the day when the wind rose to over 16 meters a second we made more than a hundred glides with much less physical exhaustion than resulted from twenty or thirty glides on days when the wind was light. No complete record was kept of all the glides made during the season. In the last six days of experiment we made more than 375, but these included our very best days. The total number for the season was probably between 700 and 1,000. The longest glide was 622½ feet, and the time 26 seconds.

The prime object in these experiments was to obtain practice in the management of a man-carrying machine, but an object of scarcely less importance was to obtain data for the study of the scientific problems involved in flight. Observations were almost constantly being made for the purpose of determining the amount and direction of the pressures upon the sustaining wings; the minimum speed required for support; the speed and angle of incidence at which the horizontal resistance became least; and the minimum angle of descent at which it was possible to glide. To determine any of these points with exactness was found to be very difficult indeed, but by careful observations under test conditions it was possible to obtain reasonably close approximations. It was found that a speed of about sixteen miles an hour would produce a pressure sufficient to support machine and operator, but the angle of incidence was too great for general gliding purposes. At eighteen miles the angle of incidence was about eight degrees, and the machine would glide on the Little Hill, descending at an angle of a little over seven degrees. Although the wings were inclined slightly above the horizon the machine continued to glide without loss of velocity. With a speed of 22 miles an hour, the angle of incidence required for support was four or five degrees, and the angle of descent a little less than seven degrees. At this speed the surfaces were inclined several degrees below the horizon. As the speed became greater the angle of incidence continued to grow less, but the angle of descent became greater again, thus showing that the point of minimum resistance had been passed. Scores of glides were made at angles of descent under six degrees, and in a few cases we reached five degrees. On the last day of experiment we made a few attempts at records. A line was drawn a short distance up the slope as a starting mark, and four trials were made. Twice the machine landed on the same spot. The distance was 156½ feet, and the angle of descent exactly five degrees. Time, 6½ seconds. From a point higher up on the slope the best angle was 5 degrees and 25 minutes, for a glide of 225 feet. Time, 10¼ seconds. The wind was blowing about nine miles an hour. The glides were made directly to windward and straight down the slope. Taking seven degrees as a conservative estimate of the normal angle of descent, the horizontal resistance of the machine was 30 pounds, as computed by multiplying the total weight, 250 pounds, by the tangent of the angle of descent. This resistance remained nearly constant at speeds between 18 and 25 miles an hour. Above or below these limits there was a somewhat rapid increase. At 18 miles the power consumed was one and one-half horse-power; at 25 miles, two horse-power. At the slower speed, 166 pounds were sustained for each horse-power consumed; at the higher speed, 125 pounds per horse-power. Between 18 and 25 miles the horse-power increased almost in exact ratio to the increase in speed, but above or below these limits the power increased rapidly, and with a constantly accelerating ratio.

On two occasions we observed a phenomenon whose nature we were not able to determine with certainty. One day my brother noticed in several glides a peculiar tapping as if some part of the machine were loose and flapping. Careful examination failed to disclose anything about the machine which could possibly cause it. Some weeks later, while I was making a glide, the same peculiar tapping began in the midst of a wind gust. It felt like little waves striking the bottom of a flat bottomed row-boat. While I was wondering what the cause could be, the machine suddenly, but without any noticeable change in its inclination to the horizon, dropped a distance of nearly ten feet, and in the twinkling of an eye was flat on the ground. I am certain that the gust went out with a downward trend which struck the surfaces on the upper side. The descent was at first more rapid than that due to gravity, for my body apparently rose off the machine till only my hands and feet touched it. Toward the end the descent was slower. It may be that the tapping was caused by the wind rapidly striking the surfaces alternately on the upper and the lower sides. It is a rule almost universal that gusts come on with a rising trend and die out with a descending trend, but on these particular occasions there must have been a most unusual turmoil during the continuance of the gust which would have exhibited a very interesting spectacle had it been visible to the eye. Irregularities of the wind are most noticeable when the wind is high, on account of the greater power then exhibited, but light winds show almost equal relative variations. An aviator must expect to encounter in every flight variations in velocity, in direction, and in upward or downward trend. And these variations not only give rise to those disturbances of the equilibrium which result from the travel of the center of pressure due to the changed angle of incidence, but also, by reason of the fact that the wind changes do not occur simultaneously or uniformly over the entire machine, give rise to a second series of disturbances of even more troublesome character. Thus a gust coming on very suddenly will strike the front of the machine and throw it up before the back part is acted upon at all. Or the right wing may encounter a wind of very different velocity and trend from the left wing and the machine will tend to turn over sidewise. The problem of overcoming these disturbances by automatic means has engaged the attention of many very ingenious minds, but to my brother and myself it has seemed preferable to depend entirely on intelligent control. In all of our machines the maintenance of the equilibrium has been dependent on the skill and constant vigilance of the aviators.

In addition to the work with the machine we also made many observations on the flight of soaring birds, which were very abundant in the vicinity of our camp. Bald eagles, ospreys, hawks and buzzards gave us daily exhibitions of their powers. The buzzards were the most numerous and were the most persistent soarers. They apparently never flapped except when it was absolutely necessary, while the eagles and hawks usually soared only when they were at leisure. Two methods of soaring were employed. When the weather was cold and damp and the wind strong, the buzzards would be seen soaring back and forth along the hills or at the edge of a clump of trees. They were evidently taking advantage of the current of air flowing upward over these obstructions. On such days they were often utterly unable to soar except in these special places. But on warm clear days when the wind was light they would be seen high in the air soaring in great circles. Usually however it seemed to be necessary to reach a height of several hundred feet by flapping before this style of soaring became possible. Frequently a great number of them would begin circling in one spot, rising together higher and higher till finally they would disperse, each gliding off in whatever direction it wished to go. At such times other buzzards only a short distance away found it necessary to flap frequently in order to maintain themselves. But when they reached a point beneath the circling flock they too began to rise on motionless wings. This seemed to indicate that rising columns of air do not exist everywhere, but that the birds must find them. They evidently watch each other and when one finds a rising current the others quickly make their way to it. One day when scarce a breath of wind was stirring on the ground, we noticed two bald eagles sailing in circling sweeps at a height of probably 500 feet. After a time our attention was attracted to the flashing of some object considerably lower down. Examination with a field glass proved it to be a feather which one of the birds had evidently cast. As it seemed apparent that it would come to earth only a short distance away some of our party started to get it. But in a little while it was noticed that the feather was no longer falling but on the contrary was rising rapidly. It finally went out of sight upward. It apparently was drawn into the same rising current in which the eagles were soaring, and was carried up like the birds.

The days when the wind blew horizontally gave us the most satisfactory observations, as then the birds were compelled to make use of the currents flowing up the sides of the hills and it was possible for us to measure the velocity and trend of the wind in which the soaring was performed. One day four buzzards began soaring on the northeast slope of the Big Hill at a height of only ten or twelve feet from the surface. We took a position to windward and about 1,200 feet distant. The clinometer showed that they were 4½ to 5½ degrees above our horizon. We could see them very distinctly with a field glass. When facing us the under side of their wings made a broad band on the sky, but when in circling they faced from us we could no longer see the under side of their wings. Though the wings then made little more than a line on the sky the glass showed clearly that it was not the under side that we saw. It was evident that the buzzards were soaring with their wings constantly inclined about five degrees above the horizon. They were attempting to gain sufficient altitude to enable them to glide to the ocean beach three-fourths of a mile distant, but after reaching a height of about 75 feet above the top of the hill they seemed to be unable to rise higher, though they tried a long time. At last they started to glide toward the ocean but were compelled to begin flapping almost immediately. We at once measured the slope and the wind. The former was 12½ degrees; the latter was six to eight meters per second. Since the wings were inclined 5 degrees above the horizon and the wind had a rising trend of fully 12 degrees, the angle of incidence was about 17 degrees. The wind did not average more than seven meters, 15 miles an hour. For the most part the birds faced the wind steadily, but in the lulls they were compelled to circle or glide back and forth in order to obtain speed sufficient to provide support. As the buzzard weighs about .8 pounds per square foot of wing area, the lifting power of the wind at 17 degrees angle of incidence was apparently as great as it would have been had it been blowing straight upward with equal velocity. The pressure was inclined 5 degrees in front of the normal, and the angle of descent was 12½ degrees.

On another day I stood on top of the West Hill directly behind a buzzard which was soaring on the steep southern slope. It was just on a level with my eye and not more than 75 feet distant. For some time it remained almost motionless. Although the wings were inclined about five degrees above the horizon, it was not driven backward by the wind. This bird is specially adapted to soaring at large angles of incidence in strongly rising currents. Its wings are deeply curved. Unless the upward trend amounts to at least eight degrees it seems to be unable to maintain itself. One day we watched a flock attempting to soar on the west slope of the Big Hill, which has a descent of nearly nine degrees. The birds would start near the top and glide down along the slope very much as we did with the machine, but we noticed that whenever they glided parallel with the slope their speed diminished, and when their speed was maintained the angle of descent was greater than that of the hill. In every case they found it necessary to flap before they had gone two hundred feet. They tried time and again but always with the same results. Finally they resorted to hard flapping till a height of about 150 feet above the top of the hill was reached, after which they were able to soar in circles without difficulty. On another day they finally succeeded in rising on almost the same slope, from which it was concluded that the buzzard's best angle of descent could not be far from eight degrees. There is no question in my mind that men can build wings having as little or less relative resistance than that of the best soaring birds. The bird's wings are undoubtedly very well designed indeed, but it is not any extraordinary efficiency that strikes with astonishment but rather the marvelous skill with which they are used. It is true that I have seen birds perform soaring feats of almost incredible nature in positions where it was not possible to measure the speed and trend of the wind, but whenever it was possible to determine by actual measurement the conditions under which the soaring was performed, it was easy to account for it on the basis of the results obtained with artificial wings. The soaring problem is apparently not so much one of better wings as of better operators.

Discussion

MR. CHANUTE: Mr. Wright has advised you heretofore as to the advance made by others, but he has not advised you of the advance achieved by his recent experiments.

As regards the weight sustained per horse-power, which will perhaps strike you as being very small in comparison with the weights that are propelled either upon the land or water, you may remember that the machine experimented with by Mr. Maxim sustained only 28 pounds to the horse-power, and that the model experimented with in 1896 by Prof. Langley sustained only 31 pounds to the horse-power, while the machine experimented with by the Messrs. Wright sustains 165 pounds to the horse-power. It is true that a large deduction must be made from those figures when a motor is applied, but nevertheless they constitute a very great advance. Moreover, it is only when support is obtained at flat angles of gliding advance, that we may hope to apply power successfully and to fly through the air. The best experiments which I had been able to make in 1896 were to obtain angles of descent of 7½ to 11 degrees. Mr. Wright has been enabled to obtain angles of descent of 6 to 7 degrees, and in one case, as he has told you, a descent of only 5 degrees. This constitutes a very great progress and gives out a good hope of further advance hereafter.

I presume that some of you may desire to ask some questions of Mr. Wright, which I am sure he will be very glad to answer. The paper is now open for discussion.

MR. CHURCHILL: Is it true that, according to your results, to propel an airship by means of a motor or other means of propulsion, horizontally, the wings would have to be inclined about 17 degrees? That is to say, the angle would be 5 degrees plus 12½ degrees, as in the case of the buzzard?

MR. WRIGHT: No, that was simply an example of soaring. If it were desired to fly by mechanical means horizontally through the air, the best angle would be about 5 to 7 degrees; that is, the wings should be set probably in the neighborhood of 5 to 7 degrees above the horizon. In our machine the weight was about 250 to 260 pounds, on a little over 300 square feet area of the main surfaces—about .8 pound to the square foot—and we found that with a speed of 25 miles per hour the wings only had to be inclined about 3 or 3½ degrees.

MR. BAINBRIDGE: Do you think it is impossible for a bird to soar in a horizontal wind?

MR. WRIGHT: I do not think any bird soars in a horizontal wind. In order to soar it is necessary that the resultant of all the pressures produced by the relative wind be exactly vertical, but in a horizontal wind this pressure is always inclined at least 6 degrees backward from the vertical. It therefore has a horizontal component which would cause the bird to drift with the wind until the relative speed required for support was entirely lost. It is only in a rising trend of wind that the bird can obtain propelling forces to balance the drift and thus make the resultant of all the pressures vertical.

MR. WARDER: I would like to ask in regard to the covering and framework of this last machine.

MR. WRIGHT: In our frame the main body is made of spruce—the very best straight-grained spruce—which is almost as strong as the hard woods. The uprights and nearly all of the spars are made of spruce. The covering is of cloth.[12]

MR. CHURCHILL: Have you made any experiments in propelling a machine with a motor?

MR. WRIGHT: We have not applied a motor to any of our machines. The driving force has been gravity.

MR. SEDDON: Have you followed the late experiments of Prof. Bell,[13] and what do you think of them?

MR. WRIGHT: It is very bad policy to ask one flying-machine man about the experiments of another, because every flying-machine man thinks that his method is the only correct one. Prof. Bell is working on the plan of getting a machine of very great structural strength and one which he thinks can be maintained easily. I think his principal idea is simply the method of construction—to get something strong.

MR. W.J. WILSON: I would like to ask Mr. Wright how he arrives at the area of the bird's wings.

MR. WRIGHT: The statement in regard to the area of the buzzard's wing was made on the authority of others. I have never measured one myself. As I understand it, the method is this: The bird, after being killed, is laid out flat, as nearly as possible in its position when flying and a line is drawn around the contour, and then the area is computed.

MR. WARDER: Does the bird throw the wing up or down without changing the axis of the body, or is it necessary to change the axis of the body at the same time he changes the plane of the wings?

MR. WRIGHT: Most birds incline the body to change the plane of the wings. Some years ago Prof. Marey[14] made photographs of the flight of birds, employing a camera making fifty exposures a second. From these pictures it would appear that the bird's body rocks. The wings are moved diagonally forward on the down stroke, and backward on the up stroke. At the end of the down stroke the wings are in front of the center of gravity so that the bird's body turns up in front and remains so while the wings are being raised with a backward movement. But the wings being thus brought back of the center of gravity the axis of the body tilts downward again. By this backward and forward motion of the wings the bird rocks its whole body and thus inclines the plane of its wings upward and downward with every stroke.

MR. CHURCHILL: Do you not utilize that principle, to a certain extent, in the front rudder? Has it that same effect?

MR. WRIGHT: We use the same principle that the bird uses in turning upward. That is, we get more pressure in front of the center of gravity. It may be that you misunderstood my statement in regard to my brother's experiments in low-gliding. I did not mean that he touched the ground; he kept 5 or 6 inches off the ground. Of course now and then he made a mistake and touched the ground.

MR. WARDER: In these glides that your brother made so close to the ground, do you not suppose there might have been a little more pressure than at 10 or 20 feet above the ground?

MR. WRIGHT: I do not think there is very much difference. We have found, by experimenting, that if you hold a surface stationary—almost touching the ground, it will have less lift than when it is up in the air. In gliding I do not think there will be very much difference.

A VISITOR: I would like to ask first, whether you consider that the future flying machine will be the machine of the type you have been using, driven by screws, or whether it will be a machine having a flapping motion.

Another thought that occurred to me was that perhaps the machine would be less liable to capsize if the wings were on a dihedral angle of about 45 degrees on a horizontal line.

MR. WRIGHT: The dihedral angle is the system used by Mr. Maxim and by Prof. Langley. The Maxim machine was overturned by a side gust of only moderate force. The Langley machine was tested only in dead calms when there were no side gusts to contend with. In our first machine we set the wings at a dihedral angle, but when we found that every little side wind threatened to capsize it, we drew the tips down like the wings of a gull. The gulls fly in the stormiest weather, while buzzards which use the dihedral angle avoid high winds. We found the gull position much the best. The dihedral angle is the proper solution of the problem for flight in still air, but it makes matters worse instead of better when the wind blows. Unfortunately the wind usually blows, so we have found it best to abandon this method and employ other means of securing lateral equilibrium.

As none of our experiments have been with power machines, my judgment of the relative merits of screws and wings may be of little value. I suspect that in efficiency they are not far from equal, but that screws possess mechanical advantages.

MR. F.E. HERMANNS: I would like to ask whether you regard 160 pounds per horse-power as the maximum amount that can be obtained?

MR. WRIGHT: I think not. Theoretically the horse-power required to sustain a given weight could be reduced to almost nothing by greatly increasing the wing area and thus reducing the speed through the air. But this ignores some practical considerations. To reduce the speed one-half, it would be necessary to increase the wing area four times in order to sustain the original weight, and much more than four times in order to sustain the increased weight resulting from the additions to the machine. It is evident, therefore, that while there is a way by which the weight carried per horse-power can be increased, the road is difficult and becomes steeper at every step. The same result could be obtained by reducing the angle of descent, but here also a limit is being approached. Until the limit is reached in both respects it is possible to increase the weight carried per horse-power. I think 200 pounds is attainable, possibly a little more.

---

1. *Journal of the Western Society of Engineers,* August 1903, 400–417 (address presented to the Western Society of Engineers in Chicago on June 24, 1903). An abridged version of this article was combined with an abridged version of the previous article (document 28), "Some Aeronautical Experiments," and published as "How to Glide and Soaring Flight," in *Flight,* October 2, 1909, 607–8, 621–22, 647–48, 672–73, 693–94, 721–23, 757–58 (not included in this work).
2. See document 28: "Some Aeronautical Experiments."
3. After the disappointing performance of their 1901 glider, the Wrights decided to no longer rely on the aerodynamic data compiled by Otto Lilienthal and others, and they began a series of wind tunnel experiments in October 1901. The brothers generated lift and drag coefficients for dozens of different wing shapes and curvatures with a pair of imaginatively designed test instruments mounted in their wind tunnel. This aerodynamic research was central to the Wrights' successful design of their next glider, in 1902, and of the first powered airplane, in 1903. The Wrights did not invent the wind tunnel, but they were the first to use one to gather data that was directly incorporated into the design of an aircraft in ways subsequently employed by modern aerospace engineers. Their pioneering use of this pivotal tool was as significant as making the first flight itself. For a detailed description and analysis of the Wrights' wind tunnel experiments, see Peter L. Jakab, *Visions of a Flying Machine: The Wright Brothers and the Process of Invention* (Washington, D.C.: Smithsonian Institution Press, 1990), 115–42, and Marvin W. McFarland, ed., *The Papers of Wilbur and Orville Wright,* 2 vols. (New York: McGraw-Hill, 1953), appendix 2, "1901 Wind Tunnel," 1:547–93.
4. Their camp was four miles from the village of Kitty Hawk.
5. See document 28, note 19.
6. The Wrights had by now adopted the practice of initially flying each of their new gliders as a kite before making free glides. See document 28, note 15.

7. See photo 17.
8. Wilbur had done all the flying in 1900 and 1901 and thus far in 1902. This day, September 23, 1902, was Orville's first opportunity to make free glides in a heavier-than-air flying machine.
9. The Wrights understood that learning to fly was just as important as building the airplane itself. They recognized that an airplane is not a single device but a system of discrete mechanical and structural entities that all had to work in proper unison to achieve flight, with no one element more important than another. Realizing that the pilot is a part of this system, they devoted as much attention to learning to fly their aircraft as they did to designing and building them.
10. When making turns with their tailless 1901 glider, the Wrights occasionally experienced the phenomenon of control reversal. When they banked the glider to make a turn, sometimes the craft would begin a normal turn in the desired direction but would then begin to rotate back in the opposite direction. This problem typically occurs when an aircraft is flying at very low airspeeds, close to stall, such as was the case with the Wrights' early gliders. At these low airspeeds, the amount of drag created by the control surface deflection can become high enough to inhibit the rotational motion of the turn. In this situation, the high wing of a banked aircraft experiences more drag than the low wing, causing the aircraft to rotate about the high wing tip, opposite from the direction of the initiated turn. To cure the control reversal problem of their 1901 glider, the Wrights added a fixed vertical tail to their next glider, in 1902. If the glider began to reverse direction in a turn, the fixed tail would naturally present itself such that the airstream exerted pressure on the appropriate side of the vertical surface to force the glider back onto the proper course. For the most part, the fixed vertical tail on the 1902 glider solved the problem experienced in 1901. Sometimes in 1902, however, the Wrights experienced a new, but related, problem with their lateral control system, and when this happened, the fixed tail seemed to make the untoward action even worse than the situation that occurred with no tail at all. In this case, rather than *rotating* in the wrong direction, that is, around the high wing, the glider would "slide" sideways out of control toward the low wing. In this instance the air pressure would exert itself on the wrong side of the fixed vertical tail, exacerbating the situation rather than forcing the glider back on track. This caused the glider to fall out of the sky at a frightening rate, eventually planting a wing tip in the sand. The Wrights called these episodes "well digging," referring to the small crater left in the sand after the wing hit the ground. The Wrights solved this problem by making the vertical tail movable. Thus the pilot could position the vertical tail so as to avoid the pressure buildup that contributed to the loss of control and could safely bring the wings back to equilibrium.
11. The movable vertical tail was linked to the wing-warping mechanism so that both control inputs were applied with a single movement by the pilot.
12. The cloth covering on the Wrights' first glider in 1900 was a fine French sateen fabric. On their subsequent gliders and the powered airplane of 1903, they used a tightly woven muslin that went by the trade name "Pride of the West."
13. The reference is to Alexander Graham Bell. The famous inventor of the telephone became ardently interested in aeronautics at the end of the nineteenth century. He was a strong supporter and close personal friend of Samuel P. Langley's. At the time of this presentation to the Western Society of Engineers, Bell was experimenting with large multiple triangular and tetrahedral cell kites. In 1907 he formed the Aerial Experiment

Association with several young aeronautical enthusiasts, including Glenn H. Curtiss. The group built a number of powered airplanes in 1908 and 1909, including the *Silver Dart,* the first airplane to fly in Canada. This historic flight of the *Silver Dart* was made on February 23, 1909, by J. A. D. McCurdy. For a detailed description of Bell's aeronautical work, see J. H. Parkin, *Bell and Baldwin* (Toronto: University of Toronto Press, 1964).

14. See document 28, note 12.

30 • THE RELATIONS OF WEIGHT, SPEED, AND POWER OF FLYERS[1]

Wilbur and Orville Wright

The flyer of 1903 carried a four-cylinder gasolene motor of four-inch bore and four-inch stroke. Complete with magneto, radiators, tanks, water, fuel, etc., the motor weighed a little over 200 lbs.; and at 1200 revolutions per minute, developed 16 horse-power for the first 15 seconds after starting. After a minute or two the power did not exceed 13 to 14 horse-power. At 1020 revolutions per minute—the speed of the motor in the flights at Kitty Hawk on the 17th of December, 1903,—it developed about 12 horse-power.

The flyer of 1904 was equipped with a motor similar to the first, but of ⅛ inch larger bore. This engine at 1500 revolutions per minute developed 24 horse-power for the first 15 seconds, but only 16 to 17 horse-power after a few minutes' run. Complete with water, fuel, and other accessories, it weighed 240 lbs.

The same engine, with a few modifications in the oiling device and the carburetor, was used in all the flights of 1905. A test of its power made soon after the flights of October, 1905, revealed a gain of 3 horse-power over tests made just before mounting it on the flyer in 1904. This gain is attributed to the increased smoothness of the cylinders and pistons produced by wear. The small output of these engines was due to lack of experience in building gasolene motors.

During the past year further improvements have been made, and our latest engines of four-inch bore and four-inch stroke produce about 25 horse-power continuously. The improvement in the reliability of the motor has been even more marked, so that now flights of long distances can be attempted without danger of failure on account of the stopping of the motor.[2]

A comparison of the flyers of 1903, 1904, and 1905 shows interesting facts. The flyer of 1903 weighed, complete with operator, 745 lbs. Its longest flight was of 59 seconds' duration with a speed of 30 miles an hour and an expenditure of 12 horse-power. The flyer of 1904 weighed about 900 lbs., including a load of 70 lbs. in iron bars.[3] A speed of more than 34 miles an hour was maintained for a distance of three miles with an expenditure of 17 horse-power. The flyer of 1905 weighed, including load, 925 lbs. With an expenditure of 19 to 20 horse-power it traveled over 24 miles at a speed of more than 38 miles an hour. The flights of 1904 and 1905 would have been slightly faster had they been made in a straight line, as were those of 1903.

In 1903, 62 lbs. per horse-power were carried at a speed of 30 miles an hour; in 1904, 53 lbs. at 34 miles an hour; and in 1905, 46 lbs. at 38 miles an hour. It will be noticed that the weight carried per horse-power is almost exactly in inverse ratio to the speed, as theory demands—the higher the speed, the smaller the weight carried per horse-power.

Since flyers can be built with approximately the same dynamic efficiency for all speeds up to 60 miles an hour, a flyer designed to carry a total weight of 745 lbs. at 20 miles an hour would require only 8 horse-power, or two-thirds of the power necessary for 30 miles an hour. At 60 miles 24 horse-power would be necessary—twice that required to carry the same weight at 30 miles an hour. At 120 miles an hour 60 to 75 horse-power would probably be necessary, and the weight carried per horse-power would be only 10 or 12 lbs. At such high speed the resistance of the operator's body and the engine is a formidable factor, consuming 64 times as much horse-power as at 30 miles an hour. At speeds below 60 miles an hour this resistance is almost negligible.

It is evident that the limits of speed have not as yet been closely approached in the flyers already built, and in the matter of distance, the possibilities are even more encouraging. Even in the existing state of the art it is easy to design a practical and durable flyer that will carry an operator and supplies of fuel for a flight of over 500 miles at a speed of 50 miles an hour.

---

1. The Aero Club of America, *Navigating the Air: A Scientific Statement of the Progress of Aëronautical Science up to the Present Time* (New York: Doubleday, Page, and Co., 1907), 6–12.
2. For a detailed discussion of the Wright brothers' motors, see Leonard S. Hobbs, *The Wright Brothers' Engines and Their Design* (Washington, D.C.: Smithsonian Institution Press, 1971), and Marvin W. McFarland, ed., *The Papers of Wilbur and Orville Wright*, 2 vols. (New York: McGraw- Hill, 1953), appendix 5, "Aeroplanes and Motors," 2:1210–17.
3. The ballast was added to the canard at the front of the airplane in an attempt to improve stability in pitch by moving the center of gravity forward.

31 • INVERTED AEROPLANE STRESSES[1]

Orville Wright

On March 13th, Lieut. Henri Paul Seville met with a fatal accident. The cause was ascribed to the breaking of the guys on the top of the wings of his Bleriot,[2] due to excessive downward pressure on the surfaces.—Editor's Note

It is true that in flying, especially in gusty weather, pressure sometimes comes on the upper sides of aeroplanes, tending to force them downwards. This is usually caused by the aeroplane running into a current of air, which is revolving about a horizontal axis. When the plane strikes the side of the whirl which is rising, the aeroplane is lifted and when it strikes the side which is descending, if the whirl is violent enough, the air strikes the planes on top, and not only is all lifting effect destroyed, but the machine is actually pushed downward. I have many times, in our early experiments, experienced cases in which the machine and the seat were pushed from under me and I was left sitting on air. Our later machines are not so subject to these whirls, so that it is now quite uncommon to have the seat forced from under one. But it frequently happens that wind pressures come on the top of the surfaces, causing the machine to drop and destroying the support of the planes, so that the machine sinks rapidly.

Our principle reason for the use of the biplane is that the biplane can be trussed much stronger in both directions. While the monoplanes have but little trussing to resist downward pressures on the wings.[3] It does not seem to me likely that any of the strains encountered on the top side of the surface in flight would be greater than the downward strain on the wings in making a rough landing. While it is possible for wings to collapse downwards, as suggested in the death of Lieut. Seville, I do not think it likely to occur in any of the better constructed machines.

---

1. *Aeronautics*, April 1912, 119.
2. The correct spelling of the name of Seville's airplane should be "Blériot."
3. For an excellent engineering analysis of pioneer monoplane wing failures, see Tom D. Crouch, *Blériot XI: The Story of a Classic Aircraft* (Washington, D.C.: Smithsonian Institution Press, 1982), chapter 4, "The Problem with Monoplanes," 69–82.

32 • STABILITY OF AEROPLANES[1]

Orville Wright

The subject of "Stability of Aeroplanes" is too broad to permit of a discussion of all of its phases in one evening. I shall, therefore, confine myself more particularly to a few phases of the fore-and-aft or longitudinal equilibrium. Although in learning to fly the beginner finds most difficulty in mastering the lateral control, it is his lack of knowledge of certain features of the fore-and-aft equilibrium that leads to most of the serious accidents. These accidents are the more difficult to avoid because they are due to subtle causes which the flyer does not at the time perceive.

A flying machine must be balanced in three directions: about an axis fore and aft in its line of motion; about an axis extending in a lateral direction from tip to tip of the wings, and about a vertical axis. The balance about the lateral axis is referred to as fore-and-aft or longitudinal equilibrium; that about the fore-and-aft axis as lateral equilibrium, and that about the vertical axis is generally referred to as steering, although its most important function is that of lateral equilibrium.

If the center of support of an aeroplane surface would remain fixed at one point, as is practically the case in marine vessels and in balloons and airships, equilibrium would be a simple matter. But the location of the center of pressure[2] on an aeroplane surface changes with every change in the angle at which the air strikes the surface. At an angle of 90 deg. it is located approximately at the center of the surface. As the angle becomes less, the center of pressure moves forward. On plane surfaces[3] it continues to move forward as the angle decreases until it finally reaches the front edge. But on cambered surfaces[4] the movement is not continuous. After a certain critical angle of incidence is reached, which angle depends upon the particular form of the surface, the center of pressure moves backward with further decrease in angle until it arrives very close to the rear edge. At angles ordinarily used in flying, angles of 3 deg. to 12 deg., the travel of the center of pressure is in this retrograde movement and is located, according to the angle of incidence, at points between 30 per cent. and 50 per cent. back of the front edge of the surface. The location of the center of pressure on any given surface is definitely fixed by the angle of incidence at which the surface is exposed to the air.

The placing of the center of gravity of the machine below its center of support appears, at first glance, to be a solution of the problem of equilibrium. This is the method used in maintaining equilibrium in marine vessels and in balloons and airships, but in flying machines it has the opposite of the desired effect. If a flying machine consisting of a supporting surface, without elevator or other means of balancing, were descending vertically as a parachute, the center of gravity vertically beneath the center of support would maintain its equilibrium. But as soon as the machine begins to move forward the center of pressure, instead of remaining at the center of the surfaces, as was the case when descending vertically, moves toward that edge of the surface which is in advance. The center of gravity being located at the center of the surface and the center of pressure in advance of the center of the surface, a turning moment is created which tends to lift the front of the machine, thus exposing the surfaces at a larger angle of incidence and at the same time to a greater resistance to forward movement. The momentum of the machine, acting through its center of gravity below the center of forward resistance, combines with the forward center of pressure in causing the surface to be rotated about its lateral axis. The machine will take an upward course until it finally comes to a standstill. The rear edge of the surface will now be below that of the front edge and the machine will begin to slide backward. The center of pressure immediately reverses and travels towards the rear edge of the surface, which now in the backward movement has become the front edge. The center of gravity again being back of the center of pressure, the advancing edge of the surface will be lifted as before, and the pendulum effect of the low weight will be repeated. A flying machine with a low center of gravity, without rudders or other means to maintain its equilibrium, will oscillate back and forth in this manner until it finally falls to the ground.

It will have been observed from the foregoing that the equilibrium in the horizontal plane was disturbed by two turning moments acting about the lateral horizontal axis of the machine; one produced by the force of gravity and the lift of the surface acting in different vertical lines, and the other by the center of momentum and the center of resistance acting in different horizontal lines.

It is evident that a low center of gravity is a disturbing instead of a correcting agent. The ideal form of flying machine would be one in which the center of gravity lies in the line of the center of resistance to forward movement and in the line of thrust. In practice this is not always feasible. Flying machines must be built to land safely as well as to fly. A high center of gravity tends to cause a machine to roll over in landing. A compromise is therefore adopted. The center of gravity is kept high enough to be but a slight disturbing factor in flight and at the same time not so high as to interfere in making safe landings.

The three forces acting on an aeroplane in the direction of its line of motion are the thrust of the propellers, the momentum or inertia of its weight, and the resistance of the machine to forward travel. If travelling in any other than a horizontal course, a component of gravity in the line of motion will have to be reckoned with. When these forces are exerted in the same line, with the centers of thrust and momentum acting in the opposite direction to that of the center of resistance, a variation in the quantity of any one, or of all, of these forces will not in itself have a disturbing effect on the equilibrium about the lateral horizontal axis. But these forces in the ordinary flying machine do not act in the same line. Usually the center of thrust is high in order to give proper clearance between the propellers and the ground; the center of gravity is low to enable the machine to land without danger of being overturned; and the center of resistance is usually between the centers of thrust and gravity. When a flying machine is travelling at uniform speed the propelling forces exactly equal the resisting forces. In case the thrust of the propellers is diminished by throttling the motor, the momentum of the machine acting below the center of resistance carries the lower part of the machine along faster than the upper part, and the surfaces thus will be turned upward, producing a greater angle and a greater resistance. The same effect is produced if the machine be suddenly struck by a gust of wind of higher velocity from in front. The thrust of its propellers will be temporarily slightly decreased, the resistance due to the greater wind pressure will be increased, and the momentum of the machine (the center of gravity being low) will in this case also turn the surfaces upward to a larger angle. While these variations in the forces acting in the horizontal line have of themselves a certain amount of disturbing effect, yet it is from the changes of incidence which they introduce that one encounters the greatest difficulty in maintaining equilibrium.

The two principal methods used in preserving fore-and-aft equilibrium have been, first, the shifting of weight so as to keep the center of gravity in line with the changing center of lift; and, second, the utilization of auxiliary surfaces, known as elevators, to preserve the position of the center of pressure in line with a fixed center of gravity. The first method has been found impracticable on account of the impossibility of shifting large weights quickly enough.[5] The second method is that used in most of the flying machines of to-day.

Flying machines of this latter type should have their auxiliary surfaces located as far as possible from the main bearing planes, because the greater the distance the greater is the leverage and consequently the smaller the amount of surface required. The auxiliary surfaces are usually placed either in front or in the rear of the main supporting surfaces, since they act with greater efficiency in these positions than when placed above or below.

With a view to high efficiency, no part of either the main surfaces or the auxiliary surfaces should be exposed on their upper sides in a way to create downward pressures. One pound of air pressure exerted downward costs as much in propelling power as two pounds of downward pressure produced by actual weight carried. This is due to the fact that the total pressure on an aeroplane is not vertical, but approximately normal to the plane of the surface. This pressure may be resolved into two forces, one acting in a line parallel with the direction of travel, and the other at right angles to the line of travel. One is termed "lift" and the other "drift."[6] With a given aeroplane surface, the drift and lift for any given angle of incidence always bear a definite ratio to one another. This ratio varies from 1 to 12 to 1 to 1, according to the angle of incidence and the shape of the surface. On an average it is about 1 to 6, so that the thrust required of the propeller in the ordinary flying machine is approximately one-sixth of the weight carried. When travelling on a horizontal course the lift is vertical and is exactly equal to the total weight of the machine and load. This load may be real weight, or it may be partly real weight and partly downward pressures exerted on parts of the surfaces. For every pound of weight carried, a thrust of approximately one-sixth pound is required. If, however, instead of real weight a downward air pressure is exerted on some part of the machine, this downward pressure must be overcome by an equal upward pressure on some other part of the machine, to prevent the machine from descending. In this case the horizontal component of the one pound downward pressure will be about one-sixth pound, and the horizontal component of the compensating upward pressure also will be about one-sixth pound, making a total of one-third pound required in thrust from the propellers, as compared with one-sixth pound thrust required by one pound actual weight carried. It is, therefore, evident that the use of downward air pressures in maintaining equilibrium is exceedingly wasteful, and, as far as possible, should be avoided. In other words, when the equilibrium of an aeroplane has been disturbed, instead of using a downward air pressure to depress the elevated side an upward pressure should be utilized to elevate the low side. The cost in power is twice as great in one case as in the other.

The dynamically less efficient system of downward air pressures is used to some extent, however, on account of its adaptability in producing more or less inherently stable aeroplanes. An inherently stable aeroplane may be described as one in which equilibrium is maintained by an arrangement of surfaces, so that when a current of air strikes one part of the machine, creating a pressure that would tend to disturb the equilibrium, the same current striking another part creates a balancing pressure in the opposite direction. This compensating or correcting pressure is secured without the mechanical movement of any part of the machine.

The first to propose the use of this system for the fore-and-aft control of aeroplanes was Penaud,[7] a young French student, who did much experimenting with model aeroplanes in the 70's of the last century. His system is used only to a slight extent in the motor-driven aeroplanes of to-day, on account of its wastefulness of power and on account of its restriction of the manoeuvring qualities of the machine.

Penaud's system consists of a main bearing surface and a horizontal auxiliary surface in the rear fixed at a negative angle in relation to the main surface. The center of gravity is placed in front of the center of the main surface. This produces a tendency to incline the machine downward in front, and to cause it to descend. In descending the aeroplane gains speed. The fixed surface in the rear, set at a negative angle, receives an increased pressure on its upper side as the speed increases. This downward pressure causes the rear of the machine to be depressed till the machine takes an upward course. The speed is lost in the upward course, the downward pressure on the tail is relieved, and the forward center of gravity turns the course again downward. While the inherently stable system will control a machine to some extent, it depends so much on variation in course and speed as to render it inadequate to meet fully the demands of a practical flying machine.

In order to secure greater dynamic efficiency and greater manoeuvring ability, auxiliary surfaces mechanically operable are used in present flying machines instead of the practically fixed surfaces of the inherently stable type. These machines possess the means of quickly recovering balance without changing the direction of travel and of manoeuvring with greater dexterity when required. On the other hand, they depend to a greater extent upon the skill of the operator in keeping the equilibrium. It may be taken as a rule that the greater the dynamic efficiency of the machine and the greater its possibilities in manoeuvring, the greater the knowledge and skill required of the operator.

If the operator of a flying machine were able to "feel" exactly the angle at which his aeroplane meets the air, 90 per cent. at least of all aeroplane accidents would be eliminated. It has been the lack of this ability that has resulted in so large a toll of human lives. Instruments have been produced which indicate closely the angle of incidence at which the machine is flying, but they are not in general use. Nor does the average flyer realize how exceedingly dangerous it is to be ignorant of this angle. Most of the flyers are aware that "stalling" is dangerous, but do not know when they really are "stalling."

A flying machine is in great danger when it is flying at its angle of maximum lift. A change either to a smaller or a larger angle results in a lesser lift. There is this important difference, however, whether the angle be increased or decreased. While a smaller angle gives less lift, it also has less drift resistance, so that the machine is permitted to gain speed. On the other hand, the larger angle gives not only less lift but encounters a greater resistance, which causes the speed of the machine to be rapidly checked, so that there is a double loss of lift—that due to angle and that due to a lesser speed.

The maximum lift is obtained in most flying machines at some angle between 15 deg. and 20 deg. If the machine be gliding from a height with the power of the motor throttled or entirely turned off, and the operator attempts to turn it to a level course, the speed of the machine will soon be reduced to the lowest at which it can support its load. If now this level course be held for even only a second or two, the speed and the lift will be so diminished that the machine will begin to fall rapidly.

The center of pressure on a cambered aeroplane surface at angles greater than 12 deg. to 15 deg. travels backward with increase of angle of incidence, so that when a machine approaches the "stalled" angles, the main bearing surfaces are generally carrying practically all of the weight and the elevator practically none at all. Under these conditions the main surfaces fall more rapidly than does the rear elevator. The machine noses downward and plunges at an exceedingly steep angle toward the earth. This plunge would tend to bring the machine back to normal speed quickly were the machine flying at its usual angle of incidence. But at the large angles of incidence the drift is a large part of the total pressure on the surfaces, so that, although plunging steeply downward, speed is recovered but slowly. The more the operator tries to check the downward plunge by turning the elevator, the greater becomes the angle of incidence, and the greater the forward resistance. At ordinary stalled angles the machine must descend at an angle of about 25 deg. with reference to the horizontal in order to maintain its speed. If the speed be already below that necessary for support, a steeper angle of descent will be required, and considerable time may be consumed before supporting speed can be recovered. During all this time the machine is plunging downward. If the plunge begins at a height of less than 200 or 300 ft., the machine is likely to strike the ground before the speed necessary to recover control is acquired.

The danger from "stalling" comes in the operator attempting to check the machine's downward plunge by turning the main bearing surfaces to still larger angles of incidence, instead of pointing the machine downward, at a smaller angle of incidence, so that the speed can be recovered more quickly. It is safe to say that fully 90 per cent. of the fatal accidents in flying are due to this cause. Most of the serious ones occur when, after long glides from considerable heights, with the power of the motor reduced, an attempt is made to bring the machine to a more level course several hundred feet in the air. The machine quickly loses its speed and becomes "stalled." All of us who have seen the novice make a "pancake" landing have seen the beginning of a case of "stalling" which might have been fatal had it taken place at a height of 100 or 200 ft.

The greatest danger in flying comes from misjudging the angle of incidence. If a uniform angle of incidence were maintained, there would be no difficulty in fore-and-aft equilibrium. As has already been stated, for any given surface and any given angle of incidence the position of the center of pressure is fixed. Under these conditions, if the center of gravity were located to coincide with the center of pressure and a uniform angle of incidence maintained, the machine would always be in equilibrium.

It is in accordance with this principle that experiments the past year have brought about a considerable advance in the development of automatic stability.[8] A small horizontal wind vane is so mounted on the machine as to ride edge-wise to the wind when the machine is flying at the desired angle of incidence. In case the machine varies from the desired angle, the air will strike the vane on either its upper or lower side. The slightest movement of the vane in either direction brings into action a powerful mechanism[9] for operating the controlling surfaces.

If the wind strikes the vane on the under side, as would be the case when the machine takes a larger angle of incidence, the elevator is turned to cause the machine to point downward in front till the normal angle is restored. If the air strike the vane from above, a smaller angle of incidence is indicated, and an opposite action on the elevator is produced. In this system no particular angle of the machine with the horizontal is maintained. It is the angle at which the air strikes the aeroplane surface that is important. If the vane is set at an angle of with the main supporting surfaces, and the machine is travelling on a level course, increasing the power of the motor will cause it to begin taking on more speed. But as the lifting effect of an aeroplane surface is the product of two factors—its speed and its angle of incidence—any increase in speed will produce a greater lift and cause the machine to rise. The machine will now be turned upward, with the surfaces meeting the air at an angle of

5 deg. On the contrary, if the power of the motor be reduced or entirely turned off, the machine will immediately begin to decrease in speed, requiring a larger angle of incidence for support. But as soon as the angle begins to increase the air will strike the regulating vane on the underside and the elevator will be turned, pointing the machine downward till the component of gravity in the direction of travel becomes sufficient to maintain the normal speed. In this case the planes will be inclined downward with reference to the horizontal. It is evident that a machine controlled by regulating the angle of the machine with reference to the impinging air is not liable to the dangers of "stalling" already described.

Several other methods of maintaining fore-and-aft equilibrium automatically have been proposed. One utilizes the force of gravity acting on a pendulum or a tube of mercury; the other, the gyroscopic force of a rapidly revolving wheel. In both of these systems the angle of the machine is regulated with reference to the horizontal, or some other determined plane, instead of with the angle of the impinging air.

In the case just referred to, in which the power of the motor was suddenly turned off while travelling on a level course, with these systems, the planes would be maintained at their original angle with the horizontal without any regard to the angle of incidence. The machine would continue forward till, through the loss of momentum, its speed would become so reduced and its angle of incidence so great that it would be exposed to the dangers of diving.

The pendulum and mercury tube have other serious faults which render them useless for regulating fore-and-aft equilibrium. If the machine suddenly meets with a greater resistance to forward travel, either as a result of change in direction or of meeting a stronger gust of wind from in front, and its speed be ever so slightly checked, the pendulum will swing forward and instead of turning the machine downward, so as to maintain the normal speed, will cause the machine to be inclined upward in front and thus further increase its forward resistance.

The pendulum has proved itself an exceedingly useful device, however, in regulating the lateral stability of aeroplanes. In this case the effects of momentum and centrifugal force act on the pendulum in the proper direction to produce desired results.

I believe the day is near at hand when the flyer will be almost entirely relieved of the work of maintaining the equilibrium of his machine, and that his attention will be required only to keeping it on its proper course and in bringing it safely in contact with the ground when landing.

---

1. Address presented at the Franklin Institute in Philadelphia on May 20, 1914, on the occasion of Orville Wright's receipt of the Institute's Elliott Cresson Medal in recognition of his pioneering work in aeronautics, published in *Aeronautics,* September 15, 1914, 67–68, 78.

2. The center of pressure is the point between the leading and the trailing edges of a wing surface at which the lifting force acting on the wing is focused. The center of pressure naturally moves back and forth along the wing with the changing angle of attack.
3. "Plane surfaces" are perfectly flat surfaces with no curvature in profile.
4. "Camber" refers to the curvature of a wing profile.
5. This was the method used by Otto Lilienthal.
6. See document 28, note 16.
7. Orville is referring to Alphonse Pénaud.
8. The Wrights' interest in developing an automatic stability device began as early as 1905. In 1913 Orville received a patent for an automatic pilot system using a vane-and-pendulum design. On February 5, 1914, three months before delivering this address, he was awarded the prestigious Collier Trophy for this advancement to aeronautics. His was a short-lived moment of glory, however. The Wright system worked but was immediately supplanted by the much superior gyroscope-based automatic pilot system developed by Lawrence Sperry and unveiled in June 1914. The Sperry gyroscope became the standard automatic stability system thereafter.
9. The "powerful mechanism" was a servomotor powered by a wind-driven generator.

33 • POSSIBILITIES OF SOARING FLIGHT[1]

Orville Wright

Readers of *U.S. Air Service* may possibly have overlooked the fact that Orville Wright as long ago as 1911 set up a world's record for soaring by hovering over the same spot for nine minutes forty-five seconds. A writer in Discovery, the British "Journal of Knowledge," points out that Orville Wright's achievement "possibly remains unequalled as a demonstration of control by all the long gliding and circling flights, up to three hours in duration, made in Germany during August of this year."—Editor's Note

The soaring experiments of the past year in Germany, France and England have excited much interest in this branch of aviation. Several of these flights have been so sensational as to mislead some into thinking that other means than a motor have been discovered for supporting and propelling an airplane from place to place. Because sailplanes based on standard type airplanes have not always led in these contests others have been misled into believing the data secured from wind tunnel experiments to be erroneous and of no value, and that soaring and gliding experiments will supplant the wind tunnel and laboratory experiments in the investigation of aerodynamic phenomena. In my opinion this is not true. The chief factors in soaring flight are the hill, the wind, the plane and the skill of the operator, ranking in importance about in the order named. The plane best adapted to one hill and one wind condition may be ill-suited to another hill and another wind condition. There is not now and probably never will be a type of soaring plane most suitable for all conditions of wind and hill, any more than there is a most suitable type of airplane for all conditions of speed and loading.

Hentzen's flight[2] of three hours six minutes without a motor is remarkable for its duration only. No new principle of flight was utilized. The longer duration of the flight was due in part to improvements in the glider itself, natural results of the progress made in aerodynamics in the last ten years; in part to the skill acquired in handling aircraft during this period; but especially to the more advantageous topography of the ground over which the flight was made.

For several reasons a ridge is better than a conical hill for purposes of soaring. If the wind is too light for support when facing directly into it, additional velocity can be obtained by quartering across the wind along the top of the ridge. On a conical hill this is scarcely possible, since lateral motion across the face of the hill will bring the machine into currents of air having less and less rising trend as the machine gets farther from the apex of the hill. But another disadvantage of the conical hill is the fact that the current of air is split by the hill, a part of the air flowing around it to the right and a part to the left. This sudden change in direction makes control of the machine difficult—so difficult in fact that often the ordinary controlling surfaces on an airplane are entirely inadequate.

These were the difficulties encountered in the soaring experiments at Kitty Hawk, N.C., in 1911.[3] The machine with which the experiments were commenced had elevators and rudders abundantly powerful for all purposes of power flight, yet under the conditions encountered on the conical face of the Big Kill Devil Hill these controls were so powerless as to allow, on one occasion, the machine to be turned completely over on its back. After the effectiveness of the controls had been greatly increased a number of flights were made of more than five minutes duration, the longest of which was nine minutes, forty-five seconds. This was the record for soaring flight from 1911 till 1921 when it was beaten in Germany by Herr Harth,[4] who remained in the air twenty-one minutes without a motor, and this year by Herr Hentzen with a flight of three hours and six minutes.

The French held a soaring contest in August of this year in which the longest flight was five minutes, eighteen seconds—inconsiderable in comparison with the German record, and not even so good as the American record of eleven years ago. But a mere record of time is not a certain criterion of the efficiency of the machine used nor of the skill of the operator, when records are made on different hills and under different wind conditions, since the wind and the hill are the two most important factors in soaring.[5]

No soaring flight has been made as yet by man, nor, as far as my own observation goes, by bird, in other than rising currents of air. The theory has been advanced that birds sometimes soar in horizontal winds, without any advantage from rising trends, by utilizing the irregularities in the velocity of the wind. Mouillard,[6] the great French pioneer student of soaring flight, in "The Empire of the Air," published in 1881, was the first, I believe, to put forth this theory. He explained the principle as follows:

> The wind gust is the very essence of the uprise; it is the magic wand, which striking the child's hoop, keeps it upright in rolling, drives it along, or raises it up to overleap elevations on its way. Suppose the toy to be placed on a steep inclined descent; gravity will cause it to roll to the bottom. If beyond this an ascending plane follows, the hoop, urged forward by momentum of acquired velocity, will rise to a height equal to that of fall, minus the losses by friction on the soil and by air resistance.
>
> Let us suppose further, when the hoop is about to ascend, we can displace the ascending plane, in contrary direction to the toy's course, so that the plane shall glide under the hoop, then we would still more assist the ascension.

Mouillard here states clearly the principle, which he imagined to be involved in soaring, but he gives no figures to show how great must be the irregularities in the wind to sustain the bird.

In 1893 Dr. Langley published his well-known paper, "The Internal Work of the Wind," in which he supported Mouillard in this theory. He repeated at greater length, though scarcely more clearly, the proposition laid down by Mouillard. Langley furnished some measurements of irregularities found in winds of different velocities, but he made no attempt to calculate the amount of support a bird would be able to secure from them. The rate of acceleration in winds of ten to fifteen miles average velocity, as shown in his charts, was less than five per cent of what would be required to sustain a bird in soaring flight.

In calm air the buzzard is able to glide on a path descending about one foot in each eight feet forward. In other words, its resistance to forward travel is equal to one-eighth of its weight, and its velocity when gliding on a horizontal course will be retarded at a rate equal to

$$g(32 \text{ ft. per sec.})/8$$

or four feet per second. It follows that if the velocity of the wind increased constantly at the rate of four feet per second, the buzzard would be able to just sustain itself. But wind gusts are composed of retardations as well as accelerations in velocity. Since approximately only one-half of the time is occupied in acceleration the actual rate of acceleration would have to be much more than four feet per second in order that the average would be equal to that amount.

Soaring in rising trends of air deflected upward by hills, trees, waves, etc., always occurs on windy days. But it is well known that over level ground, where there are no hills or other obstacles to deflect the air upward, soaring is done on comparatively calm days and not on windy days when the fluctuations in the velocity of the wind are greatest.

I have seen thousands of buzzards in soaring flight over level ground on calm, sunny days, but I have yet to see one case of soaring over this same ground on a windy day with the sky overcast. If the bird depended on getting its support from the "internal work of the wind" it would do its soaring on days when the fluctuations of the wind were greatest, instead of on days when they were least. My brother and I calculated many years ago the support to be obtained from gusts of greater intensity than those actually encountered in nature. I believe that anyone who takes the trouble to make this calculation will be convinced that the explanation of soaring flight is not to be found in the internal work of the wind.

On the other hand it is well known that soaring can be done in rising currents of air produced not by objects on the ground, but by the difference in temperature of the air at the surface and that above. These currents of rising air are most frequent on calm days when the sun is shining. We see them in the whirl winds which lift leaves and dust into the air. When you see one of these "whirls" stirring up the dust on a country road, look into the sky, a little to the direction toward which the wind is blowing. You will often find a buzzard circling there. He circles to keep within the area of the "whirl" which increases in diameter with height.

An aviator frequently runs into these rising currents and feels a slight "bump," but as the diameter of the "whirl" is usually not much in excess of a hundred feet his machine is out of it in a second. With the lightly loaded, slow machines of ten to fifteen years ago these "bumps" were more pronounced and the distance the machine was lifted by one of them was much greater than that experienced by the fast machines of today. In 1910, while training some of the early aviators, I had an unusual experience of this kind near Montgomery, Ala.[7]

I had ascended to a height of a little over one-half mile and was descending when at a height of about fifteen hundred feet I suddenly discovered that I was not able to descend further, although my motor was throttled to the limit and the machine was pointed downward as steeply as I felt it safe to point it. I remained at a height of about fifteen hundred feet for a period of five minutes without making any appreciable descent. Suddenly the machine again began to descend and was on the ground in less than a minute.

The flight was made in an almost perfect calm. The descent was in a spiral of not more than five or six hundred feet diameter. This probably accounted for the long time the machine remained in the uptrend of air. No doubt, if I had steered out of the spiral into a straight course, I would have been out of the rising trend in a few seconds; but I did not think of this at the time. In fact, I was so astonished that I did not think at the time of any reason for the phenomenon. But it is evident the machine was in a whirlwind of unusual diameter, in which the air was rising as fast as the machine could descend. These whirlwinds and other rising trends of air are not present everywhere and on some days do not exist at all. We, therefore, cannot hope to get much use of them as a means of travel.

The news reports of the contests abroad have created in the public mind an exaggerated impression of the importance of this kind of flying. My brother and I, as well as Lilienthal, Chanute and others before us, experimented in this way. We found, however, that while it was a most delightful sport, and furnished a safe and cheap means of acquiring skill in operating an airplane, it was too slow and expensive as a means of obtaining scientific data for the design of aircraft. I feel safe in predicting that it will never rival the powered airplane as a means of transportation nor the wind tunnel as a means of obtaining more exact scientific knowledge in aerodynamics.

---

1. *U.S. Air Service,* December 1922, 7–9.
2. Heinrich Hentzen set a glider duration world record of three hours, six minutes, on August 26, 1922.
3. The last of the Wrights' flying at Kitty Hawk was done by Orville in 1911 with a new glider. The aircraft was built to test the brothers' prototype automatic stability device. But several reporters were there when Orville and his party arrived, so to avoid premature publicity, he decided not to test the automatic pilot. The flights were thus confined to testing the glider and experimenting with soaring. After some test flights and modifications to the glider, Orville made a spectacular flight of nine minutes, forty-five seconds, on October 24.
4. The precise time of Frederic Harth's flight was twenty-one minutes, thirty seconds.
5. [This footnote appeared with the original article:] Hentzen's record has been broken lately in the *Daily Mail* contest at Lewes, England, by the Frenchman [Alexis] Maneyrol with a record of three hours twenty-one minutes.
6. See Wilbur Wright's comments on the work of Louis-Pierre Mouillard in document 38: "What Mouillard Did."
7. In the spring of 1910, Orville Wright trained pilots at a winter flying site in Montgomery, Alabama, for the brothers' newly created Wright exhibition team and for the U.S. military, which had recently contracted with the Wrights to train army pilots. The flights were made on the site of the present Maxwell Air Force Base.

31. *Top:* Mrs. Hart O. Berg, the wife of the Wrights' representative in Europe, being taken up as a passenger by Wilbur on October 7, 1908, at Camp d'Auvours. The cord securing her skirts inspired the hobble skirt fad.

32. *Above:* Takeoff in 1908. After Kitty Hawk, the Wrights used a tower with a drop-weight to help launch their aircraft. Here soldiers raise the weight in preparation for a flight at Fort Myer, Virginia, during the U.S. Army Signal Corps flight trials conducted by Orville in 1908.

33. Orville Wright flying over the parade ground at Fort Myer, Virginia, on September 9, 1908

34. *Top:* Orville (in cap) and Lieutenant Thomas E. Selfridge moments before their ill-fated flight at Fort Myer in 1908

35. *Above:* The Fort Myer crash, September 17, 1908. Lieutenant Selfridge became the first fatality in a powered airplane when he and Orville crashed due to a malfunction. Orville survived, though he suffered the effects of his injuries for the rest of his life. In this photo, shocked observers retrieve Orville and Selfridge from the wreckage.

36. *Top:* Wilbur Wright, captured in an unusually casual and candid moment with Charlie Taylor at Fort Myer, Virginia, in 1909. Orville's crash in 1908 postponed the completion of the U.S. Army Signal Corps trials. The Wrights returned to Fort Myer the following year with a new aircraft. Flying in Europe, Wilbur had not been present at Fort Myer in 1908.

37. *Above:* Wilbur Wright flying at Pau, France, in 1909

38. Orville and Wilbur (in cap) explaining their aircraft to King Edward VII at Pau, France, on March 17, 1909

39. Orville (left) and Wilbur with their sister, Katharine, returning to America in May 1909 after their successful European tour. Orville was still using a cane due to his injuries from the Fort Myer crash eight months earlier.

40. *Top:* President William H. Taft (center) presenting gold medals from the Aero Club of America to Wilbur and Orville at the White House on June 10, 1909. Katharine is on Orville's left.

41. *Above:* Wilbur in flight, passing over the New York skyline. On October 4, 1909, Wilbur made a twenty-mile flight up the Hudson River from Governor's Island to Grant's Tomb and back as part of New York's Hudson-Fulton Celebration. More than one million people witnessed the flight. Note the canoe Wilbur strapped under the airplane in case he had to come down over water.

42. *Top:* The Wright Model B. In early 1910 the Wrights began to manufacture aircraft for sale. The first product of the Wright Company was the Model B. It was the first Wright aircraft that had wheels, eliminating the need for the tower, drop-weight, and launching rail, and it was also the first of the brothers' airplanes that had the horizontal stabilizer mounted in the rear.

43. *Above:* Model B aircraft being assembled at the Wright factory, Dayton, Ohio

44. *Top:* Orville (with cap and goggles) with several of the Wright Exhibition Company pilots in Montgomery, Alabama, in 1910: (from left) A. L. Welsh, Spencer Crane, Orville, Walter Brookins, James Davis, and Arch Hoxsey. The show team, formed in early 1910, performed until November 1911.

45. *Above:* The Wrights in Kitty Hawk in 1911 with a new experimental glider. On October 24 Orville set a new soaring endurance record of 9 minutes, 45 seconds, a record that stood for ten years.

46. The Wright Model F. After Wilbur's death in 1912, Orville managed the Wright Company on his own for three more years. In 1913 the firm produced the Wright Model F, the first Wright aircraft with a modern-style fuselage.

47. *Top:* The Wright Model G flying boat, powered by a six-cylinder, sixty-horsepower engine

48. *Above:* Orville (left) standing before the Dayton-Wright Airplane Company's version of the British-designed de Havilland DH-4, in 1917. During World War I, Orville lent his influential name to the Dayton-Wright Airplane Company.

49. Orville with Amelia Earhart in the mid-1930s

50. Orville (right) with Igor Sikorsky, inventor of the helicopter, in front of Sikorsky's prototype XR-4 at Wright Field on May 17, 1942

51. Orville with Charles Lindbergh

52. The Wright Brothers Memorial at Kitty Hawk. Carved into the base of the sixty-foot granite monument is the following inscription: "In commemoration of the conquest of the air by the brothers Wilbur and Orville Wright. Conceived by genius, achieved by dauntless resolution and unconquerable faith."

53. *Top:* Orville Wright (center left) with family members at the dedication of the Wright Memorial on November 19, 1932

54. *Above:* Orville (left) conferring with Henry Ford, with Charlie Taylor looking on

55. Samuel P. Langley's piloted *Great Aerodrome* collapsing on itself immediately after takeoff on December 8, 1903, just nine days before the Wright brothers flew successfully at Kitty Hawk

56. The heavily modified *Great Aerodrome* lifting off Lake Keuka at Hammondsport, New York, with Glenn Curtiss at the controls in 1914

57. *Top:* The Wright Flyer on display at the Science Museum in London. Orville sent the airplane there in 1928 as a gesture of protest in the face of the Smithsonian Institution's position on Langley's aircraft.

58. *Above:* The precious relic on its way home. Paul E. Garber (right), of the Smithsonian Institution, escorts the original 1903 Wright Flyer to Washington, D.C., in 1948 after its twenty-year stay at the Science Museum in London.

59. *Top:* The official installation of the Wright Flyer at the Smithsonian Institution. An elaborate ceremony was held on December 17, 1948, the forty-fifth anniversary of the historic flights at Kitty Hawk. Lindbergh's *Spirit of St. Louis* can be seen hanging behind the Flyer.

60. *Above:* Forever the mechanic: Orville Wright a few months before his death on January 30, 1948, at the age of seventy-six

3 • "THE GREATEST OF THE PRECURSORS"

THE WRIGHTS ASSESS THEIR CONTEMPORARIES

ONE OF THE DISTINGUISHING CHARACTERISTICS of the Wrights' achievement, beyond the revolutionary technical leap it embodied, was that the brothers accomplished the age-old dream to fly essentially alone. When Wilbur and Orville began their aeronautical research, they—like all other good engineers—investigated the work of their predecessors. In the course of their literature search, however, they were somewhat surprised to find how little advancement had been made, considering the caliber of people who had addressed the problem of flight and how long it had been a subject of inquiry. The corpus of aeronautical research produced during the preceding centuries left many questions inadequately answered and others unaddressed altogether. The Wrights' reading turned up numerous dead ends and mistakes to avoid. Although they had some modest assistance from their hired mechanic, Charlie Taylor, in fabricating the engine of their powered Flyer in 1903, the Wrights defined the key problems, conceptualized the solutions, and built their test equipment and aircraft virtually on their own. In the purest sense of the term, the Wright brothers *invented* the airplane.

Nevertheless, the brothers' survey of the still nascent field of aeronautics was not a totally fruitless exercise. To an extent, preexisting ideas and technology were incorporated in their first efforts. Certain concepts about wing shapes and stability, the basic aerodynamic formulas for calculating lift and drag, and fundamental engineering data regarding the sizing and materials needed to design the structure of their flying machines were all in place when the Wrights took up the problem of flight. They quickly refined this information as they improved their designs and their flying technique, but they did use it in its basic form to build and test their initial gliders. Unquestionably the Wrights demonstrated a hitherto unknown grasp of the essential problems and an ability for devising practical solutions. As they broke onto the aeronautical scene, they rapidly made conceptual breakthroughs that raised aeronautics to a completely new level. But in so doing, they did not work from a blank slate, nor was that slate filled entirely with erroneous entries.

Part 3 shines a bit of light on how the Wrights interpreted their relationships with fellow aeronautical experimenters. Before the brothers began their own experiments, they not only wrote but also printed two brief documents related to aeronautics (documents 34 and 35). Later, especially after 1905, the Wrights put considerable energy into establishing their priority of invention and affirming their unique achievement. But on a few occasions after their success, the Wrights commented about other investigators. Two individuals in particular were central to the Wrights' story—Otto Lilienthal and Octave Chanute. In documents 37 and 40, Wilbur acknowledges the brothers' debt to these two men by lauding their contributions to aeronautics.

Lilienthal influenced the Wrights more than did any other single experimenter. He was the preeminent pre-Wright aeronautical pioneer. In the 1860s, 1870s, and late 1880s, Lilienthal performed an extensive series of aerodynamic experiments using a whirling-arm device and other techniques. In 1889 he published his magnum opus, *Der Vogelflug als Grundlage der Fliegekunst* (Birdflight as the Basis of Aviation), in which he outlined his theories and documented his experiments. Lilienthal followed up his impressive program of flight research and data collection by constructing and testing a series of elegant, full-sized gliders. Between 1891 and 1896, when he was killed in an accident while flying one of his gliders, he made close to two thousand brief flights in sixteen different designs. His best efforts covered more than one thousand feet and were twelve to fifteen seconds in duration. The Wrights' beginning wing designs were based on a published table of air pressure data developed by Lilienthal, and most significantly, they adopted Lilienthal's approach of beginning with gliders to test their ideas and gain practical experience in the air as pilots. In his memorial to Lilienthal (document 40), Wilbur referred to him as "the greatest of the precursors."

During the last quarter of the nineteenth century, Chanute emerged as the elder statesmen of the fledgling field of aeronautics. He had gained professional prominence as a railroad engineer before turning his interests, and reputation, toward aviation. A person of his stature gave credibility to a pursuit that many thought pointless. He published a landmark book in 1894 entitled *Progress in Flying Machines,* a compendium of almost all the important work on heavier-than-air flight before the death of Lilienthal.

Although Chanute offered little genuine technical assistance and few if any useful theoretical ideas to the Wrights, his relationship with the brothers was very close and consequential. His significant contribution was as a source of moral support and confidence builder to Wilbur and Orville during times of difficulty and frustration. Chanute was only rarely able to point out errors or correctly suggest that the Wrights were exercising bad judgment. But given Chanute's stature in the field, just the fact that he was always ready and willing to respond promptly to their latest letter was a major source of encouragement to Wilbur and Orville. The interest and reinforcement of Chanute played no small part in their seeing the project through to completion. Even though at times Chanute had difficulty comprehending what the Wrights were doing, he understood one thing fully: he astutely recognized that Wilbur and Orville had done more in the short time that they had been at work on human flight than had the numerous other young experimenters he helped and sometimes supported financially. Thus, Chanute eagerly assisted the brothers however he could. Sadly, their relationship became strained after the Wrights' success. Chanute felt Wilbur and Orville had become too obsessed with maintaining secrecy about their invention and with becoming wealthy and famous. But after Chanute's death in 1910, Wilbur wrote a tribute to his old friend (document 37).

In contrast to the other articles, the final piece in this section, "The Mythical Whitehead Flight" (document 41), presents Orville's view on one of the curiosities of aviation history. In the 1930s a claim surfaced about a powered heavier-than-air flight made before the Wright brothers' flight, thus challenging the Wrights' status as the first to fly. The story, which still draws ardent believers, asserted that a German-born experimenter named Gustave Whitehead (formerly Weisskopf) had flown a powered airplane near Bridgeport, Connecticut, in the summer of 1901, more than two years before the Wrights' flights at Kitty Hawk. Historians have repeatedly demonstrated that the scant evidence for the claim does not hold up to scrutiny. Nevertheless, three books and numerous articles have been published supporting the apocryphal claim since the 1937 publication of Stella Randolph's book *Lost Flights of Gustave Whitehead.* One of the best analyses of the Whitehead story appears in chapter 6 of Tom D. Crouch's *A Dream of Wings: Americans and the Airplane, 1875–1905.* Crouch places Whitehead in his true historical context within the aeronautical community of the late nineteenth century and demonstrates convincingly that no Whitehead flights ever took place, before or after the Wrights flew at Kitty Hawk. Orville's personal opinion on the matter is included here.

34 • HE CAN HALF FLY[1]

Wilbur and Orville Wright

A German, named Lilienthal, after experimenting for twenty-three years with artificial wings, has succeeded in raising himself, weighing 160 pounds, with the aid of counter weights lifting eighty pounds. How to raise the other eighty pounds is still beyond him.

---

1. The *Evening Item* (Dayton), July 17, 1890, 4. This article was repeated in the July 26, 1890, issue of the *Evening Item* under the title "Needs More Wings."

35 • AIR SHIP SOON TO FLY[1]

Wilbur and Orville Wright[2]

"Within three weeks we will sail into Chicago in the first of our air ships," declared E. J. Pennington, at the Grand Pacific Hotel, Chicago. Mr. Pennington, who is the principal inventor of the air ship soon to be tried for the first time, had gone to Chicago to attend a meeting of the stockholders of the Mount Carmel Aeronautic Navigation Company, that convened at the hotel December 10th. It was virtually the first meeting of the stockholders of this corporation, which, it is alleged, has already a paid-up stock of $20,000,000. It is proposed to invest this great sum in the manufacture of ships for traveling in the air.

Mr. Pennington, a neatly dressed, intelligent and studious-looking man of about thirty years of age, explained that the first of the ships was nearing completion, and that the plans for a trial trip over the country had already been completed. This trial will occur in about three weeks. The ship, he said, will start from the place of its manufacture at Mount Carmel and travel to St. Louis, a distance of 185 miles. From there it will sail up to Chicago, and from there to New York. Mr. Pennington and his associate, Mr. R. H. Butler, propose to make the trip, taking with them a half dozen newspaper representatives and any of the stockholders who wish to accompany them. The vessel with which the first trial will be made is two hundred feet in length. The cabin will be made of aluminium.

---

1. *Dayton Tattler,* December 27, 1890, 1. Reprinted with the permission of the Paul Laurence Dunbar Collection, Dayton and Montgomery County Public Library, Dayton, Ohio.
2. This article appeared with no byline, but very likely one or the other of the Wrights wrote it, or at least discovered it, and offered it to Paul Laurence Dunbar for the *Dayton Tattler,* since the Wright brothers were printing the newspaper.

36 • WRIGHT'S STATEMENT CONCERNING JOHNSTONE'S FATAL FALL[1]

Interview with Wilbur Wright

NEW YORK, DEC. 3.—Wilbur Wright, who arrived here tonight, gave his first account of the causes which he believes led to the death of Ralph Johnstone, who fell 800 feet to his death at Denver on Nov. 17. Johnstone was a Wright aviator.[2]

"I thought it all out," said Wilbur Wright. "Hitherto I have expressed no opinion, because I wanted to analyze the probabilities. The day before Johnstone started for Denver I said to him:

"'Ralph, you must obey orders from now on, or there will be serious trouble. You took unnecessary risks at Boston and at Belmont Park, against definite orders, and it must stop.' He answered:

"'Mr. Wright, I've thought it all over, and I've made up my mind to obey orders. You don't seem to appreciate fancy flying, and I'm not going to do any more of it.'

"He was a little hot about it, and I told him, 'Ralph, we do not value a man by the number of times he outdoes his fellow-aviators, but by the ability he has to restrain himself when the crowd yells for the uselessly sensational.'

"On the day that Johnstone was killed he was doing all right. On the day before, though, he had disobeyed a standing order by landing with the wind instead of against it. The result was that he ran into a fence and broke a wing.

"I think there must have been some little detail omitted in making repairs to the wing which failed him the next day when he was killed."

Asked about the plans of Mrs. Johnstone and her four-year-old son, Ralph, Mr. Wright said they would soon return to Germany, to the home of her parents.

---

1. *The Mobile Era: A Monthly Magazine Containing the General News of the Air Craft*, December 1910, 16.
2. In early 1910, the Wrights formed a flying exhibition team to promote their recently established aircraft-manufacturing firm, the Wright Company, and to generate income from flying. They assembled a stable of pilots, trained by Orville, and flew their first exhibition at the Indianapolis Motor Speedway on June 13–18, 1910. Ralph Johnstone was one of the Wright team's star performers. A daredevil by nature, Johnstone was always bending, and frequently breaking, the Wrights' strict rules against excessive risk-taking in the air. The brothers expected "plain flying" only—no "stunts" or "spectacular frills" (W. Wright to Arch Hoxsey, September 19, 1910, in Marvin W. McFarland, ed., *The Papers of Wilbur and Orville Wright*, 2 vols. [New York: McGraw-Hill, 1953], 2:998–99). Feeding on the crowd's desire for more than gentle circles, Johnstone and Arch Hoxsey, a fellow Wright exhibition pilot, pushed the limits of their aircraft and their skills. Despite consistent admonitions from Wilbur and Orville, these two pilots continued their stunts, resulting in more accidents, much to the Wrights' frustration. On November 17, 1910, at a Denver air show, Johnstone crashed again when he failed to pull out from a spi-

raling dive. This time he did not survive. A horrible scene ensued: ghoulish spectators broke through the police line, pounced on the wreckage, and stripped gloves and other pieces of clothing from Johnstone's mangled body. Johnstone was the first American pilot to die in an airplane crash.

37 • THE LIFE AND WORK OF OCTAVE CHANUTE[1]

Wilbur Wright

By the death of Mr. O. Chanute the world has lost one whose labors had to an unusual degree influenced the course of human progress. If he had not lived the entire history of progress in flying would have been other than it has been, for he encouraged not only the Wright brothers to persevere in their experiments, but it was due to his missionary trip to France in 1903[2] that the Voisins, Bleriot,[3] Farman, DeLagrange[4] and Archdeacon[5] were led to undertake a revival of aviation studies in that country, after the failure of the efforts of Ader and the French government in 1897[6] had left everyone in idle despair.

Mr. Chanute's own experiments have been quite fully described in papers written by himself in *The Journal of the Western Society of Engineers,* for 1897; *The Aeronautical Annual,* 1897; *McClure's Magazine* of June, 1900; *Cassier's Magazine,* June, 1901; *Popular Science Monthly,* March, 1904, and in numerous other publications. The grand object of his experiments was the attainment of automatic stability, his belief being that human intelligence would be inadequate to cope with the difficulties encountered in the tumultuous aerial seas. Every machine he built had this prime object in view. As he stated in the *Cassier's* article, referring to his own experiments, "He has confined his endeavors wholly to the evolution of automatic stability." In carrying out this purpose he not only constructed a vast number of small gliders, but also proceeded to the construction of four different types of man-carrying gliders, in addition to the full size Lilienthal glider which he had constructed to begin with. In the "multiple wing" machine, the wings were mounted on vertical axes so as to swing backward at the tips when struck by a wind gust. The "double-decker" had an elastically mounted tail which yielded under the pressure of the wind.[7] These machines were built and operated by Messrs. Herring and Avery in 1897.[8] A third type, in which the curvature of the wings from front to rear was automatically variable, was undertaken under the superintendence of Mr. E. C. Huffaker in 1901, and partially tested in a small model, but the large machine was never finished. The "multiple wing" machine was rebuilt and tried by Mr. Herring at Wright brothers' camp at Kitty Hawk in 1902, but the results were unsatisfactory. In the same year a fourth method of obtaining automatic stability was tested for him at the same place by Mr. Herring. This was the "oscillating wing" machine built under his instruction by Mr. Lamson. In it the "triple deck" wings were mounted on a horizontal axis and were intended to oscillate as the wind pressure and center of pressure varied. It also failed to give positive results.[9]

On the whole, Mr. Chanute's experiments were rather disappointing to him so far as his main purpose was concerned. As he said in the *McClure* article: "In my judgment neither of the machines above described is as yet perfected, and I believe it is still premature to apply an artificial motor. This is sure to bring about complications which it is preferable to avoid until the equilibrium has been thoroughly evolved." This view he consistently maintained through all the years of his active work. When, after the experiments of 1897, a wealthy gentleman of Chicago proposed to furnish the money necessary to construct a motor-driven flying machine, Mr. Chanute courteously but firmly declined the offer.

Mr. Chanute's active experiments closed with the trials of the two gliders above mentioned at Kitty Hawk in 1902. His increasing years, the difficulty of obtaining satisfactory assistants, and the growing prospect that the efforts of the Wrights to obtain a sufficient control by human intelligence acting through adjustable wings and rudders were the main factors in bringing about this result. On his return from Europe in May, 1903, he made a trip to Dayton and stated to my brother and myself that after thinking over the flights of the 1902 Wright glider, which he had witnessed at Kitty Hawk, he had come to the conclusion that whatever the final merits of the two systems might be, the first success would be obtained in all probability by our system, i.e., human control, rather than by his own system, i.e., automatic control. He then advised us to undertake the application of a motor and was much pleased as well as surprised when we told him that the designs were already completed for such a machine, and the work of construction well under way.

Although his experiments in automatic stability did not yield results which the world has yet been able to utilize, his labors had vast influence in bringing about the era of human flight. His "double deck" modification of the old Wenham and Stringfellow machines will influence flying machine design so long as flying machines are made. His writings were so lucid as to provide an intelligent understanding of the nature of the problems of flight to a vast number of persons who would probably never have given the matter study otherwise,[10] and not only by published articles, but by personal correspondence and visitation, he inspired and encouraged to the limits of his ability all who were devoted to the work. His private correspondence with experimenters in all parts of the world was of great volume.[11] No one was too humble to receive a share of his time. In patience and goodness of heart he has rarely been surpassed. Few men were more universally respected and loved.

---

1. *Aeronautics,* January 1911, 3–4, 35. This article contained a section on Chanute written by James Means and an introduction by the editors. Wilbur Wright's section, reproduced here, appeared on page 4.

2. In January 1903 Chanute began a four-month tour of Europe. In every city he visited he sought out all those he knew who were interested in aviation and discussed with them the latest developments. On April 2 he was in Paris to deliver a lecture before the Aéro-Club de France, whose members were leaders in the European aviation community. In his talk, which would have important ramifications for the future of European aviation, he presented details of his own work and of the Wrights' gliders and their flying experiments. Numerous articles reporting and enlarging on the lecture quickly followed. Given Chanute's revered standing in Europe's aviation community, his visit, or "missionary trip" as Wilbur termed it, was a powerful impetus to reinvigorating European aeronautical research, which had remained somewhat dormant since the death of Otto Lilienthal in 1896. Chanute's news of significant American progress toward a practical flying machine spurred the French, in particular, to redouble their efforts in aeronautical experimentation. Despite this positive effect, however, Chanute's lecture also engendered much confusion. Chanute's understanding of the technical aspects of the Wrights' design was limited at best, and as a result many inaccuracies were imparted to the French. Chanute made matters worse by exaggerating the success of his own gliders and his influence on the Wright brothers. The flawed information led to many ill-fated European attempts to replicate the Wrights' success, undermining the credibility of the brothers' claims for the capabilities of their aircraft. Chanute's embellishments of his role as the Wrights' adviser and mentor also contributed to later personal dissension between Chanute and the brothers.
3. This name was properly spelled Blériot. Louis Blériot was one of the dominant figures in the early history of the airplane. A wealthy manufacturer of automobile headlamps, he turned to aviation in 1901. He first experimented with an ornithopter (flapping-wing) design that was a total failure. In 1904 he commissioned Gabriel Voisin to build a float-mounted, biplane glider, which was tested on the Seine in 1905 with little success. After a few more collaborative efforts, Blériot split with Voisin in 1907 and began experimenting with monoplane designs. His first several were only marginally successful, but with his Type XI, first flown in January 1909, Blériot's luck changed. On July 25, 1909, Blériot achieved world fame when he successfully flew the English Channel in his Type XI, winning the £1,000-prize offered by the *London Daily Mail* for the first crossing of the Channel by airplane. Following the flight, Blériot was flooded with orders for copies of his monoplane. The Blériot XI was one of the most significant airplanes of the pioneer era. Approximately eight hundred were produced between 1909 and 1914, and they were flown by many of the most celebrated pilots of the period.
4. This name was properly spelled "Delagrange." See document 3, note 3.
5. For further information on the Voisins, Farman, and Archdeacon, see the notes to document 3.
6. See document 39: "What Clement Ader Did."
7. The "double-decker," also known as the Chanute "two-surface machine," was the one glider designed by Chanute and his assistants that achieved some meaningful success and influence. In its final biplane configuration, it accomplished a number of flights in September 1896, ranging from 250 to 350 feet. The Chanute "double-decker" was even more significant for its structural design. The wings were trussed one above the other with struts and cross wires, forming a light, sturdy biplane wing cell. The concept was derived from Chanute's knowledge and experience with trussed bridge designs. The trussed biplane form was adopted by the Wrights and became the dominant structural

configuration of the first two decades of powered flight. The trussed biplane concept was not exclusively Chanute's, but his version of it was among the most important.

8. Actually they were built in 1896 and 1897.
9. For a detailed discussion of Chanute's glider experiments and the work of his assistants—A. M. Herring, William Avery, E. C. Huffaker, and Charles Lamson—see Tom D. Crouch, *A Dream of Wings: Americans and the Airplane, 1875–1905* (New York: W. W. Norton and Co., 1981). Wilbur was being charitable when he stated that Herring's attempts to fly the Chanute gliders at Kitty Hawk in 1902 "failed to give positive results." The two gliders were near total failures. Chanute no doubt left Kitty Hawk feeling rather embarrassed, especially in light of the Wrights' spectacular controlled glides of several hundred feet made with their perfected 1902 glider.
10. Chanute's highly influential book *Progress in Flying Machines,* published in 1894, was a compendium of virtually every credible aeronautical investigation up to that time. All serious late-nineteenth-century and early-twentieth-century experimenters consulted this rich and valuable treatment of the field.
11. Chanute exchanged some four hundred letters with the Wright brothers alone between 1900 and his death in 1910.

38 • WHAT MOUILLARD DID[1]

Wilbur Wright

Until a few months ago the name Louis Pierre Mouillard was known to only a few deep students of aeronautics and to them he appeared as an elusive personality, a French student—farmer—poet—who had lived in Egypt and had written a remarkable book upon bird flight. Of his life and the value of his work nothing definite was known. Two years ago, during the Heliopolis meet, somebody remembered that Mouillard had lived and died in Cairo and started an investigation, which ended with the finding of a boxful of papers of Mouillard in the cellars of the French Consulate, where they had been stored on the death of Mouillard. These papers were acquired by an officer of the Ligue Aerienne who undertook to edit them. From time to time since then the Ligue has advanced for Mouillard the claim of his having discovered the principle of wing warping. Because there were found among the Mouillard papers letters of Chanute showing that in their correspondence he and Mouillard had discussed the peculiarities of bird flight, and in particular a belief of Mouillard's that birds turn by creating a resistance at the tip of the wing upon the side toward which they wish to go, it has been sought to intimate that the principle of warping was revealed by Mouillard to Chanute, and by him was communicated to the Wrights. These claims have never been advanced officially, nor substantiated with proof. To clear this point, for historical purposes, we asked the Wright brothers to define both Mouillard's place in history and the value of his contribution. The following article by Wilbur Wright is made especially

timely by the inauguration of a monument to Mouillard at Heliopolis, February 25, 1912.—Editor

The erection at Cairo, Egypt, of a monument to L. P. Mouillard, recalls attention to one of the greatest missionaries of the flying cause which the 19th century produced. Mouillard was a Frenchmen who passed a large part of his life in Algeria and Egypt, where his attention was attracted by the wonderful soaring of vultures on fixed wings. His imagination was greatly excited by what he saw and during the remainder of his life he was like a prophet crying in the wilderness, exhorting the world to repent of its unbelief in the possibility of human flight. In 1881 he published a book called "The Empire of the Air," which is one of the most remarkable pieces of aeronautical literature that has ever been published. In his introduction he says:

> If there be a domineering, tyrant thought it is the conception that the problem of flight may be solved by man. When once this idea has invaded the brain it possesses it exclusively. It is then a haunting thought, a walking nightmare, impossible to cast off. If now we consider the pitying contempt with which such a line of research is appreciated, we may somewhat conceive the unhappy lot of the poor investigator whose soul is thus possessed.

He deplores the incredulity of the world and exhorts it to cast aside its unbelief:

> O! blind humanity! open thine eyes and thou shalt see millions of birds and myriads of insects cleaving the atmosphere. All these creatures are whirling through the air without the slightest float; many of them are gliding therein, without losing height, hour after hour, on pulseless wings without fatigue; and after beholding this demonstration, given by the source of all knowledge, thou wilt acknowledge that Aviation is the path to be followed.

His observations upon the habits of vultures led him to the conclusion that flight without motors was possible to man, and this idea he presented to his readers with an enthusiasm so inspiring and convincing that his book produced results of the greatest importance in the history of flight. The man was himself almost fanatical in his enthusiasm. Speaking of his first sight of a vulture in full soaring flight, he says:

> All my life shall I remember the first flight which I saw of the Gyps fulvus, the great tawny vultures of Africa. I was so impressed that all day long I could think of nothing else; and indeed there was good cause, for it was a practical, perfect demonstration of all my preconceived theories concerning the possibilities of artificial flight in a wind. Since then I have observed thousands of vultures. I have disturbed many of the vast flocks of these birds, and yet, even now, I cannot see one individual passing through the air without following him with my eyes until he disappears in the distant horizon.

The vulture's needs are few, and his strength is moderate. To earn his living he but needs to sight the dead animal from afar. And so what does he know? He knows how to rise, how to float aloft, to sweep the field with keen vision, to sail upon the wind without effort, till the carcass is seen, and then to descend slowly, after careful reconnaissance and assurance that he may alight without danger, that he will not be surprised, and compelled to precipitous and painful departure. And so he has evolved a peculiar mode of flight; he sails and spends no force, he never hurries, he uses the wind instead of his muscles, and the wing flap occasionally seen is meant to limber up rather than to hasten through the air. And so the true model to study is the vulture—the great vulture. Beside him the stork is as a wren, the kite a mere butterfly, the falcon a pin feather.

Whoso has for five minutes had the fortune to see the oricou vulture in full sail through the air, and has not perceived the possibility of his imitation by man, is—I will not say of dull understanding, but certainly inapt to analyze and to appreciate.

Throughout the book are to be found passages of high literary quality, and the charm is so great that more than one cold blooded reader has been incited to emulate the example of the birds. There is no doubt that the reading of this book was one of the main factors in inducing Mr. Chanute to undertake his experiments, and I know that it was one of the inspiring causes of the efforts of the Wright brothers. Compared with this book, which is devoted almost entirely to observations relating to birds, the ordinary books on ornithology are childish. With the possible exception of Lilienthal, none of the men who wrote on aviation in the 19th century possessed such power to draw recruits to a belief in the possibility of motorless human flight.

As a missionary, Mouillard stood at the very top along with Lilienthal and Chanute. As a scientific student of the laws and principles of aerodynamics he is not to be mentioned in the same class with such men as Cayley,[2] Wenham,[3] Penaud,[4] Langley, Lilienthal, Chanute and Maxim.[5] He was a careful observer of birds, and possessed a genius for expressing his thoughts and feelings in words, but beyond that he was mediocre. He made a few feeble attempts to construct soaring machines, but their design and construction were so crude that he failed to surpass the futile attempts at gliding made by Cayley and Wenham who long antedated him. It remained for Lilienthal to definitely employ this mode of experiment, and thereby win for himself a glory which the world will never forget.

It is most unfortunate that the project of erecting a monument to a man well worthy of the thanks and the remembrance of the world should have become entangled with an unworthy attempt to seek to add to the glory of France by filching the credit justly due to Lilienthal, and by falsely accusing Mr. Chanute, the benefactor of Mouillard, of having stolen the latter's secrets and transmitted them to the Wright brothers. There is in France a little group of misguided individuals who bring disgrace upon their country by their too zealous attempts to add to its glory.

Fortunately they do not represent the real France, which has shown by numerous manifestations of various kinds its high appreciation of the work of foreigners, including even Lilienthal, a native of a country greatly disliked by French people.

This group some years ago formed a society known as the "Ligue Aerienne" and made it their purpose to convince themselves and the world that France was the birthplace of human flight.[6] To begin with they hailed Santos Dumont as the "father of aviation," because of his flights in 1906.[7] When it was proved that flights had been made outside France long before that, they then fell back on Ader and hailed him as the "father of aviation," on account of a mythical flight in 1897.[8] But when the Minister of War permitted the publication of the official report on the trial of this machine, which showed that it had never left the ground, but had been wrecked while running along the track with only a small part of the power turned on, this indefatigable group went on back to Mouillard and proceeded to erect a monument to him as the "father of aviation." If they had been content with this, their activity might have been passed with a smile, but when in addition they attempted to pervert history and accuse Mr. Chanute of dishonestly getting from Mouillard the secret of warping the wings to control lateral balance, and transmitting it to the Wright brothers, it is well to expose their errors.

The position of Lilienthal as the founder of gliding experiments is too fully established to make it necessary to defend it here. The facts are well known.

The fact that the Wright brothers had been using wing warping several years before Mr. Chanute became acquainted with them, effectually disposes of the part of the story accusing Mr. Chanute of transmitting any of Mouillard's secret to them. The fact that Mouillard never had the idea of warping the wings to control lateral balance, and never communicated such an idea to Mr. Chanute, is also sufficient of itself to refute the charge.

It only remains to discuss that part accusing Mr. Chanute of having received from Mouillard the manuscript of a proposed book and, after reading it, of having dishonestly advised him to suppress it. It is quite clear that the men who manufactured this shameful attack on the memory of a dead man had never read Mr. Chanute's book, "Progress in Flying Machines," published in 1893.[9] This book contains the fullest and most appreciative account of Mouillard which is to be found in the literature of flying. It discusses not only his book, "The Empire of the Air," and his attempts to construct apparatus, but also makes copious extracts, with full credit to Mouillard, from the manuscript which these ignoramuses accuse him of trying to keep from the knowledge of the world. Not only that, but Mr. Chanute, learning that Mouillard was an invalid and without funds, furnished the money to secure a United States patent on his invention, and gave him a considerable sum of money in addition. The patent issued and was published in 1897. Mr. Chanute never received a cent of benefit from it. *In this patent, Mouillard proposed to make the right and left rear corners of the wings double so that one or the other could be distorted to create a resistance in order to turn the machine to right or left. No vertical tail was to be used. The subject of lateral balance was not even mentioned.*

The Mouillard patent was cited by the defendants in the case of The Wright Company *vs.* Louis Paulhan,[10] and Judge Hand in his decision refers specifically to it and says, "In no one of the nineteen claims is there anything which in any way even foreshadows the patent [of the Wright brothers][11] in suit." Mr. Chanute's book and the patent clearly show that he made every effort to spread the fame and improve the finances of Mouillard.

The memory of Mouillard is well deserving of perpetuation by a monument, but it is a pity that it should have been used by a self-constituted group of pretended champions of French glory, in a disgraceful Chauvinistic campaign of slander and detraction not approved by the mass of the French people.

---

1. *Aero Club of America Bulletin,* April 1912, 2–4.
2. Sir George Cayley was an English experimenter working throughout the first half of the nineteenth century. He was the first to mount a well-conceived, systematic program of aeronautical research grounded in scientific method. He was among the first to study bird flight beyond casual observance. Cayley was also the first to apply a whirling-arm apparatus to aeronautical experimentation. He built the world's first successful model glider in 1804 and later experimented with two full-size gliders capable of brief hops with a pilot aboard. Most importantly, Cayley set down several fundamental concepts that, in general terms, define the airplane in its modern form. He conceived the airplane to be a machine with fixed wings, a fuselage, and a tail, with separate systems to provide lift, propulsion, and control. Seemingly a simplistic and self-evident, it was a major intellectual leap over all that come before. Cayley published his groundbreaking ideas in a pivotal three-part article in *Nicholson's Journal of Natural Philosophy, Chemistry and the Arts* in 1809 and 1810. For a detailed treatment of Cayley's aeronautical work, see Charles Harvard Gibbs-Smith, *Sir George Cayley's Aeronautics, 1796–1855* (London: Her Majesty's Stationery Office, 1962).
3. See document 5, note 8.
4. Properly spelled "Pénaud." See document 17, note 9.
5. See document 5, note 7.
6. The first human ascension in a free balloon took place in France when the Marquis d'Arlandes and Pilâtre de Rozier made a flight of five miles on November 21, 1783, in a Montgolfier hot air balloon. With this event, the French proclaimed their nation as the birthplace of aviation. A little more than a century later, as heavier-than-air flight became a reality, the French aeronautical community struggled with what they saw as a loss of face over a Frenchman not being the first to fly an airplane. Regarding aviation as a French invention, more than a few in France attempted to attribute claims of pre-Wright success to native experimenters.
7. Alberto Santos-Dumont, a Brazilian-born experimenter living in France, had gained great fame with a series of successful lighter-than-air dirigibles at the turn of the century. A flamboyant personality, Santos-Dumont turned his interest to heavier-than-air flight in 1906 with a powered biplane known as the *14bis.* On October 23, 1906, he made

a hop of 60 meters (197 feet), capturing the Archdeacon prize for a flight of at least 25 meters. On November 12, 1906, he had his best performance with the *14bis*, another straight-line flight covering 220 meters (722 feet). With little public knowledge beyond rumor of the Wrights' success at Kitty Hawk and their impressive extended flights of 1905, many Europeans hailed Santos-Dumont as the first to fly. Though not the first flights in the world, Santos-Dumont's efforts in 1906 were the first public flights in Europe of a powered heavier-than-air flying machine. More significantly, however, the *14bis* had no effective means of lateral control and was structurally unsound. Unlike the Wright design, it could not have been developed into a practical airplane. Still, Santos-Dumont became a hero in France and was frequently cited as evidence of French priority as the home of aviation.

8. See document 39: "What Clement Ader Did."
9. It was actually published in 1894.
10. This was one of the patent-infringement cases filed by the Wrights in 1910 regarding their basic 1906 airplane patent.
11. This insertion was part of the original text of the article.

39 • WHAT CLEMENT ADER DID[1]

Wilbur Wright

Who was the first man to leave the ground in a self propelled heavier-than-air craft? is a question that has been asked over and over since human flight became an actuality and has elicited considerable discussion. The Wright brothers are, of course, known to have made the first real flight, but the full honor has never been accorded them in some quarters on account of rumors which credited Clement Ader, the French pioneer, with first leaving contact with the ground during a trial of the machine which he constructed for the French Government in the year 1897. The experiments of Ader were never made in secret, but the outcome being unsatisfactory were discontinued. Nothing was heard about the matter thereafter until three years ago when some French patriots advanced for Ader the claim of having been the man who first broke the shackles of gravity in a power-driven aeroplane. This claim was investigated by French aeronautical authorities, who obtained from the French Government the official report of the Ader experiment, and finding that the claim was not clear rejected it. But as is often the case with matters of similar nature, while the first claim was published broadcast, the final outcome was known only to the few directly concerned, so that so far as the public is concerned, the Ader claim still stands unsettled; and it is not unusual to find in books statements crediting Ader with the feat. The following authoritative article by Mr. Wilbur Wright is therefore of historical value. It is the first comprehensive presentation of the subject and the first definition of Ader's place in the history of aviation ever written.—Editor

Clement Ader was a French electrical engineer, who during the last quarter of the nineteenth century devoted a great deal of study and money to the problem of human flight.[2] In his youth he had become interested in the flight of birds, and at a later period had made a study of bats, with a view to imitating their structure in a flying machine. Between the years 1882 and 1890 he built a number of pieces of apparatus of which the last, finished in 1890, was fitted with a steam engine.

Having exhausted his own resources, he succeeded in enlisting the aid of the French Government and proceeded to the construction of a large machine, having a steam motor of 40 horsepower. This apparatus was tried under conditions of great secrecy in October, 1897, at the military field at Satory, near Paris, in the presence of a Commission, representing the French Government, but the results were so unsatisfactory that the French Government, which had spent more than one hundred thousand dollars on the project, refused to advance further funds, and Ader abandoned the attempt to solve the problem.

Ader Did Not Leave the Ground

After the possibility of human flight had been demonstrated by the Wright brothers, claims began to be made that the Ader machine, before being wrecked, had flown nearly one thousand feet in 1897. After a time a systematic attempt was begun to establish by constant repetition a legend which might eventually displace the truth. But the friends of M. Santos-Dumont, who claimed the honor of being the first man to fly within the borders of France,[3] became aroused and a heated controversy arose.

At length M. Archdeacon[4] succeeded in obtaining permission of the French Ministry of War to publish the official report of the Commission which supervised the trials of the Ader machine in 1897. The report, which conclusively shows that the Ader machine never left the ground, was as follows:

GENERAL MENSIER'S REPORT

Paris, October 21, 1897

Report of the Trials of Mr. Clement Ader's Aviation Apparatus

Mr. Ader having notified the Minister of War by letter, July 21, 1897, that the Apparatus of Aviation which he had agreed to build under the conditions set forth in the Convention of July 24, 1894, was ready, and therefore requesting that trials be undertaken before a Committee appointed for this purpose as per the decision of August 4, the Committee was appointed as follows:

Division General Mensier, Chairman; Division General Delambre, Inspector General of the Permanent Works for Coast Defense, Member of the Technical Committee of the Engineering Corps; Colonel Laussedat, Director of the Conservatoire des Arts et Metiers; Sarrau, Member of the Institute, Professor of Mechanical Engineering at the Polytechnique School; Leaute, Member of the Institute, Professor of Mechanical Engineering at the Polytechnique School.

Colonel Laussedat gave notice at once that his health and work as Director of the Conservatoire des Arts et Metiers did not permit him to be a member of the Committee; the Minister therefore accepted his resignation September 24, and decided not to replace him.

Later on, however, on the request of the Chairman of the Committee, the Minister appointed a new member, General Grillon, commanding the Engineer Corps of the Military Government of Paris.

To carry on the trials which were to take place at the Camp of Satory, the Minister ordered the Governor of the military forces of Paris to requisition from the Engineer Corps, on request of the Chairman of the Committee, the men necessary to prepare the grounds at Satory.

After an inspection made on the 16th an aerodrome was chosen. Mr. Ader's idea was to have it of circular shape with a width of 40 meters and an average diameter of 450 meters. The preliminary work, laying out the grounds, interior and exterior circumference, etc., was finished at the end of August; the work of smoothing off the grounds began September 1 with 45 men and two rollers and was finished on the day of the first tests October 12.

The first meeting of the Committee was held August 18 in Mr. Ader's workshop; the object being to demonstrate the machine to the Committee and give the members all the information possible on the tests that were to be held. After a careful examination and after having heard all the explanations by the inventor which were deemed useful and necessary, the Committee decided that the apparatus seemed to be built within a perfect understanding of the purpose to be fulfilled as far as one could judge from the study of the apparatus at rest; they therefore, authorized Mr. Ader to take the machine apart and carry it to the Camp of Satory so as to proceed with the trials.

By letter of August 19 the Chairman made a report to the Minister of the findings of the Committee.

The work on the grounds having taken longer than was anticipated, the Chairman took advantage of this delay to call the Committee together for a second meeting during which Mr. Ader was to run the two propulsive screws situated at the forward end of the apparatus.

The meeting was held October 2; it gave the Committee an opportunity to appreciate the motive power in all its details; firebox, boiler, engine, under perfect control, absolute condensation, automatic fuel and feed of the liquid to be vaporized, automatic lubrication and scavenging; everything in a word seemed well designed and executed.

The weights in comparison with the power of the engine realized a considerable advance over anything made to date, since the two engines weighed together 42 kg., the firebox and boiler 60 kg., the condenser 15 kg., or a total of 117 kg. for approximately 40 horsepower or a little less than 3 kg. per horsepower.

One of the members summed up the general opinion by saying: "Whatever may be the result from an aviation point of view, a result which could not be foreseen for the moment, it was nonetheless proven that from a mechanical point of view Mr. Ader's apparatus was of the greatest interest and of real ingeniosity. He expressed a hope that in any case the machine would not be lost to science."

The second experiment in the workshop was made in the presence of the Chairman, the purpose being to demonstrate that the wings, having a spread of 17 meters, were sufficiently strong to support the weight of the apparatus. With this aim in view, 14 sliding supports were placed under each one of these, representing imperfectly the manner in which the wings would support the machine in the air; by gradually raising the supports with the slides, the wheels on which the machine rested were lifted from the ground. It was evident at that time that the members composing the skeleton of the wings supported the apparatus, and it was quite evident that when the wings were supported by the air on every point of their surface the stresses thereon would be better equalized than when resting upon a few supports, and that therefore the resistance to breakage would be considerably greater.

After this last test, the work on the grounds being practically finished, the machine was transported to Satory, assembled again and made ready for trial.

At first Mr. Ader was to maneuver the machine on the grounds at a moderate speed, then increase this until it was possible to judge whether there was a tendency for the machine to rise; and it was only after Mr. Ader had acquired sufficient practice that a meeting of the Committee was to be called to be present at the first part of the trials; namely, volutions of the apparatus on the ground.

The first test took place on Tuesday, Oct. 12, in the presence of the Chairman of the Committee. It had rained a great deal during the preceding night and the clay track would have offered considerable resistance to the rolling of the machine; furthermore a moderate wind was blowing from the southwest, too strong during the early part of the afternoon to allow for any trials.

Towards sunset, however, the wind having weakened, Mr. Ader decided to make his first trial; the machine was taken out of its hanger, the wings were mounted and steam raised. Mr. Ader in his seat had, on each side of him, one man to the right and one to the left, whose duty was to rectify the direction of the apparatus in the event that the action of the rear wheel as a rudder would not be sufficient to hold the machine in a straight course.

At 5:25 p.m. the machine was started, first slowly then at an increased speed after 250 or 300 meters, the two men who were being dragged by the apparatus were exhausted and forced to fall flat on the ground in order to allow the wings to pass over them and the trip around the track was completed, or a total of 1,400 meters, without incident at a fair speed, which could be estimated to be from 300 to 400 meters per minute. Notwithstanding Mr. Ader's inexperience, this being the first time that he had run his apparatus, he followed approximately the chalk line which marked the center of the track and he stopped at the exact point from which he started.

The marks of the wheels on the ground, which were rather soft, did not show up very much, and it was clear that a part of the weight of the apparatus had been supported by the wings, though the speed was only about one-third of what the machine could do, had Mr. Ader used all of its motive power; he was running at a pressure of from 3 to 4 atmospheres, when he could have used ten or twelve.

This first trial, so fortunately accomplished, was of great importance; it was the first time that a comparatively heavy vehicle (nearly 400 kg. including the weight of the operator, fuel and water) had been set in motion by a tractive apparatus, using the air solely as a propelling medium. The favorable report turned in by the Committee after the meeting of October 2 was found justified by the results demonstrated on the grounds, and the first problem of aviation, namely, the creation of efficient motive power could be considered as solved, since the propulsion of the apparatus in the air would be a great deal easier than the traction on the ground, provided that the second part of the problem, the sustaining of the machine in the air, would be realized.

The next day, Wednesday the 13th, no further trials were made on account of the rain and wind.

On Thursday the 14th the Chairman requested that General Grillon, who had just been appointed as a member of the Committee, accompany him so as to have a second witness.

The weather was fine, but a fairly strong, gusty wind was blowing from the south. Mr. Ader explained to the two members of the Committee the dangers of these gusts since at two points of the circumference these would strike him sideways. The wind was blowing in the direction A. B., the apparatus starting from C. and running in the direction shown by the arrow. The first dangerous spot would be at B.[5] The apparatus had been kept in readiness in the event of the wind dying down. Toward sunset the wind seemed to die down, as it had done on the evening of the 12th. Mr. Ader hesitated, which unfortunately further events only justified, but decided to make a new trial.

At the start which took place at 5:15 p.m. the apparatus having the wind in the rear seemed to run at a fairly regular speed, it was nevertheless easy to notice from the marks of the wheels on the ground that the rear part of the apparatus had been lifted and that the rear wheel, being the rudder, had not been in constant contact with the ground. When the machine came to the neighborhood of B. the two members of the Committee saw the machine swerve suddenly out of the track in a semicircle, lean over to the right and finally stop. They immediately proceeded to the point where the accident had taken place and endeavored to find an explanation for the same. The Chairman decided as follows:

Mr. Ader was the victim of a gust of wind which he had feared as he explained before starting out; feeling himself thrown out of this course, he tried to use the rudder energetically, but at that time the rear wheel was not in contact with the ground and therefore did not perform its function; the canvas rudder, which had as its purpose the maneuvering of the machine in the air, did not have sufficient action on the ground. It would have been possible without any doubt to react by using the propellers at unequal speed, but Mr. Ader being still inexperienced had not thought of this. Furthermore he was thrown out of his course so quickly that he decided in order to avoid a more serious accident to stop both engines. This sudden stop produced the half circle already described and the fall of the machine on its side.

The damage to the machine was serious; consisting at first sight of the rupture of both propellers, the rear left wheel and the bending of the left wing tip. It will only be possible to tell after the machine is taken apart whether the engines and more particularly the organs of transmission have been put out of line.

Whatever the damage may be, though comparatively easy to repair, it will take a certain amount of time, and taking into consideration the time of the year it is evident that the tests will have to be adjourned for the present.

As has been said in the above report, the tests, though prematurely interrupted, have shown results of great importance, and though the final results are hard to foresee, it would seem advisable to continue the trials. By waiting for the return of spring there will be plenty of time to finish the tests and it will not be necessary to rush matters, which was a partial cause of the accident. The Chairman of the Committee personally has but one hope and that that a decision be reached accordingly.

Division General,
Chairman of the Committee,
Signed, Mensier.

Boulogne-sur-Seine, October 21, 1897

Annex to the Report of October 21

General Grillon, who was present at the trials of the 14th and who saw the report relative to what happened during that day, made the following observations in writing which are reproduced herewith in quotation marks. The Chairman of the Committee does not agree with General Grillon and he answers these observations paragraph by paragraph.

1.—"If the rear wheel (there is only one of these) left but intermittent tracks on the ground, does that prove that the machine has a tendency to rise when running at a certain speed?"

Answer.—This does not prove anything in any way and I was very careful not to mention this in my report, this point being exactly what was needed and that was not demonstrated during the two tests made on the grounds.

"Does not this unequal pressure of the two pairs of wheels on the ground show that the center of gravity of the apparatus is placed too far forward and that under the impulse of the propellers the machine has a tendency to tilt forward, due to the resistance of the air?"

Answer.—The tendency of the apparatus to rise from the rear when it was running with the wind seemed to be brought about by the effects of the winds on the huge wings, having a spread of 17 meters, and I believe that when the machine would have faced the wind the front wheels would have been lifted.

During the trials of October 12, when a complete circuit of the track was accomplished without incidents, as I and Lieut. Binet witnessed, there was practically no wind. I was therefore unable to verify whether during this circuit the two front wheels or the two rear wheels were in constant contact with the ground because when the trial was over it was dark (it was 5:30), and the next day it was impossible to see anything, because it had rained during the night and during Wednesday morning. But what would prove that the rear wheel was in contact with the ground at all times is the fact that Mr. Ader, though inexperienced, did not swerve from the circular track, which would prove that he steered pretty well with his rear wheel—this he could not have done if he had been in the air.

In the tests of the 12th, the speed was at least as great as on the 14th.

2.—"It would seem to me that if Mr. Ader thought that his rear wheels were off the ground he should have used his canvas rudder in order to regain his proper course; this was the best way of causing the machine to rotate, since it would have given an angular motion to the front axle."

Answer.—I state in my report that the canvas rudder whose object was the maneuver of the apparatus in the air could have no effect on the apparatus on the ground, and to convince oneself of this point it is only necessary to consider the small surface of the canvas rudder compared with a mass to be handled on the ground, a weight of approximately 400 kg. According to my idea and as I have stated in my report, Mr. Ader should have steered by increasing the speed on one of his propellers and slowing down the other. He admitted afterward that this remark was founded, but that he did not have time to think of it owing to the suddenness of the accident.

3.—"When the apparatus fell on its side it was under the sole influence of the wind, since Mr. Ader had stopped the machine. Haven't we a result here which will always be the same when the machine comes to the ground since the engines will have to be stopped or slowed down when coming to the ground? Here seems to be a bad defect of the apparatus under trial."

Answer.—I believe that the apparatus fell on its side after coming to a stop, not on account of the wind but because the semicircle described was on rough ground and one of the wheels had collapsed.

October 27, 1897

Signed, Mensier

It will be seen that the report shows that the Ader machine never left the ground. *It started with the wind on its back and rolled along on the ground at a speed not greater than twelve or fourteen miles an hour. The wind on its back and the pull of the screws tended to force the upper part of the apparatus forward, while the friction of the wheels on the ground retarded the machine below, so that there was a tendency of the apparatus to turn over on its nose and lift the rear wheel from the ground.* A puff of wind rolled the machine over and smashed it to pieces.

The official report accords exactly with the statement made to us in 1906 by a member of the French Commission which came to America to negotiate with us in that year.[6] He said that the machine never flew at all, but while running on the ground rolled over and was smashed. He also remarked, that if the machine had really flown, the Commission would not be in America negotiating with us. The failure of the Ader machine was the real cause of the failure of this negotiation with us, because the French officials at home could not believe that we had succeeded where Ader with the assistance of the French Government had failed, and they feared being laughed at if they closed a contract with us.

The Value of Ader's Works

M. Ader occupies a different position in the history of attempts at flight from that of Lilienthal, Maxim, Langley and Chanute, by reason of the fact that his experiments were conducted in secret. Although Lilienthal, Maxim, Chanute and Langley fell short of success in solving the flying problem, nevertheless their efforts contributed to the final success.

The Wright brothers had heard of Ader only as a man who was rumored to have attempted to solve the problem of human flight by a slavish imitation of nature, and had met with disastrous failure. He deserved great credit for the persistence and energy with which he carried on experiments for a great number of years, but unfortunately he did not succeed himself in solving the problem nor in making his labors useful to others. Consequently his work contributed nothing to the final success.

Rumors have been circulated that the Ader machine was designed to control lateral balance by a method similar to that invented and given to the world by the Wright brothers. During the trial of the Wright French patent suit the Court visited the museum where the Ader machine is preserved and found that it contained no provision for varying the angles of the wings. Mr. Ader was present and stated that the machine of 1890 possessed means for distorting the wings, but that the use of two propellers capable of being run at different speeds had made this distortion unnecessary in the 1897 machine. This statement proved that the abandoned device related to steering and not to lateral balancing.

---

1. *Aero Club of America Bulletin,* May 1912, 17–19. Ader's first name is properly spelled "Clément."
2. For a detailed discussion of the aeronautical work of Clément Ader, see Charles Harvard Gibbs-Smith, *Clément Ader: His Flight-Claims and His Place in History* (London: Her Majesty's Stationery Office, 1968).
3. See document 38, note 7.
4. Ernest Archdeacon was a wealthy lawyer-sportsman and patron of aviation. He built several gliders of his own and offered a number of lucrative aviation prizes to foster developments in the field. In May 1903 he created the Aviation Committee in the Aéro-Club de France to promote heavier-than-air flying. He was intent on spurring French aeronautical experimenters to beat the Wright brothers into the air with a powered airplane.
5. The diagram to which the report refers was omitted from Wilbur Wright's transcription of the report in his article on Ader. See photo 8.
6. The French government sent a commission to the United States in March 1906 to negotiate with the Wrights for the sale of an airplane for the French military. The Wrights were unwilling to demonstrate, or even show, their airplane to the French officials until they had a signed contract in hand. Without firsthand proof that the Wright airplane could perform as the brothers said it did, the members of the French commission were not willing to pay the Wrights' $200,000 asking price and risk public ridicule if the airplane failed to meet expectations. Negotiations broke down, and the commission was recalled in April.

40 • OTTO LILIENTHAL[1]

Wilbur Wright

In the history of aviation, particularly the period covering the last half of the 19th century, there are to be found several leading figures; enthusiastic workers whose experiments and studies, either by being material contributions or by the interest they created, led up to the final achievement—the realization of a practical aeroplane. How much each of those workers actually contributed, and what was the nature of their contributions—these things are still undecided and undefined. Scores of books have been written on aeronautics, and in some can be found detailed particulars of the works of most of the

pioneers, but, unfortunately, only in one or two can there be found an authoritative valuation of those works; and whereas the actual flying machine has hardly any of the characteristics of the early models, and as a rule the experiments were based on theories since then proved fallacious, it follows that we have no definite knowledge of just what each of those workers contributed to the final achievement. Of the few people in the world who could speak on the matter authoritatively, the Wright brothers were the best qualified, they alone having put the theories and deductions of the pioneers through tests to find their practicability and fallaciousness. But the Wright brothers, reticent and busily engaged in working out big problems, never thought it of immediate importance to enlighten the world on the subject, until recently, when Wilbur Wright consented, at our request, to write articles on the subject for the *Bulletin*. The first of these articles, "What Mouillard Did,"[2] was published in the April number; the second, "What Clement Ader Did,"[3] appeared in the May number.

In the present article which, Mr. Orville Wright advises, was written for the *Bulletin* by Wilbur a day or two before he was taken down with fever, Wilbur Wright does more than define the place of Lilienthal in history. He defines a code by which not only the pioneers but all workers in aviation can be judged.—Editor

Of all the men who attacked the flying problem in the 19th century, Otto Lilienthal was easily the most important. His greatness appeared in every phase of the problem. No one equaled him in power to draw new recruits to the cause; no one equaled him in fullness and clearness of understanding of the principles of flight; no one did so much to convince the world of the advantages of curved wing surfaces; and no one did so much to transfer the problem of human flight to the open air where it belonged. As a missionary he was wonderful. He presented the cause of human flight to his readers so earnestly, so attractively, and so convincingly that it was difficult for anyone to resist the temptation to make an attempt at it himself, even though his sober judgment and the misfortunes of all predecessors warned him to avoid touching it. If Lilienthal had done nothing more than this he still would have been one of the greatest contributors to the final success. But he was much more than a mere missionary. As a scientific investigator none of his contemporaries was his equal. He set forth the advantages of arched wings in such convincing manner as to make him the real originator of this feature. Others had noted that bird wings were arched, and had speculated on the possibility that an arched wing was superior to an absolutely true plane, but Lilienthal demonstrated the reasons why it was better, and changed mere speculation into accepted knowledge. He also devoted an enormous amount of time and patience to experiments with test surfaces for the purpose of determining the best shapes for wings and the amount of pressures to be obtained at the various angles of incidence. For nearly twenty years his tables and charts were the best to be found in print. His work in this line alone would have been sufficient to place Lilienthal in the front rank, yet there still remains to be mentioned his greatest contribution to the cause.[4] Lilienthal was the real founder of out-of-door experimenting. It is true that attempts at gliding had been made hundreds of years before his time, and that in the nineteenth century, Cayley,[5] Spencer,[6] Wenham,[7] Mouillard, and many others were reported to have made feeble attempts to glide, but their failures were so complete that nothing of value resulted.

Lilienthal pursued the undertaking so persistently and intelligently that although his own death and that of Pilcher for a time caused a cessation of this mode of experiment, nevertheless his efforts constituted the greatest contribution to final success that had been made by any of the nineteenth century group of workers.

When the general excellence of the work of Lilienthal is considered, the question arises as to whether or not he would have solved the problem of human flight if his untimely death in 1896 had not interrupted his efforts. Many people believe that success was almost within his grasp. Others think that he had limitations which rendered such an outcome at least doubtful. One of the greatest difficulties of the problem has been little understood by the world at large. This was the fact that those who aspired to solve the problem were constantly pursued by expense, danger, and time. In order to succeed it was not only necessary to make progress, but it was necessary to make progress at a sufficient rate to reach the goal before money gave out, or before accident intervened, or before the portion of life allowable for such work was past. The problem was so vast and many sided that no one could hope to win unless he possessed unusual ability to grasp the essential points, and to ignore the nonessentials. It was necessary to have a genius for solving almost innumerable difficult problems with a minimum expenditure of time, a minimum expenditure of money, and a minimum risk of accident. A study of the failures of the nineteenth century shows clearly that none of the important workers stood still, but that the rate of progress was so slow that each one was overcome and removed from the race by one of the causes just mentioned before the goal was reached. If they had possessed the faculty of doing things more quickly, more simply, and less expensively, they might not have been overtaken by old age, lack of funds, or accident. Some were traveling at a rate which would have required fifty years or more to reach success. Others were spending money at a rate which would have necessitated an expenditure of millions of dollars in order to complete the task. When the detailed story is written of the means by which success in human flight was finally attained, it will be seen that this success was not won by spending more time than others had spent, nor by spending more money than others had spent, nor by taking greater risks than others had taken.

Those who failed for lack of time had already used more time than was necessary; those who failed for lack of money had already spent more money than was necessary; and those who were cut off by accident had previously enjoyed as many lucky escapes as reasonably could be expected.

Lilienthal progressed, but not very rapidly. His tables of pressures and resistances of arched aeroplane surfaces were the results of years of experiment and were the best in existence, yet they were not sufficiently accurate to enable anyone to construct a machine with full assurance that it would give exactly the expected results. Under such conditions progress could not but be slow. His methods of controlling balance both laterally and longitudinally were exceedingly crude and quite insufficient. Although he experimented for six successive years 1891–1896 with gliding machines, he was using at the end the same inadequate method of control with which he started. His rate of progress during these years makes it doubtful whether he would have achieved full success in the near future if his life had been spared, but whatever his limitations may have been, he was without question the greatest of the precursors, and the world owes to him a great debt.

---

1. *Aero Club of America Bulletin,* September 1912, 20–21. This was Wilbur Wright's last article. Written in May 1912, a day or two before he was stricken with the typhoid fever that would kill him one month later, it was published posthumously.
2. See document 38.
3. See document 39.
4. The results of Lilienthal's principal aerodynamic research were published in Otto Lilienthal, *Birdflight as the Basis of Aviation,* trans. A. W. Isenthal (New York: Longmans Green, 1911), originally published as *Der Vogelflug als Grundlage der Fliegekunst* in 1889, and in Hermann W. L. Moedebeck, *Pocket-Book of Aeronautics,* trans. W. Mansergh Varley (London: Whittaker and Co., 1907), 287–94, originally published as *Taschenbuch zum praktischen Gebrauch für Flugtechniker und Luftschiffer* in 1895. For a detailed historical analysis of Lilienthal's aerodynamic research, see Peter L. Jakab, "Otto Lilienthal: 'The Greatest of the Precursors,'" *AIAA Journal* 35 (April 1997): 601–7. For biographical material on Lilienthal, see Tom D. Crouch, *A Dream of Wings: Americans and the Airplane, 1875–1905* (New York: W. W. Norton and Co., 1981), 157–74.
5. See document 38, note 2.
6. In l868 Charles Spencer built a glider with fixed wings, 110 square feet in area, equipped with 15-square-foot flappers attached to the outer ends, and a tail. The flappers were human-powered and were intended to provide supplemental propulsion to the aircraft. Spencer may have had some minor success with this machine but apparently developed it no further. He followed this with one or two other flapper-assisted glider designs but made no additional flight attempts.
7. See document 5, note 8.

41 • THE MYTHICAL WHITEHEAD FLIGHT[1]

Orville Wright

In *Reader's Digest* for July, 1945, p. 57, under the heading "The Man Who Knows Everything," appears an article by Mort Weisinger, condensed from Liberty. We were astounded to read therein the following:

"It was during one of these programs [radio] that Kane presented Charles Whitehead of Bridgeport, Conn., as 'the son of Gustave Whitehead, the first man to fly a heavier-than-air machine, two years, four months and three days previous to the Wright flight at Kitty Hawk.'"

This is the second time that *Reader's Digest*, we don't know why, has placed itself seemingly in the position of wishing to prove that the Wright brothers were not the first to fly. It was not so long ago, as the crow flies, that *Reader's Digest* published an article by a woman, under the head: "Santos Dumont: Father of Flight."[2]

We asked the first man in the world to fly—with his brother Wilbur co-inventor of the airplane—to give us the facts.—Editor's Note

The myth of Gustave Whitehead having made a power flight in 1901 was founded upon the story which appeared in the *Bridgeport Herald* of August 18, 1901. Although this mythical flight was alleged to have taken place on August 14th, and to have been witnessed by a *Herald* reporter, the news was withheld four days and appeared as a feature story in a Sunday edition of that paper! Would the editor of the *Herald* have held back for four days a story of such great human and historical interest, if he believed it to be true? The strangest part of all is that anyone should think that Howell's story was intended to be taken as fact. It was printed with a large heading entitled "Flying," illustrated with four witches riding astraddle their brooms.

The *Herald* represented that just four persons were present on the occasion—"Gustave Whitehead, Andrew Cellie and James Dickie, his two partners in the flying machine, and a representative of the *Herald*."

In an affidavit dated April 2, 1937, the above-mentioned James Dickie, after saying that he had worked with Gustave Whitehead when Whitehead was constructing and experimenting with aeroplanes, said:

"I do not know Andrew Cellie, the other man who is supposed to have witnessed the flight of August 14th, 1901, described in the *Bridgeport Herald*. I believe the entire story in the *Herald* was imaginary, and grew out of the comments of Whitehead in discussing what he hoped to get from his plane. I was not present and did not witness any airplane flight on August 14, 1901. I do not remember or recall ever hearing of a flight with this particular plane or any other that Whitehead ever built."

John J. Dvorak, a Chicago business man, who in 1904 was on the teaching staff of

Washington University of St. Louis, spent some months that year with Whitehead at Bridgeport, while Whitehead was building a motor financed by Dvorak. Dvorak finally came to the conclusion that Whitehead was incapable of building a satisfactory motor and in disgust he left. In an affidavit dated July 18, 1936, Dvorak said:

"I personally do not believe that Whitehead ever succeeded in making any airplane flights. Here are my reasons: 1. Whitehead did not possess sufficient mechanical skill and equipment to build a successful motor. 2. Whitehead was given to gross exaggeration. He was eccentric—a visionary and a dreamer to such an extent that he actually believed what he merely imagined. He had delusions."

In May, 1901, Stanley Y. Beach visited Whitehead at Bridgeport and wrote an illustrated article about Whitehead's machine, which was published in the *Scientific American* of June 8, 1901. Later he induced his father to advance money to continue Whitehead's experiments. Although Beach saw Whitehead frequently in the years from 1901 to 1910, Whitehead never told him that he had flown. Beach has said that he does not believe that any of Whitehead's machines ever left the ground under their own power, in spite of the assertions of persons thirty-five years later who thought they remembered seeing them. Beach's nine years' association with Whitehead placed him in a better position to know what Whitehead had done than that of other persons who were associated with Whitehead but a short time, or those who had so little technical training, or so little interest that they remained silent for thirty-five years about an event which, if true, would have been the greatest historic achievement in aviation up to that time. If Whitehead had really flown, certainly Beach, who had spent nearly ten thousand dollars on the experiments, would have been the last to deny it.

---

1. *U.S. Air Services,* August 1945, 9.
2. See document 38, note 7.

4 • "IT IS NEVER SAFE TO PROPHESY"

THE WRIGHTS ON THE FUTURE OF AVIATION

DURING THE YEAR 1905, AT an isolated cow pasture eight miles east of Dayton, Ohio, the world changed. As the hot, sweltering afternoons of summer drifted into the cool, crisp mornings of fall that year, nearby residents and local farmers tending their fields witnessed a recurring scene, one that would become a defining characteristic of twentieth-century life: the sight and sound of an airplane flying overhead. Throughout September a noisy, frail-looking, wood-and-fabric machine frequently circled the hundred-acre meadow known locally as Huffman Prairie. Small groups of friends and family of the "birdmen" began turning up to see them fly. Even commuters passing by on the interurban railway adjacent to the field caught glimpses of what appeared to be a huge, white, box kite, skimming effortlessly over the cow pasture. For weeks after observing an especially spectacular flight of nearly forty minutes on October 5 a three-year-old Dayton boy named Charley Billman raced through his parents' house, arms outstretched, mimicking the sound of the engine. Like the craft that so enthused him, young Charley's playful imitation would become a ubiquitous cultural feature of the century. Indeed, the age of the airplane had arrived.

The pilots who were causing passersby to turn their eyes skyward in the autumn of 1905 were, of course, Wilbur and Orville Wright. Although the brothers were drawing more and more spectators as their sustained flights became increasingly routine, their aeronautical work had become quite well known in their hometown even before they were turning circles over the local countryside. For years, the Wrights' regular customers at the bicycle shop had been vaguely aware that something having to do with flying machines was going on upstairs. And though filled with wild inaccuracies, the local papers had carried the story of the breakthrough flights at Kitty Hawk on December 17, 1903. Most of the Wrights' neighbors considered their flying experiments rather eccentric, but Wilbur and Orville were still regarded as solid, stable members of the community. When the clattering of their crude engine first began to break the bucolic calm of Huffman Prairie in the spring of 1904, most people simply shrugged it off. The Wright boys' efforts to fly might have been a bit crazy, but they were harmless. So it was during 1904 and 1905 over this unkept patch of Ohio grassland. One of the great technological innovations of the century was ushered in not with spirited public fanfare but with quiet fascination.

At the close of their 1905 flying season, Wilbur and Orville Wright stood alone in the aeronautical world. After six short years of research and experimentation, they had achieved what countless other would-be aviators had strived for without success. The Wrights had an airplane that could take off under its own power, stay aloft as long as the fuel supply lasted, maneuver precisely through the sky under the full and sure command of the pilot, and land safely to fly again. The brief flights of the Kitty Hawk airplane two years earlier had proven the Wrights' basic design to be sound. But their third experimental powered machine brought mechanical flight to practicality in 1905. Wilbur and Orville now had something to show the world.

Yet it would be another two and a half years before the Wrights stunned the aviation community with their first major public flying demonstrations in America and Europe in 1908. They did not want to disclose the details of their invention until they had secured patent protection and laid the groundwork for the sale of their unique creation. When they did go public, their lives changed forever. They were among the first true celebrities of the twentieth century. By the time of the extravagant homecoming celebration mounted by the citizens of Dayton in June 1909 to honor the brothers, they had flown before adoring crowds of thousands, had been hosted by the royalty of Europe, and had won the respect of the aeronautical establishment on both sides of the Atlantic. They stood without peer at the opening of the aerial age, their place in history forged.

Not surprisingly, with this fame came public interest in the Wrights' views on the future of aviation. Surely the men who had conceived this modern wonder could offer wisdom on the direction it should take. The documents in part 4 compose the brothers' public attitudes and commentary on aviation as the airplane evolved. In addition to articles actually written by the Wrights, their thoughts found expression in published interviews, letters to editors, and testimony before various government boards examining different aspects of aviation. Publications of this sort have been included here because they too convey the Wrights' public viewpoint, in the brothers' own words.

As the airplane emerged from infancy and matured into a technology of broad utility, debate regarding its applications grew. The breadth of issues that engaged public discourse during the first decades of aviation history is reflected in the collection of Wright material gathered here. Beyond the development of the basic technology of flight itself, the brothers commented on the future of commercial aviation and air travel, civil and sport flying, military aviation, air safety, and the growth and control of the aircraft industry in the United States. Their words shed light on the general pattern of aviation development before 1950, as well as on how they felt the technology they pioneered should be guided and exploited.

As was the brothers' custom before Wilbur's death in 1912, the elder sibling spoke for the team most of the time. Before 1912, only one article was written by Orville on the future of aviation (document 44). With Wilbur gone, however, the role of aeronautical prophet shifted to Orville, as did also the chore of protecting the Wrights' standing as the inventors of the airplane. Orville alone had to service the reputation of the brothers when the world sought the wisdom of the first to fly.

After 1912 Orville slowly disengaged himself from the business and legal interests that he and Wilbur had pursued together. In 1915 he sold his assets in the aircraft-manufacturing company they had formed in 1909, and he retired as an active inventor and businessman. In 1918 he made his last flight as a pilot. Financially secure, Orville settled into what was, for him, the uncomfortable role of aviation elder statesman and national folk hero. The situation only grew worse for Orville as the passage of time magnified his legendary stature. With this reputation came unending demands to lend the Wright name to private and government research and business endeavors and to exhibit a public image. There was nothing that Orville found more distasteful than stepping onto the popular stage in this way, but he felt it was his obligation. Orville's feeling of personal duty to Wilbur to uphold the Wright name in the proper public light was constantly at odds with his desperate desire, his almost crippling need, for privacy. The published material gathered here is just one manifestation of the requirements of this unwanted public life.

In addition to consulting for private companies, Orville served on numerous government aeronautical boards and commissions. In 1920 President Woodrow Wilson appointed him a member of the National Advisory Committee for Aeronautics (NACA). Founded in 1915, NACA aided the infant U.S. aircraft industry by identifying key technical problems and performing basic research to assist in opening the way to further progress. Orville also served on the board of the Daniel and Florence Guggenheim Fund for the Promotion of Aeronautics. Among other aviation safety and technical projects, the Guggenheim Fund established a number of high-caliber aeronautical engineering programs at major universities across the United States during the late 1920s. Although Orville's name on the programs and his regular attendance at the meetings of these organizations formed a distinct asset for this work, his specific contributions to discussions rarely had an impact on the projects.

Beyond consulting and serving on various committees, Orville was continually invited as the honored guest at countless banquets, award ceremonies, and public programs. He detested these functions more than anything else because he was frequently expected to speak. Since he was extremely shy, he always refused to offer even the briefest of remarks. (Even though he lived until 1948, there are no known recordings of Orville's voice.) Between 1915 and 1947, he received eleven honorary degrees from colleges and universities in Europe and America and dozens of medals and awards including the American Distinguished Flying Cross and the French Legion of Honor. Orville was also often obliged to receive distinguished visitors who were traveling through Dayton and who invariably wanted to pay their respects to the famous inventor.

As the years passed, all the accolades and public attention forced Orville into a role that he had never wanted but that he knew he could not escape. He was keenly aware of his responsibility to represent Wilbur and the rest of the family with dignity whenever the world spotlight was upon him. As the year 1948 began, aviation was beginning a new era. The jet engine, first successfully tested less than a decade before, was now becoming practical. Less than three months earlier, on October 14, 1947, Chuck Yeager had marked yet another aviation milestone when he became the first to fly faster than the speed of sound. The advances that Orville had witnessed since he and Wilbur had inaugurated the aerial age with their frail little craft forty-four years earlier were truly astonishing. But in 1948, the man who had helped create one of the most revolutionary technologies in history was generally content tinkering with one of the many temperamental systems he installed in Hawthorn Hill, the lavish mansion he had built in 1913. On January 27, 1948, Orville occupied himself fixing a doorbell. Later that day, he suffered his second heart attack in four months. He died three days later, at the age of seventy-six, in a Dayton hospital. The burden of carrying on alone had finally been lifted.

42 • FLYING AS A SPORT—ITS POSSIBILITIES[1]

Wilbur Wright

Up to the present time men have taken up flying partly from scientific interest, partly from sport, and partly from business reasons, but a time is rapidly approaching when the art will have reached a state of development such that men can practice it without the necessity of maintaining a private laboratory or a manufacturing plant.

Considered as a sport, flying possesses attractions which will appeal to many persons with a force beyond that exercised by any of the similar sports, such as boating, cycling, or automobiling. There is a sense of exhilaration in flying through the free air, an intensity of enjoyment, which possibly may be due to the satisfaction of an inborn longing transmitted to us from the days when our early ancestors gazed wonderingly at the free flight of birds and contrasted it with their own slow and toilsome progress through the unbroken wilderness. Though methods of travel have been greatly improved in the many centuries preceding our own, men have never ceased to envy the birds and long for the day when they too might rise above the dust or mud of the highways and fly through the clean air of the heavens.

Once above the tree tops, the narrow roads no longer arbitrarily fix the course. The earth is spread out before the eye with a richness of color and beauty of pattern never imagined by those who have gazed at the landscape edgewise only. The view of the ordinary traveler is as inadequate as that of an ant crawling over a magnificent rug. The rich brown of freshly-turned earth, the lighter shades of dry ground, the still lighter browns and yellows of ripening crops, the almost innumerable shades of green produced by grasses and forests, together present a sight whose beauty has been confined to balloonists alone in the past. With the coming of the flyer, the pleasures of ballooning are joined with those of automobiling to form a supreme combination.

The sport will not be without some element of danger, but with a good machine this danger need not be excessive. It will be safer than automobile racing, and not much more dangerous than football. The motor flyers will always be somewhat expensive, as the best of materials and workmanship will be required in their construction, but there is a possibility that men will eventually learn to fly without motors, after the manner of soaring birds, which sail for hours on motionless wings. In such case the flyer would be so small and simple that the original cost would be very moderate, and the fuel expense done away with entirely. Then flying will become an every-day sport for thousands. We may not live to see that day, but with thousands of buzzards, eagles, hawks, and sea birds giving demonstration of the possibility of soaring flight every day of the year, no good reason exists for asserting that human flight without motors is entirely visionary.[2] Meanwhile the motor-driven flyers will become sufficiently numerous to afford great sport, not only to the amateur aviators, but also indirectly to the general public, for the flying machine races of the future will surpass anything the world has yet seen as spectacular performances.

In ballooning, a few glorious hours in the air are usually followed by a tiresome walk to some village, an uncomfortable night at a poor hotel, and a return home by slow local trains. With a flyer, which returns the sportsman to his starting point, thus eliminating the uncomfortable features of the balloon trip, aerial sport will appeal to a wider class than has heretofore been the case.

---

1. *Scientific American,* February 29, 1908, 139.
2. Compare this with Orville Wright's view on the future of soaring in his 1922 article "Possibilities of Soaring Flight" (document 33).

43 • THE AEROPLANE: WHAT IT WILL BE LIKE IN FIVE YEARS TIME, OPINIONS OF PROMINENT AEROISTS[1]

Interview with Wilbur Wright

WHAT WILBUR WRIGHT THINKS[2]

"Back again?" said Wilbur Wright, as the *Motor* representative stepped from the rain-sodden military plateau into the plain deal shed which housed the flying machine, its pilot and two mechanics, but which at this moment was so filled with thick smoke from an open chimneyless fire that only the outlines of the men could be distinguished.

"Yes, I'm looking for a prophet."

"Well, I guess you have come to the wrong shop; I'm no hand at prophesying."

"But you know something about aeroplanes, and you can tell me what is going to happen during the next five years."

"Yes, I have had ideas on that subject for a long time, but it is never safe to prophesy."

Here Wilbur Wright looked away in the distance, his keen, searching glance evidently riveted on some object beyond the limits of the vast, dreary plain, and declared: "This is a military proposition, and it will develop along military lines."

"But is it not also a sporting proposition, in even a greater degree than the early motorcar?"

"Yes, to a certain extent, but only in a limited degree. A certain number of sportsmen will be drawn to it, but I do not think their number will be great, and the future of the flying machine is entirely along military lines. It may develop in directions that we do not think of now; frequently we map out a course for a great invention and it takes a quite different one. But the future I see for the flying machine is with armies. Every army will have not one, but hundreds of these machines, carrying three or four men and ammunition, and capable of keeping the enemy continually harassed. Naturally, these machines will take the place of cavalry, and will be very much more effective than that branch of military service."

"But will the flying machine not develop sufficiently as a sport to influence the motorcar industry?"

"No, I do not think so; the sportsmen who will be attracted to the flying machine will not abandon their automobiles; in all cases they will be men who can afford to keep the two, and when they take up the flying machine they will not sell their automobiles. The automobile industry will not suffer at all."

"Do you see any future for the flying machine in connection with a special mail service, for instance, between France and England, or from England and Ireland?"

"No; it could be done, but there is no advantage in doing it. The few minutes gain would be obtained at such a great cost in other directions that it is not worth it, and international main service is not likely to come during the next five years."

"Was the advent of flying dependent on the petrol engine, or could you have done what you have done if the petrol engine had not come along?"

"The petrol engine was not necessary. It has undoubtedly helped us, but it was not essential to success. If the petrol engine had not been developed we could have flown with the steam engine. There are steamers built now sufficiently light to enable us to fly with them."

"Then engineers are wrong in searching for special lightweight engines?"

"It would be folly to carry unnecessary dead weight, but reliability is much more important than lightness. There is really no need for a special type of engine. There are plenty of automobile engines that I could place on my flying machine and use successfully without any changes whatever. As you know, a lot of the weight on a motorcar engine is altogether unnecessary, more especially when that engine has to be used in the air, where there are no road vibrations. My own engine is rather lighter than one of the same power for car work, but nothing has been sacrificed to make it light."

"What are the possibilities in carrying several passengers?"

"Doubtless we shall be limited to six or eight passengers at the most. With this machine I can fly just as well alone as with a very heavy passenger giving a load equal to three ordinary people. No, there is no danger by reason of a passenger moving about during a flight, and if he had to shift his position two or three feet it would make no real difference to the machine, for I am constantly correcting the equilibrium. As a matter of fact, if it were possible to control from there I could fly on the tip of the wing without upsetting the balance of the machine."

"Is this obtained by the working of the wing tips?"

"Yes, principally; but there are other features too.

"Dangerous? Well, there certainly is a certain element of danger. But even the railroads manage to kill a lot of people every year, and anyway I would rather be on my machine than on Paris streets. There will be no more danger on a properly-constructed flying machine than on an automobile."

Questioned on the manner in which he would train his pupils, and the length of time necessary to make them efficient, Wilbur Wright declared that he had no special plans, he did not know how long it would take to be able to fly with ease, but he did not think his task would be a long one.

"Of course," he added, "a lot depends on the man, and, as in motorcar driving, a man might learn to handle the machine in two or three lessons, then spend years in perfecting himself."

"Will some outside means of starting always be necessary?"

"We believe the starting rail with falling weight will always have to be used. For military purposes there will be no difficulty, for the apparatuses are cheap, easily constructed, and can be kept in readiness wherever likely to be needed. In any case a preliminary run will always be necessary, either by the use of an apparatus like our own, or by means of wheels.[3] I have no faith in the helicopeter as a means of starting. We might possibly get away without the use of a starting rail, but generally it is not advisable to do it."

"What form will the flying machine of the future take?"

"Probably it will maintain the same proportions as at present. It all depends on what you want to do. Big planes would give a greater lifting capacity, but they would reduce speed. The flying machine of the immediate future will have a capacity of two or three passengers and a range of action of about 200 miles. They could be made to go further, but there is no particular advantage in doing so."

"Have you succeeded as much as you expected when you commenced experimenting?"

"When my brother and I set out on this game we did not think it would be possible for a man to fly within fifty years."

"Then you have done in eight years what you expected would occupy fifty?"

"No, in two years; for although we started in 1900,[4] all the real work was done in two years."

"What was your greatest difficulty?"

"There is no greatest difficulty; there are a thousand problems in one, and as soon as you settle one you tread on the toes of another."

"Is there any special advantage in the use of two propellers?"

Wilbur Wright smiled as he replied, "Well, I use two. It is untrue that my brother's accident was caused by having two propellers. The first story that got abroad was that one propeller broke off and the other one running caused the apparatus to swing round as if on a pivot. People accepted this report, for there were plenty willing to say 'I told you so.' As a matter of fact the accident would have happened just the same if there had been but one propeller. The engine was shut off so quickly that the undamaged propeller had no time to swing the machine round. All the damage was done by the breakage of the rudder.[5]

"My future plans?" Wilbur Wright remained silent a minute, then declared: "I never talk business."

"But will you not seek to place your patents with other countries in the same way as you have done with France?"

"We never imagined France was the only country in the world." On further questioning, Wilbur Wright admitted that he was free to negotiate with countries other than France.

"How will the Lazare-Weiller committee develop your machine?"

"Ask them," was the firm reply, "I can tell you nothing about their doings."[6]

"And the cross-Channel trip, is it possible, will you attempt it?"

"Don't ask me," came the equally firm reply. "It is not a thing that particularly interests me, and I am not going to criticise other men's schemes."

"When you have trained your pupils and won the height prize, will your mission be finished in France?"

"Yes, I suppose I shall make an attempt at the height prize some morning, and when the three pupils have been trained for the Lazare-Weiller committee I shall have finished my work in France, for the present at any rate.[7] I shall then return to the States."

---

1. *Motor,* November 17, 1908, 457–58.
2. Also included in this article were interviews with three other prominent aviators of the day: Léon Delagrange, Henri Farman, and Charles Voisin.
3. The first Wright airplane with wheels was the 1910 Wright Model B. Until that time, Wright airplanes continued to be launched by riding a dolly down a narrow rail in the manner of the first powered airplane at Kitty Hawk in 1903. To accommodate locations that did not possess the strong steady winds of Kitty Hawk, the Wrights used a tower and drop-weight arrangement to provide sufficient momentum at takeoff. Through a system of lines and pulleys, weights ranging from 1,200 to 1,600 pounds were used to catapult the aircraft forward on its takeoff run. See photo 32.
4. The Wrights constructed and tested their first full-size piloted glider in 1900. But they began serious research and experimentation in 1899, with a five-foot-span biplane kite built to test the viability of their lateral control system, and they had begun general reading and study a few years before that.
5. The reference is to Orville's crash at Fort Myer, Virginia, on September 17, 1908, while conducting flight trials in connection with the brothers' contract with the U.S. Army for the sale of the first military airplane. Orville was seriously hurt in the crash, and his passenger, the army representative Lieutenant Thomas E. Selfridge, was fatally injured. The crash occurred when one of the propellers split in flight, causing serious vibration and other damage to the aircraft, which led to a loss of control and a severe crash. The fact that there were two propellers had nothing to do with the cause of the accident. The Wrights returned to Fort Myer in 1909 with a new airplane and satisfactorily completed the flight trials.
6. The reference is to the Wright brothers' contract signed in March 1908 to manufacture and sell Wright aircraft under license in France. The new firm, created by a syndicate of French capitalists, was called La Compagnie Générale de Navigation Aérienne (CGNA). The name "Lazare-Weiller committee" noted in the text is inaccurate, likely the result of confusion on the part of the author of this published interview. The hyphenation of the names suggests that this is a compound last name or two individuals. Actually, Lazare (first name) Weiller (last name) is the full name of the financier who was one of the leaders of the syndicate that organized the French licensing deal with the Wrights. By "Lazare-Weiller committee," the author means the French syndicate that created the CGNA firm.
7. The terms of the contract with the French syndicate called for training several pilots in addition to meeting various flight performance standards.

44 • THE FUTURE OF THE AEROPLANE[1]

Orville Wright

The future development of the aeroplane in any line, for sport, for war, or for commerce, will be also the development of the gasolene engine. The aeroplane of to-day is more perfect than the engine which drives it. I expect that in the future—and not such a very far distant future—to see the gasolene engine so made that it is perfectly reliable. Even the best automobile engines of to-day sometimes stop running, or miss in one or more cylinders. It is of minor importance, if they do, in an automobile. But in an aeroplane, unless the engine be far more powerful than is necessary, running on one cylinder less than usual may mean coming down.

The sporting side of the aeroplane development will, I believe, speedily follow, and be continuous with, the experimental stage, in which all flying machines are at present. The exhilaration of flying is too keen, the pleasure too great, for it to be neglected as a sport. It seems to me that its use will be somewhat similar to the automobile, as far as pleasure goes; that is, that people will have aeroplanes for pleasure runs, for fresh air, and for sight-seeing—perhaps even for touring, when starting devices are either carried along, or to be found readily at stopping points. There will be races, I suppose, and contests, and many of them will be beneficial as stimuative to inventive progress, just as races and contests have improved the automobile. But the greatest development in a sporting line, as I see it, will be for the pure pleasure of flying.

The danger is less now than many people think, and the better the motor is made, the safer the sport will be, but if it is absolutely robbed of all possibilities of accident or incident, it will lose its flavor for those who love sport for sport's sake. If an automobile could go fifty miles an hour on an ordinary road with absolute and perfect safety, few people would care to go. Few people care for railroad speed as a pleasure—it is just a means of getting there. It is the spice of uncertainty, of a possible accident, which makes swift automobiling so great a pleasure, and it will be the same way with the aeroplane. While I firmly believe that aeroplaning will shortly be as safe a means of travel, of sport, or of observation as any other modern means of swift locomotion, I do not believe it will ever be a tame sport!

I have heard of a prize being offered for the first aeroplane to pass over the city of Paris. Such offers are wrong in spirit and principle. There will be, and there should be, laws made to prevent air craft from passing over large cities. The danger to those below is as great, if not greater, than to those who fly. A man who goes up in a flying-machine of any kind does so with the full knowledge of what he is doing; the man in the street, unavoidably struck down by something dropped from the machine, or by the flying pieces resulting from an accident, is in the position of the innocent bystander struck in a shooting affray. Grade crossings are eliminated in well-governed cities, and what might be called "air crossings" should be against the law.

I believe that the time is coming when the aeroplane will be as safe and as reliable as the modern locomotive—when we can start out to go anywhere with the certainty of getting there and getting back. This time will come when the explosion engine is made as near perfect as the steam-engine is to-day, and the greatest commercial development will follow immediately. I firmly believe in the future of the aeroplane for commerce, to carry mail, to carry passengers, perhaps express. I know that it is but little more difficult to learn to operate the aeroplane with which I am most familiar than it is to learn to ride a bicycle. The experiments of to-day are but the beginning. There will be dozens—hundreds—of men engaged in perfecting the art of flying in the next decade. Those who engage in flying for the love of it, the sport they get out of it, will aid in its development as they did in developing the automobile, the bicycle, and the balloon. The army and navy experiments of France and Germany, of England and the United States, will interest many men from the financial standpoint. I cannot but believe that we stand at the beginning of a new era, the Age of Flight, and that the beginnings of to-day will be mightily overshadowed by the complete successes of to-morrow.

1. *Country Life in America,* January 1909, 252–53.

45 • FLYING FROM LONDON TO MANCHESTER[1]

Wilbur Wright

SPECIALLY WRITTEN FOR THE *LONDON MAGAZINE*

When the *Daily Mail* prize[2] was offered many persons doubtless thought of it as a reward for the production of a flyer capable of making such a trip, but a study of the history of invention shows that scientists and inventors do not get their rewards in that way. It is not the men who spend their whole time in inventing instruments, but the men who spend their whole time in using them, that develop the skill necessary to win prizes of an extremely difficult nature. The men who perform exceptional feats with pianos, typesetting machines, automobiles, &c., are never the inventors. The inventor is always more interested in the development of the machine than in contests of skill or daring.

It will not be different in the case of the London to Manchester prize. The winner will be a man who is satisfied to devote his entire thought and energies to this particular task. As the risk of losing his life will be great, he must be a man who values it not too highly, or who considers the winning of the prize more important than any other purpose he may have in living. On the other hand, he must not be a mere dare-devil, or he will be killed without attaining anything. The winner will probably be of the same general type as the men who win automobile races—men having the courage to do anything that is necessary and profitable for the attainment of their object, but yet with sufficient judgment and self-control to avoid the impossible.

Before such a prize can be won, flying will have lost some of the novelty it possesses to-day, but the winner will become a popular hero for a short time, and will receive that tribute of admiration which exhibitions of exceptional courage and skill always draw forth.

It is more difficult to forecast the exact nature of the flyer with which the flight will be made. Will it be a machine of large size? Will it be one of exceptional speed? For my part, I believe it will be a machine not very different from existing models. The prize will probably be won before the type has had much time to change. The winning flyer will doubtless be capable of carrying one or two persons, but not more. Its speed will probably range between thirty-five and fifty miles an hour.

When speed is mentioned, visionary persons often talk of one hundred or even two hundred miles an hour as the best speeds for human flight, but there are scientific and mechanical reasons which make the lower speeds more desirable for long flights. The reputed speeds of birds are almost invariably over-estimated. The usual speed of the common crow is not greater than twenty miles an hour. I have frequently timed their speed over a measured course in calm air, and found it a trifle under the speed named. The wild duck is probably the bird which flies at the greatest speed in ordinary flight over long distances. I have frequently timed ducks, but I have never found the speed above forty miles an hour unless assisted by the wind. When driving a flyer, I have often noticed birds ahead of me, but the speed of the machine was always much greater than that of the birds, and they were compelled to turn aside to avoid being run down. The records of the flights of homing pigeons sometimes show speeds of more than forty miles an hour, but in such cases the birds have usually flown with the wind. Their case is exceptional, moreover, because they over-exert themselves in order to reach home quickly.

Of course, any animal for short periods can exert power very far beyond what it is able to maintain continuously. A man, whose power is usually estimated at one-eighth that of a horse, can develop for a short time two horse-power. Birds, by a similar exertion, can fly much faster than their normal speeds, and may sometimes reach sixty or seventy miles an hour, but the increase of speed cannot be proportional to the increase of power. Consequently, it is not reasonable to expect that success in winning the *Daily Mail* prize will be dependent upon the increase of speed. On the contrary, it is possible that a lowering of the speed will be desirable, since the slower speed will make it possible to carry heavier and more reliable motors.

The best speeds for human flight will probably be a little greater than that of birds; and it is probable that the average height of human flight will also be greater than that of birds. As a matter of fact, birds usually fly very low. It is more frequent to find them flying at a height of less than fifty feet than above that height. But the bird is small, and can fly through openings in trees in a way manifestly impossible to man. Moreover, the fact that the flyer will possess a less reliable motive-power than the bird will also make it necessary that men in travelling from place to place should maintain a considerable height. If the motor stops, the flyer must descend at the rate of at least one foot for each eight feet it moves forward. As it is not desirable to land among trees or houses, it is necessary to rise to sufficient height to enable the machine to glide to a suitable landing-place. From a height of half a mile it is possible to land on any spot within a radius of about four miles. This would give the operator an opportunity to choose for his landing-place a spot within an area of about fifty square miles. From a height of one mile the area would be extended to some two hundred square miles. If the height of the flyer at the time of the stopping of the motor is sufficiently great, the danger becomes negligible. But any attempt to fly at a low altitude over ground unsuitable for landing must be accompanied by constant danger. Consequently, it may be expected that the successful flight from London to Manchester will be made at a height of a thousand or more feet. In some parts of the journey an even greater elevation might be necessary. It is usual to associate height with danger, but this is true only within certain limits. Three feet is doubtless safer than thirty feet under some conditions; but when the height becomes sufficient to make it impossible to reach the earth quickly, an increase of height not only adds no danger but even decreases it. In early days sailors feared to venture far from land, just as aviators do to-day, but, once certain limits are passed, sailors prefer the high seas; and aviators will prefer the higher atmosphere of heaven for long flights. With motors a little better than we possess to-day, and with operators of somewhat greater experience and skill, men will make such journeys as that between London and Manchester without extraordinary danger. The danger to the future winner of the prize will be due to the fact that, in order to accomplish the feat before others, he will be compelled to attempt it a little before conditions are ripe.

When the London to Manchester prize was first announced, many people were surprised that my brother and I did not immediately declare a purpose to win it. Our backwardness was contrasted with the forwardness of another experimenter, and publicly made the basis of an unfavourable judgment as to the credibility of our past performances. But it was never our practice to publicly announce intentions which we had no settled purpose of promptly carrying to a successful conclusion. Consequently, it has resulted that while we have repeatedly said that we believed that the prize would be won, we have never said that we ourselves were about to make an attempt to win it.

In order to win the ten thousand pounds, it is necessary to make the aerial journey from London to Manchester within a period of twenty-four hours, and with only two landings en route. Many people would think that this prize could be easily grasped by anyone having a flyer capable of making single journeys of sixty miles each; but the person who studies the actual ways and means of carrying forward such an attempt sees difficulties which render the task one of more serious difficulty.

If a prize should be offered to the Englishman who would drive an automobile from New York to Boston, with only two stops for the purpose of inquiring the way, it is quite certain that the prize would not be won at the first attempt, even if the running of the automobile were perfect.

No more will the London to Manchester prize be won at the first attempt, even though the contestant may have a flyer fully able to perform its part of the work. In order to succeed, the operator must have a very accurate personal acquaintance with the appearance of the country over which he must fly. He must be able to recognise by bird's-eye view the various cities, towns, and roads which he may pass on the way.

Neither public safety nor the safety of the aviator will permit that he shall fly directly over cities. He therefore cannot follow a railroad line directly. He must make detours, and, after a city is passed, be able to select the right one of the many lines which diverge from each large city.

If he attempts to fly by compass, the drift of the wind will carry him many miles out of his course; and unless he is very familiar with the topography of the country he will find it difficult to find the goal with only two chances to make inquires. It is quite possible that contestants may find it profitable to mark the course by means of a series of captive balloons, or easily distinguished signals placed at short intervals along the way. Of course, the preparation and maintenance of such signals will call for a very considerable expenditure of money, and it is even possible that the winner will find his main reward in the glory of the achievement rather than in the prize itself.

Of more obvious difficulties it is scarcely necessary to speak, because even the most superficial student of the subject realises them. If one hundred automobiles should start for a prize offered for a trip from London to Manchester, at a high rate of speed, with only two stops en route, how many would succeed at the first attempt? Very few indeed.

In the race at Dieppe last summer few indeed of the racers made less than twenty stops. Yet the automobile has been brought to a very high stage of development, while the flyer is yet in its infancy. Therefore, it may be set down as practically certain that the *Daily Mail* prize will not be won at the first attempt. It may not be won at the tenth attempt.

Nevertheless, I am not such a pessimist as the reader might suppose. It is true that I realise the difficulties of the task; but it is necessary to foresee difficulties, and arm against them before success can be achieved by anyone. Notwithstanding all these difficulties, I believe the prize will be won. It is probable that the winning will cost more than the amount of the prize. It is possible that there will be a toll of human life; but as there are men in the world who will not hesitate to stake money, and even life, in order to win, and as there are machines already within reach which are capable of doing their part (if given a sufficient number of trials), it is quite reasonable to believe that the prize will be won in the near future.[3]

(signed) Wilbur Wright

1. *London Magazine,* February 1909, 617–25.
2. In 1906 the English newspaper the *Daily Mail* offered a £10,000 prize for the first flight between London and Manchester.
3. Fourteen months after Wilbur's article appeared, the £10,000 prize offered by the English newspaper the *Daily Mail* was won by the French aviator Louis Paulhan. On April 27 and 28, 1910, Paulhan flew the 185 miles from London to Manchester in a Farman biplane.

46 • AIRSHIP SAFE: AIR MOTORING NO MORE DANGEROUS THAN LAND MOTORING[1]

Wilbur Wright

No airship[2] will ever fly from New York to Paris.[3] That seems to me to be impossible. What limits the flight is the motor. No known motor can run at the requisite speed for four days without stopping, and you can't be sure of finding the proper winds for soaring. The airship will always be a special messenger, never a load-carrier. But the history of civilization has usually shown that every new invention has brought in its train new needs it can satisfy, and so what the airship will eventually be used for is probably what we can least predict at the present.

There is a misconception about the safety of flying machines, if the motor stops. We can glide to the earth. The higher we are, then, the wider our range of choice for places for descent, and, in a half a mile radius, one ought to be able to select some safe ground. Perhaps the greatest danger, at first, lies in the fact that we've recently changed our system of control. In the first machines we lay in a cradle or deck, and by moving from side to side we regulated the lateral roll. That was too tiresome to the neck muscles, and we decided a seat would be the permanent necessity for comfort. This necessitated levers for manipulating without thought, and I have now to learn the new way.

But I've made so many descents that it doesn't worry me much, and although I know I take chances, they're hardly greater than in an automobile. And it isn't any more dangerous after all than our gliding experiments.

1. *Cairo (Ill.) Bulletin,* March 25, 1909. See also "Wright Finds Ocean Crossing Risky Now" (document 52), for Orville Wright's view, five years later, on the feasibility of a transatlantic flight.
2. The term "airship" here refers to an airplane, not a lighter-than-air craft, for which the term would soon come to be used exclusively.
3. Charles A. Lindbergh accomplished the feat eighteen years later, flying his single-engine Ryan monoplane, the *Spirit of St. Louis,* from New York to Paris in 33½ hours on May 20–21, 1927.

47 • A TALK WITH WILBUR WRIGHT[1]

Interview with Wilbur Wright

"No. The next advance in the art of human flight will not be so much in improving the motor as in the practice of high flying. Personally, I am perfectly satisfied with our motor; not that one, but the later type, which has been strengthened in the very part where the cylinder gave way just now." Thus Wilbur Wright. It was in the gathering gloom of an October afternoon, and we were standing alone in the shed which had been built on Governor's Island to house the Wright aeroplane during the late Hudson-Fulton Celebration.[2] A few minutes earlier the machine was on its launching ways, with everything primed for an hour-long flight in which Wright had purposed to travel up the East River, over the four great bridges that span it, across Manhattan Island, over the Hudson and the Palisades, and return to the starting point, with a wide detour over the Jersey Meadows and across the Upper Bay. We had seen Wright and his mechanic crank the engine by a swift turn of the propellers; had heard the loud explosion and crash, as the forward cylinder tore loose from the crank case; and had seen the wrecked cylinder tear its way through the upper plane and fall at Wright's feet. At the very moment when a million people were lining both shores of the Hudson River, watching with absorbing interest to catch the first glimpse of the author and past master of the art of human flight, lo! here was his machine, rendered an absolute wreck, and the possibility of a Hudson-Fulton flight shut out for good![3] Under such dramatic conditions of disappointment a Frenchman would have wept. Not so Wilbur Wright. Picking up the broken cylinder, he turned to the small group of which the writer formed one, smiled, gave an almost imperceptible shrug of his shoulders, and quietly remarked, "It is all over, gentlemen."

If there is any appetite for the sensational or melodramatic in Wilbur Wright, he certainly keeps it under masterful control. The fact that he had been opposed to the giving of public exhibitions of flight, and that this was the first and only exception that he had made, would, for most men, have rendered the complete breakdown of his machine a most aggravating disaster. Yet, five minutes later, when we were alone with him and his disabled air craft, he was perfectly composed, and showed his philosophical estimate of the true significance of the mishap by pointing to the broken cylinder and remarking: "This is merely an incident. The machine is an old one that I used at Kitty Hawk.[4] The metal was rather light at the point of fracture. The defect has been remedied in our later motors."

A few months ago we expressed the opinion in these columns that the element which needed most attention in the aeroplane was the motor, and that until the latter had been brought up to the degree of reliability of the automobile motor, the art of flying could not make much material progress. Wilbur Wright, however, does not agree with us. "I have developed my motor to the point at which it has ceased to give me any more anxiety than the motor of an automobile. I have run the later pattern of this motor in an endurance test (not, of course, in the air) for seven consecutive hours, and my machines have made 280 consecutive flights without experiencing motor trouble."

"In what direction, then, will the development of the future be made?" we asked, and again the answer came back: "High flying; we must get up clear of the belt of disturbed air which results from the irregularities of the earth's surface. From now on you will see a great increase in the average elevation at which aviators will make their flights; for not only will they find in the higher strata more favorable atmospheric conditions, but in case of motor trouble, they will have more time and distance in which to recover control or make a safe glide to earth."

Next we raised the question of suitable starting and stopping places, and suggested that the art of flying was handicapped by the present necessity for broad open spaces for the purpose. This brought the reply that since trains, trolley cars, steamboats, and sailing yachts are all provided with special points of departure and arrival, it was a little unfair to quote the necessity for such conveniences as an objection to the aeroplane. "But the problem of alighting, especially during a cross-country flight, is not so serious as you might suppose. It will be largely solved by the high flying to which I referred just now, for, the greater the elevation, the larger the section of country from which the aviator can select a suitable alighting place. Suppose," said Wright, "in making a flight, say of 100 miles, I rose to a height of one mile, and while at that elevation motor trouble necessitated an immediate descent. Commencing to glide down the air on a grade of one in seven, I would traverse seven miles of country in a straight line before reaching the ground, that is, supposing that the ground were fairly level. But the glide could be made in any direction, and consequently I could choose a landing place on any one of the 150 square miles that would be included in a circle of 14 miles in diameter. The chances would be therefore decidedly in my favor of finding some fairly smooth field, free from obstruction, on which I could come down safely."

Of course, the question of speed came in for discussion, and the reply to the question whether we shall see any great increase in speed in the near future was characteristic. "Why should we wish to increase the speed? It was only a few years ago that the world believed the construction of a successful flying machine to be impossible, and yet there are not many birds that I cannot overtake with that machine." This was presenting the speed question from a new and very sensible standpoint; for it must be admitted that to have surpassed the average speed of the birds this early in the game is one of the most sensational achievements of this, the latest and most sensational of man's inventions.

---

1. *Scientific American,* October 23, 1909, 290.
2. The Hudson-Fulton Celebration of 1909 was a grand series of events mounted by the state of New York to commemorate the centennial of Robert Fulton's *North River Steamboat,* later called the *Clermont,* and the three-hundredth anniversary of the explorer Henry Hudson's entry into New York Harbor. As part of the commemoration, the Hudson-Fulton Celebration Aeronautics Committee offered Wilbur Wright a $15,000 contract for a flight of at least ten miles in length or one hour in duration, plus any other flights he would care to make during the festivities.
3. The interviewer gave the misimpression that Wilbur Wright completed no flights during the Hudson-Fulton Celebration. The damaged engine cylinder simply forced Wilbur to cancel a scheduled flight for the afternoon of October 4. Earlier that day he had made a spectacular round-trip flight from Governor's Island to Grant's Tomb and back, a total of twenty miles, in 33½ minutes. Since the Hudson-Fulton Celebration flights would be over water, Wilbur had strapped a locally purchased red canoe, sealed with a canvas cover, to the bottom of his airplane to serve as a flotation device in the event of a mishap, giving the aircraft a peculiar look. See photo 41.
4. The term "machine" here refers only to the engine, not the entire aircraft. The Hudson-Fulton airplane was never flown at Kitty Hawk. In the spring of 1908, the Wrights had modified their 1905 powered airplane, fitting it with this improved engine and making other changes, and had practiced with this plane at Kitty Hawk in preparation for their upcoming September flight trials in connection with their U.S. Army Signal Corps contract.

48 • W. WRIGHT ON ALTITUDE AND FANCY FLYING[1]

Wilbur Wright

To the Editor of *Aero:*

I think you do not quite understand our exact position regarding the relative merits of fancy flying and altitude efforts, as compared with cross-city, cross-sea and cross-mountain flying. We believe in all kinds of flying which demonstrate the *merits of the machine.* Among such tests we regard as valuable, demonstrations of control, duration contests, weight-carrying contests, altitude contests and speed contests.

Of all the qualities which an aeroplane should possess, capacity of control is by far the most important, since safety in the fickle air is absolutely dependent upon abundant control. The machine which is most amenable to ready control in calm air is the one which will fly most safely in high winds or in the sudden fierce whirls which are particularly abundant on quiet, sultry days. I believe that fancy flying is a more definite and much safer method of determining the merits of machines in this respect than flying in a gale, as Hoxsey, Johnstone and Brookins did at Belmont Park during the second hour on Thursday, when everyone else refused to go out.[2] That demonstration was only a proof under extremely dangerous conditions of what they had already shown many times by their fancy flying under safer conditions. I am absolutely opposed to carrying fancy flying to extremes merely to provide "thrillers," but legitimate fancy flying is safe and at the same time an exceedingly valuable training exercise for the purpose of acquiring presence of mind and facility in the control of machines. Without such practice Brookins, Johnstone, Hoxsey could not safely have flown in that high wind at Belmont.

In general I am opposed to demonstrations of any quality by tests under dangerous conditions if there is any way to determine the same quality under safer conditions. For this reason I am opposed to flights over cities, flights over seas, flights over mountains, etc., etc., in which the flying part is no different from other flying, but differs only in the consequences of a forced descent. These are not demonstrations of capacity, but of useless bravado.

Altitude flying is also an excellent test of the quality of a machine and not dangerous to a sound man until the altitude approaches 20,000 feet. At present no machine in the world has the capacity to reach a height really dangerous. Very few can reach 5,000 feet. With one exception all the men who have passed the 9,000-foot mark have been stopped by the fact that their machine practically refused to rise higher. Altitude flying, with proper consideration of horsepower and weight carried, is fully as good a proof of the scientific perfection of wings, screws, etc., as speed contests, and is *very much safer.* Altitude contests might be improved, however, by placing a time limit on them so as to make the rate of ascent the real determining factor.

The most valuable contests are those which demonstrate with greatest definiteness and least danger the presence of the quality sought. The machine which will fly longest and maneuver best over safe grounds will in time of real need fly farthest and in the worst weather over seas, cities or mountains.

Yours truly,
Wilbur Wright

1. *Aero,* December 17, 1910, 3.
2. Arch Hoxsey, Ralph Johnstone, and Walter Brookins were show pilots flying with the Wright brothers' exhibition team. Hoxsey and Johnstone in particular were inclined to risky flying to thrill spectators. See also document 36: "Wright's Statement Concerning Johnstone's Fatal Fall."

49 • IN HONOR OF THE ARMY AND AVIATION[1]

Wilbur Wright

MR. WILBUR WRIGHT

Mr. Chairman, Ladies and Gentlemen: When the Director of your Society extended me the invitation to be present at this dinner he indicated that a few remarks might be required from me. This game of after-dinner speaking is one that I have never played very much; so I said to myself, "It will be a good thing to study up on the rules of the game."

So last week I went up to New York and had an opportunity to attend a dinner there at which were present a number of distinguished speakers. The first gentleman on the program was a bishop, and he made a splendid speech. I said to myself, "If it is necessary for me to speak like that I might as well give up trying to play this game." But as the evening wore on I began to discover things. I found out after a little bit that this man had been stealing the speeches of all the men who were to follow him on the program; and not only that, but, according to the statements of the other speakers, he had not only stolen their ideas, but he expressed them better than they could express them themselves. "Well," said I, "if a man is permitted to steal the speeches of all the other men on the program, it is an easy job." So when I heard that among the speakers this evening were some of our most distinguished men, including the President of the United States, I said to myself, "This will be an easy job. I will steal their speeches and I will present them better than they could present them themselves."

But unfortunately the novice often learns some other rule that is equally as important. In this case the rule I overlooked was the rule that provides an arrangement of the speakers on the program. Instead of being on first, so that I could steal their speeches, I have been put on last, with the result that all the speech I was going to make they have made; and, as usual in banquets, according to rule, they have said it a great deal better than I could say it myself.

But I have discovered one other rule that is customary in this game, and that is to choose the subject which is appropriate to the occasion; and another rule confine your remarks strictly to the subject. Therefore I chose for my subject this evening "geography." I shall confine my remarks more particularly to that branch of geography which I discovered on the front of a book once in my father's library. The book was entitled "The Geography of the Heavens." I am not certain now whether the book treated of astronomy or whether it was a book on theology. For my part I steered clear both of astronomy and theology; and, in order to keep off the ground that might have been covered in that book, it is my intention to turn the subject exactly upside down, and instead of viewing it from the ground I will view geography from the heavens.

The ways and means of studying the earth from above have now become pretty well known. Some of the uses which may be expected to be derived from the aëroplane and similar instruments have been told you very well by our distinguished friend, General Wood.[2] The real uses of the aëroplane in warfare are so much better known to him and have been so much better presented that I shall not attempt to take up your time with that. The advantages of knowing what the enemy is doing, with the consequent advantage of being able to concentrate your own troops at the critical spot—the advantage of rising high in the air for the purpose of determining the accuracy of gun-power and giving appropriate directions for carrying on work of that kind—are so well known that it is useless for me to take it up now.

The leading nations of the earth are taking up the subject, our own nation being the first of all to begin it. But, unfortunately, there seems to be some hesitation at present. I do not know exactly what the trouble is. I presume possibly that if we were to apply the parable of the talents we would possibly arrive at something near the present situation. The Department[3] probably feels that with the small equipment it now has it is useless to do anything. On the other hand, Congress seems to feel that unless something is done with the equipment already on hand it is useless to appropriate for it now. I hope the day will soon come when more will be done with what we already have, so that Congress will see fit to appropriate more if it sees that the money will be well spent. I thank you very much.

1. *National Geographic Magazine,* March 1911, 267–84. These were Wilbur Wright's remarks given at the sixth annual banquet of the National Geographic Society in Washington, D.C., on January 14, 1911, honoring the U.S. Army and the invention of the airplane by the Wright brothers. The full article included remarks from several other honored guests at the banquet, including President William H. Taft and the ambassadors from Germany, Mexico, and Great Britain.
2. Major General Leonard Wood was chief of staff for the U.S. Army.
3. Wilbur here refers to the War Department.

50 • WRIGHT CONSIDERS HIGH SPEED TOO DANGEROUS[1]

Wilbur Wright

Wilbur Wright, in a communication to the Paris edition of an American newspaper, declared that the Wright Company did not enter a machine in the Gordon Bennett race[2] because he considered such races dangerous. He wrote as follows:—

"Now that the Gordon Bennett flying machine race for 1911 is over and the terms of next year's contest are yet to be fixed, I would like to raise a few points for discussion.

"In an article, which my brother and I contributed to the Aero Club (New York) book in 1907,[3] long before the Gordon Bennett Cup was instituted, we stated that with motors then within reach speeds exceeding one hundred miles an hour could be attained.

"This opinion we still hold. Even higher speeds could be attained to-day, but we believe that flying at the highest speed for which it is possible to design a machine is unreasonably dangerous.

"All makers agree on this point. No one dares build the fastest machines he knows how to build. Consequently, the winning of the Gordon Bennett Cup has become largely a question of the daring use of larger motors than others use.

"Each year the Gordon Bennett Cup has been won by the most powerful motor. Men who dare the most win under these conditions.

"The Wright Company refused to enter a machine in the 1911 race, as we believed the speed would reach about one hundred miles an hour, which we considered unreasonably dangerous.

"If the Gordon Bennett Cup is to receive the support of the numerous makers and become a real test of superiority in construction and design of flying machines, the rules should be so changed as to limit the size of the motors.

"I would suggest that the standard Gnome (110 mm. by 120 mm.) be taken as a maximum. This motor has a total piston area of 665 square centimeters and a total displacement of 8,000 cubic centimeters. Let these figures fix the maximum as to both area and displacement.

"With a motor of such size a speed of 80 miles an hour can be obtained with biplanes. If monoplanes are really still faster, it is certain that the race will not lack interest because of too slow speed.

"Much complaint has been made by aviators because of the dangerous character of the grounds on which the races of 1910 and 1911 were run. It is not easy, however, to find a five kilometer circuit entirely free from obstacles. If the managers of the race were permitted to fix the circuit at not less than two and a half kilometers it would be much easier to find absolutely safe grounds.

"If the rules should be amended in these respects I have no doubt many aviators and many makers who have been inclined to avoid participation in this contest would at once become interested and thus add to the importance of the event."

---

1. *Fly Magazine*, August 1911, 9.
2. See document 25, note 15.
3. See document 30: "The Relations of Weight, Speed, and Power of Flyers."

51 • WILBUR WRIGHT FAVORS RELIABILITY TESTS[1]
Interview with Wilbur Wright

Baltimore, Md., March 24

Wilbur Wright, on his way to Augusta, Ga., to see the government aeroplane tests, stopped over and spent the better part of the day with the local aviator, Howard Gill, who last year was a member of the Wright exhibition team, and who at present holds the American duration record. Speaking of the coming season's activity in aviation Wright was strongly in favor of inaugurating a form of reliability flights in preference to purely speed contests.

He said, "The speed contests are not only dangerous but also produce machines that are suitable for no practical purpose, while a cross-country reliability flight of 1,000 miles or more in length, made in daily stages of from 100 to 200 miles, with stops at the principal cities along the way, would promote safety and reliability and would develop just the type of machine most suitable for military and general use. At the different stopping points controls should be established where the committee could take charge of the planes upon their arrival. Any repairs or adjustments made during the stop would be considered in determining the winner.

"Contests of this nature, if started now will develop a future market for the aeroplane, but unless this end of the business is encouraged and development of it started soon, when the exhibition business which is slowly dying out ceases to prove profitable, manufacturers of planes will find themselves without any market for their output."

These views of Wilbur Wright coincide with those expressed editorially in *Aero*, February 10,[2] under the heading, "Demonstration of Reliability."

1. *Aero*, March 30, 1912, 514.
2. See *Aero*, February 10, 1912.

52 • WRIGHT FINDS OCEAN CROSSING RISKY NOW[1]
Orville Wright

Dayton, Ohio, Feb. 13, 1914

To the Editor of *Aero and Hydro:*
I have your letter of February 12th, enclosing clipping on the trans-Atlantic flight. What I said was, that while it was possible at the present time to design a machine to carry one man and fuel enough for a flight of about 1,500 miles, it would be foolish for an aviator to risk his life in attempting a non-stop flight across the ocean with such a machine until the motor has been perfected to the point where it can be ab-

solutely depended upon. Of course, a favorable wind of 15 miles per hour or more would be necessary to complete the trip, as the shortest distance across is between 1,800 and 1,900 miles. The longest trip in a single flight up to date is less than one-half this distance.

(signed) Orville Wright

---

1. *Aero and Hydro,* February 21, 1914, 261. See also "Airship Safe: Air Motoring No More Dangerous Than Land Motoring" (document 46) for Wilbur Wright's view, five years earlier, on the feasibility of a transatlantic flight.

53 • FLYING MACHINES AND THE WAR[1]

Interview with Orville Wright by Fred C. Kelly

"The greatest use of the aeroplane to date has been as a tremendously big factor of modern warfare. But—

"The greatest use of the aeroplane eventually will be to prevent war.

"Some day there will be neither war nor rumors of war, and the reason may be flying machines.

"It sounds paradoxical. We are building aeroplanes to use in time of war, and will continue to build them for war. We think of war and we think of aeroplanes. Later on, perhaps, we shall think of aeroplanes in connection with the wisdom of keeping out of war.

"The aeroplane will prevent war by making it too expensive, too slow, too difficult, too long drawn out—in brief, by making the cost prohibitive."[2]

The man who makes these statements about the aeroplane is Orville Wright, one of the brothers who invented it.

"Did you ever stop to think," inquires Wright, "that there is a very definite reason why the present war in Europe has dragged along for a year with neither side gaining much advantage over the other? The reason, as I figure it out, is aeroplanes. In consequence of the scouting work done by the flying machines, each side knows exactly what the opposing forces are doing.

"There is little chance for one army to take another by surprise. Napoleon won his wars by massing his troops at unexpected places. The aeroplane has made that impossible. It has equalized information. Each side has such complete knowledge of the other's movements that both sides are obliged to crawl into trenches and fight by means of slow, tedious routine rather than by quick, spectacular dashes.

"My impression is that before the present war started the army experts expected it to be a matter of a few weeks or, at the most, a few months. To-day it looks as if it might run into years before one side can dictate terms. Now, a nation that may be willing to undertake a war lasting a few months may well hesitate about engaging in one that will occupy years. The daily cost of a great war is of course stupendous. When this cost runs on for years the total is likely to be so great that the side which wins nevertheless loses. War will become prohibitively expensive. And the scouting work in flying machines will be the predominating factor, as it seems to me, in bringing this about. I like to think so anyhow."

"What, in your opinion, has the present war demonstrated regarding the relative advantages of aeroplanes and Zeppelin airships?" the inventor was asked.

"The aeroplane seems to have been of the more practical use," replied Wright. "In the first place, dirigible airships of the Zeppelin type are so expensive to build, costing somewhere around half a million dollars each, that it is distinctly disadvantageous to the nation operating them to have one destroyed. The financial risk every time your Zeppelin is shot at is too great. But what is more important is the fact that the Zeppelin is so large that it furnishes an excellent target unless it sails considerably higher than is comparatively safe for an aeroplane. And when the Zeppelin is at a safe height it is too far above the ground for your scout to make accurate observations. Similarly, when the Zeppelin is used for dropping bombs, it must be too high for the bomb thrower to show much accuracy."

"You think that the use of flying machines for scouting purposes will be of considerably more importance than their use as a means of attack?" was another question.

"That has been decidedly true so far," replied Wright. "About all that has been accomplished by either side from bomb dropping has been to kill a few noncombatants, and that will have no bearing on the result of the war.

"English newspapers have long talked of the danger of Zeppelin attacks or aeroplane attacks, but it was all for a purpose, because they did not believe the country was sufficiently prepared for war and sought to arouse the people and the War Department to action by means of the airship bogy."

"Has the war use of the aeroplane been up to the expectations you and your brother formed at the time of its invention?"

"Yes, beyond our expectations. About the first thing we thought of after we found that we could fly was the possibilities for scouting purposes, but we had little idea that the year 1915 would see so many aeroplanes in army use.

"Aside from the use of the machines for war purposes the war will give a great boost to aviation generally. It has led more men to learn to fly, and with a higher degree of skill than ever before. It has awakened people to aviation possibilities."

"Apart from war, what will be the future of the aeroplane?"

As a Sporting Proposition

"Just like the automobile, it will become more and more fool-proof, easier to handle, and safer. There is no reason why it should not take the place of special trains where there is urgent need of great speed. Maybe you never paused to think that already the aeroplane is safer than the automobile if you are going at a high rate of speed? If you want to ride sixty miles an hour, as men occasionally do, you are about ten times safer doing it in an aeroplane, granting, of course, that the man at the wheel has learned his business.

"The aeroplane has never really come into its own as a sporting proposition. Of late years the tendency has been to develop a high rate of speed rather than to build machines that may be operated successfully at comparatively low speed. The low-speed machine is necessary before the aeroplane can fill the place that it should in the world of sport. You see, a machine adapted to make from seventy to one hundred miles an hour cannot run at all except at a pretty rapid clip, and this means difficulty in getting down. One must have a good, smooth piece of ground to land on and plenty of it. When we get an aeroplane that will fly along at twenty miles an hour, one can land almost any place—on a roof, if necessary—and then people will begin to take an interest in owning an aeroplane for the enjoyment of flying. As it is now, the man who buys a flying machine for sport usually takes a trip or two to show his friends that he can do it, and then is reconciled to let the machine remain a good deal of the time in the shed.

"The problem of finding a landing place, in case one's motor ceases to work, is one of many interesting angles. If you are just a mile up in the air at the moment of beginning an enforced descent, you have your choice of nearly two hundred square miles of territory in which to alight. You can circle about and strike a point immediately below you, or, if you prefer, it is possible to soar down at an angle that will bring you to a point eight miles from there.

"Now, when you have two hundred square miles to pick from, it looks as if you ought to be able to find a smooth place, doesn't it? But the trouble is you probably are not familiar with the territory, and it is impossible to tell from where you are much about the conformation of the ground. The aviator soon learns to distinguish the shades of green that indicate the various growing crops, but when only a few hundred feet in the air he cannot tell whether the ground is hilly or level. When he gets down to a point where he can see just what he is coming to, it is then too late to have much choice in the matter."

This talk about heights and distances reminded Wright of a misunderstanding that long caused him and his late brother Wilbur to be regarded as fakers in the days before flying was recognized as a reality. The Wrights made their first flight down at Kitty Hawk, N.C., which place they had selected because the weather reports showed it to be about the most persistently windy place in the country. That night, after making their flight, they wired their father at Dayton stating that they had been in the air five minutes and had flown more than eight hundred feet over the ground.[3]

This private message was intercepted in some manner and got into the papers. The man writing the account for the newspaper got the impression that eight hundred feet over the ground meant eight hundred feet above the ground!

Persons at Kitty Hawk knew the Wrights had not ascended any eight hundred feet, and therefore branded the whole story as a pure hasheesh dream. That notion spread. The Wrights had been making successful flights for many months before the wonder of their invention attracted much attention. I asked Wright how it happened that they could fly so clandestinely. How did they keep it out of the papers?

"Chiefly," replied Wright, "because in those days everybody called an aeroplane an airship. Nobody distinguished between an airship and a flying machine.[4] There had been airships with dirigible gas bags making flights in France and staying up an hour where we would be up in our aeroplane only five minutes.[5] Naturally our performance seemed of little consequence by comparison. The man who handled the Associated Press work at Dayton lived not far from our experiment field, and doubtless heard people nearly every day speaking of our flights; yet he sent nothing to the papers, for he naturally assumed that we had an airship.

"Whenever we spoke of our device as a flying machine we placed ourselves in the same class with the man who goes crazy over perpetual motion. Old friends of our family used to shake their heads when mention was made of our experiments, and say that we ought to be at some better business. I recall that on the night following our first flight, down at Kitty Hawk, I picked up a magazine to while away the hours until bedtime, and opened it by chance at an article by a scientist explaining just why it would always be an utter impossibility to fly with a heavier-than-air machine."

"Did you think you were going to succeed even before your machine actually left the ground?" I asked Wright.

"Yes, toward the last we began to have great confidence in our figures. We had rigged up an air funnel, and experimented for months on the effects of air pressure on planes of different sizes and at different angles.[6] Our original intention, you know, was simply to build a gliding machine. Then, as we built up our system of calculation, we worked out figures for the air pressure on the blades of a propeller. Each blade is, of course, only a small plane in motion. Inasmuch as experiments had convinced us of the accuracy of our earlier figures, we began to think that they would make good with reference to the power of a propeller.[7] Except for these figures we would have built no successful aeroplane. To have arrived at the results by experiment would have cost probably $100,000—more money than we could have raised. We had to do our experimenting with paper and pencil."

"Is it true that you and your brother had a compact not to fly together?"

"Yes, we felt that until the records of our work could be made complete it was a wise precaution not to take a chance on both of us getting killed at the same time.

We never flew together but once.[8] It would surprise you to know how little we were in the air at all during the eight years following our first flight. From 1900 to 1908 the total time in the air for both Wilbur and myself, all put together, was only about four hours."

"Shall you fly much in the future?"

"I want to fly now and then for the sport of it as long as I live.[9] But I do not care to do it as a business. I would like to be clear out of any actual business occupation.

"As it is now I am a manufacturer of aeroplanes. Many another man can handle such a manufacturing enterprise much more capably than I. What I would like to do is rig up another air funnel and go ahead experimenting once more in the laboratory. There is still lots to be done."[10]

The Modesty of the Man

I talked to Wright in the reception room of his new home, a handsome colonial mansion set among big trees in one of Dayton's pretty suburbs.[11] Fame and fortune have not, however, made Orville Wright any less simple in taste or manner than when he conducted a little bicycle shop and lived in a cottage with hair-cloth furniture on an obscure side street. He is the most genuinely modest man that I know. Not once did his conversation lose its unconscious tone of unassumingness. He discusses inventing the first successful flying machine as if he were talking about a favorite cherry tree in the side yard.

---

1. *Collier's Weekly,* July 31, 1915, 24–25.
2. The idea that the airplane would become the great deterrent to war—that governments, knowing that destruction from the air was a reality, would be far more reluctant to engage in military solutions to conflicts—became widespread after the inception of flight. Orville Wright was hardly the first to advance this view. The potential world-changing effect of the aerial weapon was the subject of much literature and debate in the early twentieth century. Orville was not alone in his belief that having demonstrated its reconnaissance and combat capabilities in World War I, the airplane would be a key factor in preventing future wars. But this of course proved to be an unfulfilled hope in light of the pervasive use of airpower in World War II and after. For a historical treatment of the faith in airpower as a deterrent to war, and a general study on early popular and intellectual ideas regarding the inspirations and implications of flight, see H. Bruce Franklin, *War Stars: The Superweapon and the American Imagination* (New York: Oxford University Press, 1988), and Robert Wohl, *A Passion for Wings: Aviation and the Western Imagination, 1908–1918* (New Haven: Yale University Press, 1994).
3. The actual time of the Wrights' best flight was fifty-nine seconds. The telegram the brothers sent to their father was in error, stating the time as fifty-seven seconds—but not five minutes. The precise distance covered by that best flight was 852 feet.
4. An "airship" referred to a lighter-than-air craft, whereas a "flying machine" referred to a heavier-than-air machine.
5. Orville is referring to flights the brothers made with their subsequent powered air-

planes in 1904 and 1905 at Huffman Prairie, a local cow pasture near their home in Dayton, Ohio.

6. By "air funnel," Orville means their wind tunnel built in October 1901. See also document 5, note 15.
7. See document 5, note 16.
8. On May 25, 1910, the Wright brothers made their one and only flight together. With Orville as pilot and Wilbur as passenger, they circled Huffman Prairie, their practice field near Dayton, for 6½ minutes. Another noteworthy flight was made that day. Orville took up the brothers' father, eighty-one-year-old Bishop Milton Wright. Concerned over how his aging father might react to being in the air, Orville maintained an altitude of no more than 350 feet. Throughout the near seven-minute flight the Wright patriarch made only one comment: "Higher, Orville, higher!"
9. Orville Wright made his last flight as a pilot in 1918, at the age of forty-six. He had suffered serious injuries in a crash on September 17, 1908, while demonstrating the Wright airplane at Fort Myer, Virginia, in connection with a U.S. Army contract for the sale of the first military airplane. His passenger, the army representative Lieutenant Thomas E. Selfridge, was killed. The lingering effects of Orville's injuries resulted in lifelong pain and stiffness, especially when sitting for extended periods. The vibration and stresses of airplane flight in the pre–World War II era were generally more than Orville could stand. After 1918 he rarely flew even as a passenger. See also document 25, notes 20 and 21.
10. In the fall of 1915, three and a half years after the death of Wilbur and a few months after this interview was published, Orville Wright sold out his aeronautical interests in the Wright Company and retired from the airplane business a wealthy man. The following year he built a new laboratory near the bicycle shop in which he and Wilbur had performed so much of their pioneering aeronautical work. They had always planned to set up a specialized workshop and return to the joy of technical research and experimentation in their retirement. In November 1916 Orville finally gave up the lease on the old bicycle shop and, alone, moved into his new facility, located at 15 North Broadway.
11. See document 13, note 2.

54 • ADDRESS BY ORVILLE WRIGHT AT THE NATIONAL PARKS CONFERENCE, UNDER THE AUSPICES OF THE DEPARTMENT OF THE INTERIOR, WASHINGTON, D.C., JANUARY 5, THE DAY'S PROGRAM BEING DEVOTED TO THE SUBJECT OF "MOTOR TRAVEL TO THE PARKS," AND UNDER THE DIRECTION OF THE AMERICAN AUTOMOBILE ASSOCIATION[1]

Orville Wright

Travel to our national parks at present is confined to the few rail and wagon roads leading to them. To build these roads, paths through the forests had to be cleared; rivers and chasms bridged, and in many places extensive excavations made to reduce grades. But before long, we hope, other access to these parks will be established in a way that will require neither roadways, nor rails, nor bridges or excavations.

The rapid strides taken in aerial navigation in the past few years has demonstrated its practicability as a means of travel. While it seems certain that it never can compete with the railroad train or the steamboat in carrying large bodies of people in one company, yet it will be but a short time till parties equal in size to those now accommodated in automobiles will be easily and safely carried from place to place.

It is only thirteen years since the first flight was made by man in a heavier than air machine. Within that time the length of flight has been increased from one minute to more than twenty-four hours; the altitude from a few feet to more than twenty-six thousand feet, and the load from a few hundred to several thousand pounds.

The pleasure of travel by air is increased by its freedom from dust, smoke and vibration, met with in travel by rail or automobile. It is true that in very boisterous winds one may be tossed about somewhat as in ocean travel, but even in this the sensation is not disagreeable.

Viewed from above, the flat monotonous landscapes take on a new beauty not seen from the ground; the plowed fields, the patches of grass and grain, and the wooded spots appear as a quilt of beautiful colors; the hills and valleys are scarcely distinguishable; the earth appears to be a flat plain, marked and colored with a beauty not appreciated except when seen in this way.

Travel by air is not only the cleanest, but it is the fastest mode of transportation. All other means must follow certain routes to avoid steep grades. They often follow the winding courses of streams of water. The aerial route passes over mountain or plain, hill or dale, and river or lake with almost equal facility. Not only can low places be reached by air, but the highest mountains as well. An altitude of over 26,000 feet has been attained by aeroplane, a feat never as yet accomplished by any of the older artificial means of transportation. The aerial route is not only the most direct and fastest route; it is the safest at very high speeds. When speeds of forty or fifty miles an hour are exceeded flying is now safer than automobiling.

But in order to visit the national parks by the aerial routes, suitable landing places will have to be provided, either within the parks themselves, or in the closely adjacent country. A landing station should be on flat level ground, of smooth surface and of dimensions of at least 1,000 feet on a side. Many machines require more space than this: 1,600 to 2,000 feet in at least one direction is not too much.

In the plains west of the Mississippi and east of the Rockies, landing places can be found almost anywhere. But in the mountainous and hilly regions of the far east and far west, they are not so plentiful. Here suitable landing places either will have to be prepared, or those already existing must be found and marked so as to be easily recognized from distances of five to ten miles. When flying at a height of a mile one has a territory of nearly two hundred square miles in which to find a landing place. Unfortunately the flyer cannot know the nature of the ground until he has come within a few hundred feet of it, unless it is a marked or well known ground. Then, if the motor is not operating, it is too late to seek a landing place elsewhere.

It is true that most of our national parks do not abound with such spots already prepared by nature. Neither the rugged mountains with snowcapped peaks and rocky slopes or wooded sides; nor the deep river gorges of bouldered beds and precipitous walls, lend themselves easily to the formation of ideal landing stations. Yet it is probable that within every national park nature has provided many, or at least a few, such spots, which, with a little aid from man, will serve very well for landing stations. Probably no one as yet has ever looked over our parks with this object in view.

No doubt within a few years aeroplanes will be so improved that even smaller spaces than those already mentioned can be utilized. In Crater Lake Park, and probably in some of the others, are bodies of water large enough for landing with aeroplanes equipped with hydroplanes.

But no matter by what route we arrive, our national parks must be viewed from the ground to be fully appreciated. The giant Sequoia, when viewed from on high, will be no more impressive than the modest shrub; and the Grand Canyon of the Colorado will flatten out almost to a plain. Though the shining river will be seen winding its tortuous way in a mass of variegated colors, the grandeur of the gorge in size and sculpture will be gone.

1. *Flying,* February 1917, 64. The spoken version of this address was published in *Proceedings: National Parks Conference, Held in the Auditorium of the New National Museum, Washington, D.C., January 2, 3, 4, 5, and 6, 1917* (Washington, D.C.: Government Printing Office, 1917), 281–83.

55 • THE SAFE AND USEFUL AEROPLANE[1]

Interview with Orville Wright by Burton J. Hendrick

While the world is thundering with well-nigh universal war, the one man whose lifework has probably most influenced most military operations is spending his quiet days experimenting in his laboratory at Dayton, Ohio.[2] This is Orville Wright, the man who, with his brother Wilbur, invented the aeroplane. It was only about ten years ago that Wilbur Wright, in France, and Orville Wright, in this country, made the famous flights that first brought home to the world the fact that transportation through the air had become a reality. The last three years have shown the part that this invention was to play in history. Yet when I recently talked with Mr. Orville Wright on the aeroplane, I found him more interested in its usefulness as an instrument of peace than as an instrument of war.

"I really believe," he said, "that the aeroplane will help peace in more ways than one—in particular I think it will have a tendency to make war impossible. Indeed, it is my conviction that, had the European governments foreseen the part which the aeroplane was to play, especially in reducing all their strategical plans to a devastating deadlock, they would never have entered upon the war. Possibly they foresaw something of the present development, but not definitely. When I was in England several years ago I found the British Government not at all enthusiastic about the aeroplane, since the English military experts regarded it as a menace to England's isolation. This was the time when the nation was aroused over the fear of a German invasion; there was a widespread belief that the Germans were planning a descent in several forms of aircraft, and many very sensible people regarded such an enterprise as not impossible. Naturally they looked with suspicion upon any instrument, such as the aeroplane, which might facilitate such an operation. This illustrates the mistaken notions which were entertained concerning the practical uses of the aeroplane in warfare. Most of us saw its use for scouting purposes, but few foresaw that it would usher in an entirely new form of warfare. As a result of its activities, every opposing general knows precisely the strength of his enemy and precisely what he is going to do. Thus surprise attacks, which for thousands of years have determined the event of wars, are no longer possible, and thus all future wars, between forces which stand anywhere near equality, will settle down to tedious deadlocks. Civilized countries, knowing this in advance, will hesitate before taking up arms—a fact which makes me believe that the aeroplane, far more than Hague conferences and Leagues to enforce peace, will exert a powerful influence in putting an end to war."[3]

"I presume you would welcome such an outcome?" I said.

"Yes, indeed," answered Mr. Wright, quickly. "I should hail this as the aeroplane's greatest triumph. My main interest is in the aeroplane as a real promoter of civilization. Recent events have made us regard it almost exclusively as a weapon of war. Probably many people believe that, as soon as peace is signed, the thousands of aeroplanes that have contributed so greatly to it will be scrapped. That is not my belief. After the war we are told we shall have a new world and a new type of civilization; in my opinion one of the factors that will contribute to this changed order will be the part which will be played in it by the aeroplane. We shall have an entirely new form of transportation, which will serve many ends and contribute in many ways to the welfare and happiness of mankind."

"Yes," I remarked, "we have many prophets who tell us of the wonderful future in store for your invention."

"Yet I am not one of those," answered Mr. Wright, "who entertain extravagant ideas concerning its future. All sorts of ridiculous notions are afloat, largely fathered by people of lively imagination and of limited information. I do not believe that all transportation in future will be through the air. The aeroplane will not supplant the railroad, the trolley-car, or the automobile. All our present methods of transporting passengers and freight will continue to render excellent service; the aeroplane will merely be another agency for performing a similar kind of work. There are certain things that it will do better than the railroad or the automobile, and its use will therefore be limited to these, for we must realize at the start that the aeroplane has decided limitations. In saying this I am discussing the machine as we know it to-day. It is not impossible that other forms of aircraft, built upon other principles, may be invented, which may accomplish all the wonderful things certain imaginative people prophesy for the present aeroplane. We see numerous pictures to-day of aircraft as large as ocean-liners, but these are merely vain imaginings. We shall have no aeroplanes as large as the *Lusitania.* Any one who understands the fundamentals of air mechanics will immediately understand why this is so. The aeroplane is built essentially upon the same principles as a bird; it has the same flying capabilities as a bird, and precisely the same limitations. The best flyer among birds is the humming-bird. Have you ever noticed how it poises itself in the air, in almost identically the same place, perhaps for an hour at a time? The humming-bird is one of the smallest of birds; and certain insects, which are much smaller, such as the dragon-fly, are also wonderful flyers. It is a law of nature that, the larger the bird, the poorer its flying ability. The barnyard fowl has great difficulty in getting over a fence, while the ostrich does not fly at all. All creatures that live in the air are small; we have nothing, among flying animals, which can be compared in size to the horse or the elephant. There are excellent mechanical reasons for this. The main one is that, as a bird increases in size, its weight increases at a much greater rate than the area of its wings. Thus, if a bird doubles in size, it would need, to lift itself in the air, not twice as much power, but eight times as much. That is, its weight increases as its cube, whereas the area of the wings increases as its square. You can easily see where that mathematical principle will soon land you. This is the principle that limits the size of birds, and it is also the principle that limits the size of aeroplanes, which fly just as birds fly. Each increase in size demands a much greater proportional increase in motive power, the result being that we have to add so enormously to the weight that the aeroplane soon reaches a size where it cannot leave the ground. Many attempts have been made to make bigger machines, but nothing is gained in economy or usefulness by making them. The aeroplane is a method of transportation that works best and least expensively in small units. We can get better and cheaper service out of two aeroplanes of moderate size than we can get out of one which is twice as large. There are other factors that will limit our present aeroplane practically to its present size, but it is unnecessary to go into the matter in greater detail. Ten passengers have already been carried comfortably, yet it is a fact that a large car carrying ten passengers would not be so economical or efficient as ten little cars each carrying one."

"Most people believe," I suggested, "that what mainly stands in the way of the aeroplane is its danger. The average citizen regards it as an exhilarating and exciting sport, but not safe enough for general use."

"Yes," said Mr. Wright, "it is a new idea that the aeroplane is a safe means of transportation in safe hands, yet it is an idea that we must firmly get into the popular mind. The average citizen is still frightened at the prospect of leaving the ground and having no support except the air itself. Yet at the speed which we expect an aeroplane to maintain—seventy or eighty miles an hour—there is no means of transportation that is so safe. The obstructions that cause accidents with trains and automobiles do not exist for flying craft. A locomotive has to follow a definite track, which may be obstructed or the slightest dislocation of which may cause a frightful calamity. The aeroplane is not so circumscribed—its tracks are wherever it wishes to go. There are no obstructions in the air—unless we regard 'air-pockets' as such—no bridges to cross, no mountains to penetrate, no signals to run by, and no switches to be misplaced. Or compare this new craft to the rough road of the automobile. The slightest mistake or even inattention on the part of the driver, going, say, forty or fifty miles an hour, may hurl the machine over a precipice or overturn it on an embankment. But such a lapse on the part of an aviator has no such deplorable results; there are no precipices to fall from and no obstructions to collide with. The aeroplane is even safer than some forms of water travel. The motor-boat, going at a speed of forty miles an hour, or even slower, is a more risky form of transportation than an aeroplane. If such a boat strike even a small obstruction, such as a floating plank, its side is punctured and it sinks in a few seconds. But there are no such dangers in the air.

"Certain performers have done much to instill this notion that flying is exceedingly dangerous," Mr. Wright continued. "These are the daredevil exhibition flyers, who cultivate the circus aspects of the art. Both by words and deeds they have associated the aeroplane with the idea of danger. They have spread abroad the impression that only an immense amount of nerve, abnormal skill, and plenty of luck qualify one for aviation. And their air acrobatics—their tail-glides and their loopings-the-loop—have accentuated this idea. They have had many bad accidents, too, which have been the necessary consequences of inexperience and of taking foolish chances. Yet I do not wish to criticize too harshly these circus-performers, for they have accomplished much good. The man who first looped-the-loop made a solid contribution to the cause of aeronautics, for he demonstrated the wonderful stability and righting-power of the aeroplane. He showed that the contrivance could get into practically no position in the air from which it could not be righted. What other means of transportation, except the aeroplane, sails just as well upside as down? In what other can one turn turtle, without fear of serious consequences? We owe the demonstration of these reassuring facts to the exhibition-performers, and the discovery has the greatest value for the man or woman who prefers to fly in more prosaic fashion. It gives them a consciousness that, whatever happens, they are safe. Still these flyers, with their numerous accidents, have made the aviator's career seem a hazardous one, and of this false idea we should disabuse our minds. There is no sense of dizziness in the air. Once well up, you never know whether your elevation is a few hundred or a few thousand feet."

"Are there, then, no dangers in flying?" I asked.

"Yes, indeed," Mr. Wright answered, "but there are no difficulties which ordinary prudence and common sense cannot provide against, for the greatest danger of aeroplaning is not the flying, but the landing. If one has a wide, smooth, open place for his descent, all is well; but it is inconvenient and it may be fatal to land in the top of a tree or somewhere in the neighborhood of a skyscraper. Of actual upsetting in the air—that is, a genuine fall, such as was not infrequent in the early days—there is now very little danger, and there is no reason why accidents of this kind should ever take place, for, as I have already said, an aeroplane, no matter what position it gets into, is easily righted. What we must guard against, above everything, is flying too near the ground. Here again we must revise the popular attitude toward the aeroplane. Most people feel that they would not mind going up provided they went up only a hundred feet or so; the idea of ascending fifteen hundred or two thousand is what appals them. But in general I may say that the higher one flies the safer he is. Clearly, if you are going to fall, you will suffer no more by falling from a thousand feet than from five hundred; the chances are that you will be killed in either case. But you are less likely to have a serious fall at the higher altitude than at the lower. The reason is that, if the machine is high enough, the pilot has space in which to right himself, while if he is too near the ground he does not have sufficient space.

"We also hear much about the stopping of the motor. The public has the impression that this dead motor is one of the greatest perils of flying. As a matter of fact, the stopping of the motor is not necessarily a serious matter. The motor does not make the aeroplane fly—it merely propels it. The machine flies when the motor stops, only it does not fly on the horizontal plane. Whenever this happens, it glides easily and gracefully toward the earth. If we have a level landing-place under us, everything goes well; if we do not, the consequences are unpleasant. If we are only a hundred feet in the air, we haven't time to select a landing-place, but go down just where we are, whether it is a deep pond, a mass of telegraph wires, or the tangled roofs of the city. If we are up a thousand or more feet, however, we have much more room to glide in, and can usually select some place where we can land in comfort. The usual gliding range is about eight to one; that is, if the aeroplane is a hundred feet in the air, it lands about eight hundred feet away from the place where the motor stops, while if it is up a thousand feet, it comes down about eight thousand feet away, or about a mile and a half. A height of two thousand feet, giving a gliding range of three miles, is usually safe for all purposes, as, from this height, the flyer can discover a level spot within that large radius. Thus safety in the air is almost entirely a matter of maintaining a sufficient height. Exhibition-performers constantly take this risk; they persist in flying low over a city, taking their chances that the motor will not stop. I cannot understand why men will run such risks, unless it is that flight itself is so easy, and the aeroplane inspires such confidence, that the possibility of a mishap vanishes from the mind."

"What do you do, then, when the motor stops?" I asked.

"The stopping of the motor is not in itself dangerous," said Mr. Wright; "it merely means a descent to earth until the mechanism can be again made ready for flight. But it is inconvenient, and a deterrent to commercial aeroplaning. A motor that works with the same perfection as the automobile motor is to-day our greatest need. And we are making rapid progress toward obtaining it. This, it will be remembered, was the greatest problem of the automobile in the early days—the motor's constant tendency to break down in a distant road was a constant irritation. We have been going through this same preliminary stage with the aeroplane motor; indeed, I think we have made more progress in the same period of time in propelling the flying-machine than we did in propelling the automobile. American manufacturers are somewhat behind Europeans in making motors, simply because we have not had the opportunities to experiment. Making thousands of machines for war purposes, the European manufacturers have naturally produced motors that are superior to ours. They have spent millions in experimental work and with satisfactory results. One motor in particular weighs only 374 pounds, has developed 150 horse-power, and has the important quality of durability. This motor has given certain war aeroplanes a speed of 125 miles an hour, and with it the aviator can climb 10,000 feet in ten minutes. The Allies have placed orders for 7,000 of these machines. The war has developed other motors and American manufacturers are producing better types every day. The time has therefore arrived for the general use of the aeroplane for commercial and pleasure purposes."

"What, then, will be its uses? Will it carry passengers to any extent?"

"Yes. It will not, as I have said, supplant the railroad, but there are certain things that the aeroplane can do better than the railroad. It will be demanded whenever the necessity is for great speed. Few express trains average more than fifty miles an hour—though they make greater speed on short stretches of straight track—whereas that speed represents almost the minimum of the flying-machine. We think nothing of sixty and seventy miles, a regulation speed of one hundred miles may be expected, and, as said above, certain pursuit aeroplanes now used in the war go at the rate of one hundred and twenty-five miles an hour. At first even the suggestion of such speeds almost takes one's breath away; it seems inconceivable that human beings could physically endure such rapid traveling. But there is one great difference in traveling in the air and on the surface. On a railroad car we are always conscious of high speed; well up in the air we are not conscious of it at all. The sensation is precisely the same whether you are going forty or ninety miles an hour, or, indeed, if you are making no progress at all, as, in a high adverse wind, sometimes happens. A fly in a Pullman car has the same sensation, whether the car is standing still or rushing ahead at the rate of fifty miles an hour—the fly is simply carried along with the mass of air and has no sense of motion. The situation is the same in flying. A speed of one hundred miles an hour, therefore, causes no physical distress. Traveling under such circumstances will be far pleasanter than that furnished by the most luxurious Pullman or automobile. There is no roadbed to jar, and we never know when we are going around a curve. Indeed, the passengers will hardly realize that they are moving at all."

"How will this cut down the time of traveling?"

"The trip from New York to Boston," Mr. Wright answered, "would take about two hours, where now it takes five. From New York to Chicago will take eight or ten hours instead of twenty, as at present. You will be able to make the trip from New York to San Francisco in a couple of days. Now plenty of occasions arise in everyday life when such rapid transit is desirable. The only recourse now for unusually rapid speed is the special train. This has two disadvantages—it costs so much that only railroad presidents and millionaires can use it, and, after all, it does not go very much faster than the regular train. In a very few years, I think, the flying-machine will do all the work that the special train does now. It is not only faster, but it is more comfortable, much safer, and much less expensive. The New York business man who wishes quick transit to Chicago, where the saving of a few hours will perhaps mean a successful business deal involving millions, will use the aeroplane. So will the man who wishes to reach the bedside of a sick relative, where saving an hour or two may mean seeing his wife or child alive. We frequently read of surgeons being rushed upon a special train, so that they may arrive in time to perform an operation that may save a human life. What a godsend the speedier transit of a flying-machine will be in cases like this!"

"Why isn't such a service established at once?" The question was a natural one.

"Chiefly because of the impediment I have mentioned—the scarcity of good landing-places. It will be necessary to establish such landing-places—that is, smooth level fields—at all important points. We have two or three such model landing-places already—especially those at Dayton and at Detroit. All large cities will have to build such accommodations; future municipal planning will necessarily provide them. With these established in all important points, the day of passenger traffic will begin. This service can supplement the regular railroad in numerous ways. In particular it will make 'missing the train' much less of a calamity than it is now. Suppose, for example, you fail to catch the Twentieth Century Limited at the Grand Central Station; you can jump into an aeroplane and reach Albany in plenty of time to catch it there. Perhaps the greatest service of the passenger aeroplane is that it will make accessible parts of the world that are now little used. There are plenty of places where railroads cannot be built because of the great cost, because of engineering obstacles, and because there is not enough traffic to justify them.

"This brings me to the use of the aeroplane for transporting freight. The present type of machine will never supplant the freight-car, and I cannot foresee that it will ever be used for carrying coal or wheat. But in transporting special small packages, precious freight, it will be extremely useful. Here again we shall penetrate sections where the railroad cannot carry us. There are thousands of such places in the West, in South America, in Africa. The aeroplane will probably be one of the most potent agencies in the development of Alaska, for here we have an extremely rich country where railroads are difficult and extremely expensive to build. I can best illustrate this by a special instance. There is a certain port in Alaska back of which, about sixteen miles away, lie rich gold-fields. The problem of the company which works these mines is to get supplies to its men and to get the concentrate back to tidewater. The mines are shut off from the port by two ranges of mountains four thousand feet high, and it is inconceivable that a railroad should ever be built across these obstructions. Supplies are now sent by a circuitous route which takes three days to make in the summer-time; in winter it cannot be made at all. The company is now completing plans to install an aeroplane service. In this way the workmen can easily sail over the mountainous barriers and reach the miners in an hour. They can thus carry supplies to the workmen and bring back the concentrate. The money saved will be an important item; the great point, however, is that the mines, with all their precious output, can be successfully worked for the first time. There are thousands of places, in Alaska and elsewhere, where precisely the same situation exists. In such places the flying-machine will perform much work now done by packhorse and mule, and open up sections where even the mule is useless for transit purposes. One of the greatest obstacles to transportation in Alaska are certain large areas of 'nigger-heads'—flat stretches resembling swamps, with a growth similar to cabbage-heads, which neither man nor beast can negotiate, and across which neither railroads nor highways can be built. These obstructions, of course, will present no difficulty to the aeroplane."

"Will the aeroplane be useful for carrying mails?"

"Not to the extent that some people suppose," said Mr. Wright. "I do not think it will supplant the steamship and the railroad as a mail-carrier, because it will be too expensive. It would take a very large number of flying-machines, perhaps a hundred, to carry as much mail as we now get into a mail-car. You can easily figure how this would increase the expense. It will have the same advantage in carrying mails as in carrying passengers, and that is speed. This statement also needs some qualification, for, when it comes to quick communication, the aeroplane can never supplant the telegraph and the telephone. But we shall probably have a special rapid mail service by aeroplane, for which we shall pay a higher price and buy a special stamp. The flying-machine will give a ten-hour service between New York and Chicago and a two-day service from the Atlantic to the Pacific. It will likewise carry letters into remote sections which the mail now reaches only at long intervals or does not reach at all. The United States still has a large number of 'star routes'—routes which the mail-carrier travels on horseback, sometimes consuming days in the journey. The aeroplane can do all this work much more cheaply and much quicker. It goes in a straight line, whereas the star route man has usually to take a roundabout course, for mountains and rivers offer the flying-machine no obstacles.

"In Mexico we have had an example of the use of the aeroplane for carrying mails. Practically all the mails from Columbus, New Mexico, to Pershing's column have been carried by air.[4] My friend, Mr. Glenn Martin,[5] who spent several days down there, tells an incident that illustrates the mail- carrying possibilities of this new contrivance. While visiting Captain [Townsend F.] Dodd, commanding officer of the First Aero Squadron, stationed at Pershing's supply headquarters in Columbus, Mr. Martin and several officers were standing on the field one morning when a message came saying that Lieutenant [Thomas S.] Bowen had left Pershing's station, one hundred and twenty miles south of the border, by aeroplane with mail-matter. Captain Dodd related that a daily mail-route was maintained by air. Looking to the south the captain pointed out a familiar dust-cloud which followed the truck-trains, making trips to and from Pershing's station. The great contrast to the truck-train they were looking at was very striking at this particular time, as the message just received from Pershing said that Lieutenant Bowen was leaving his headquarters by aeroplane. On the horizon was a truck-train which had been on the way two days and a half and was still a half-day out of Columbus. An hour and twenty-two minutes later Lieutenant Bowen arrived and spiraled into the field. The incident was passed over until train time, eleven-thirty, the hour Mr. Martin was leaving Columbus for New York. As the train pulled out the dust-cloud following the truck-train was still approaching from the south; apparently it was still two or three hours away. It had taken the aeroplane not an hour and a half to make the trip; and the truck-train, covering the same distance, had been two and a half days and had not yet arrived.

"Aeroplanes in Mexico also carried extra officers from one headquarters to another, and important personal matter and express between the two bases."

"But how about the aeroplane as a sport?" I asked.

"I think," Mr. Wright replied, "that it is the greatest sport yet devised. It is far more exhilarating and delightful than the automobile for high speed, and far safer. The time is not far distant when people will take their Sunday-afternoon spins in their aeroplane precisely as they do now in their automobiles. Long tours in the air will offer greater relaxations from the daily grind than long railway journeys. People need only recover from the foolish impression that it is a dangerous sport, instead of being, when adopted by rational persons, one of the safest. It is also far more comfortable. The driver of an automobile, even under the most favorable circumstances, lives at a constant nerve tension. He must keep always on the lookout for obstructions in the road, for other automobiles, and for sudden emergencies. A long drive is therefore likely to be an exhausting operation. Now the aeroplane has a great future for sporting purposes because this element of nerve tension is absent. The driver enjoys the proceeding as much as his passengers, and probably more. He can make mistakes, even lapse in his attention, without any serious consequences. Winds no longer terrorize the airman. Newspaper readers will remember that, ten years ago, my brother and I carefully selected the days in which we made our flights. Some days, when there was too much wind, we would not fly at all. But we have learned now how to fly, and even strong gales do not now frighten the flyer. He goes up except in the very bad days. The only wind conditions that deter him now are the kind known as 'cyclonic,' when there are great twists in the atmosphere. Under these circumstances he does not fly."

In conclusion, Mr. Wright made one of his most interesting statements.

"Aeroplaning, as a sport," he said, "will attract women as well as men. Indeed, in such aviators as have come to my attention, I find that a larger proportion of women make good flyers than men. I would hardly hazard the statement that women are better aviators—merely that I have found this to be the case in those whom I have met. Just why this should be so I do not know; yet there is a fascination and exhilaration in flying that appeals strongly to the feminine mind. Women also make excellent passengers. I have never yet taken up one who was not extremely eager to repeat the experience. This fact, of course, will hasten the day when the aeroplane will be a great sporting and social diversion."

---

1. *Harper's Magazine,* April 1917, 609–19.
2. See document 53, note 10.
3. See document 53, note 2.
4. In March 1916 rebels led by the Mexican revolutionary Pancho Villa raided Columbus, New Mexico. In response to this and other previous incidents, the United States launched a punitive expedition led by General John J. Pershing. The U.S. Army's First Aero Squadron was deployed to Columbus in support of Pershing's troops.
5. Glenn L. Martin built and flew his first airplane in 1910. He quickly became a well-known exhibition pilot and was among the first prominent aviators in California. In 1912 he formed the Glenn L. Martin Company of Los Angeles and began manufacturing aircraft. After disputes with his financial backers and members of the board of directors, he quit and formed a new Glenn L. Martin Company in 1917 in Cleveland and shortly thereafter moved his operation to Baltimore, Maryland. Martin was one of the few pre–World War I aircraft manufacturers to stay in the business after the war, and he

became a major player in the burgeoning U.S. aircraft industry in the late 1920s and into World War II. See John R. Breihan, "From Amusements to Weapons: The Glenn L. Martin Aircraft Company of California, 1910–1917," *Journal of the West* 36 (July 1997): 29–38.

56 • ORVILLE WRIGHT SAYS 10,000 AEROPLANES WOULD END THE WAR WITHIN TEN WEEKS[1]

Interview with Orville Wright

When Orville Wright, inventor of the flying machine and the first man in the world to fly, was asked to express his opinion as to the probable effect of an efficient carrying out of the Aircraft Production Board's plan for an appropriation of $630,000,000 for 35,000 airplanes and thousands of aviators, he replied that, as the war was now being run absolutely from above, the United States could win it in the air. Ten thousand flying machines, he said, would end the war in ten weeks.[2]

Mr. Wright has fitted up an experimental laboratory in Dayton, Ohio,[3] at his own expense, is running it at his own expense, and offers entirely free of cost to all persons engaged in helping the Government obtain the tremendous air fleet required to defeat Germany any advice or other assistance, including the making of laboratory tests, that he has it in his power to give. He is busy today, with a few assistants, including Charles E. Taylor,[4] who has been with the Wrights since 1900[5] as chief mechanician, working out new problems which are presenting themselves to the flying men at the front. From that scientific centre, discoveries which will tend further to perfect all kinds of aircraft may therefore be expected to come.

It was in Dayton that Mr. Wright talked about the Government's airplane program and the outlook for victory in the air.

"It is my opinion," he said, "that a large airplane fleet is the way to stop the war. If it were possible for the United States to deliver tomorrow several thousand flying machines in France, the war would be won by the Allies in a few weeks. The way to stop the war is simply to drive the Germans from the skies, and this can be done only by a preponderance of fighting machines. By fighting machines I mean little airplanes carrying one man and a rapid-fire machine gun.

"When the Germans have been driven out of the air, the Allies will be supreme and the war will end. To do this we need a great number of small airplanes of the sort that have successfully chased the Zeppelins. At present the difference between five years or more of war and an early victory for the Allies is ten thousand airplanes.

"How long the war will last depends therefore on the capacity we show in coping with the very great problem of producing without unnecessary delay the small fighting machines needed at the front. The Allies long since obtained control in the air, but their present advantage in this respect falls short of being an overwhelming superiority.

"We have the industrial plants which could soon be adapted for the turning out of airplane motors. We have the men to supervise the industry, the inventive genius to adapt and improve upon the developments that have been made abroad, and, now that we are assured of the money to pay for the labor and material, there seems no reason to doubt that in a year hence we will have sent abroad thousands of fighting airplanes that will be better than anything yet produced.[6]

"The reason for this optimistic feeling is that the United States will immediately go about the business of making a huge airplane fleet, and go about it in a businesslike way. Heretofore, airplane development in this country has been seriously handicapped by the fact that the problem has not been attacked in a large way by men with money. At the present time, due to the exceptional need for straining every nerve to win the war, the airplane industry will benefit by the expert advice of various large manufacturers experienced in great output production.

"The country will also be helped by advice of men from the front who have been actually flying in fighting machines.

"The business men who will handle the tremendous problem of assembling the machines and motors are public-spirited and already have expressed their willingness to forego any personal profit, many of them even making extraordinary sacrifices in order that there may be organized at once a harmoniously working airplane industry, which will mean victory for the Allies and the end of the war.

"To my mind there is not the slightest doubt that the personnel of the Aircraft Production Board, in charge of the work of getting to the other side enormous quantities of airplanes, is of such calibre as to assure all of us that they will carry on the undertaking until the entire program has been put through. The men of this board have made a habit of success; each man on it has a record of definite accomplishment in whatever he has undertaken. And these men are working night and day, without salary and to the financial detriment, of course, of the concerns of which they are the moving spirits. They are actuated by no motives other than that there shall be assembled the greatest number of airplanes of the best sort in the least time.

"The civilian members of the Aircraft Production Board, which is the sole organization charged by the Government with the business of getting together the required number of airplanes, being responsible only to President Wilson's Cabinet, are Howard E. Coffin, Chairman; E. A. Deeds, former Vice President and General Manager of the National Cash Register Company and now at the head of industries in Dayton doing an annual business of $80,000,000; Sidney D. Waldon, formerly Vice President of the Packard Motor Company, and Robert L. Montgomery, senior partner of the banking firm of Montgomery, Clothier & Tyler of New York and

Philadelphia. The army is represented by Brig. Gen. George O. Squier, and the navy by Rear Admiral David W. Taylor.[7]

"The spirit of co-operation which they have discovered to exist among the various manufacturers to whom they have talked with a view to utilizing their plants for an intensive production of machines has really been wonderfully fine. The automobile industry, which is one of the best organized in the world, already has shown a keen desire to help.

"Owing to the backwardness of this country in airplane development from the manufacturing standpoint, it will be necessary, to call upon the automobile industry for probably nine-tenths of the production needed. The existing airplane plants will, of course, receive as much of the work as they are capable of turning out; but they have not the equipment to handle this large program."

"Do you think that it would be possible and expedient to attempt to blow up Germany's submarine bases with bombs dropped from airplanes?" Mr. Wright was asked.

"That would not stop the war," he replied. "Suppose you did blow up the submarine bases, suppose you sunk every submarine today—that would not end the war. It would mean ease of mind for England, of course, because of the freedom from fear of a lack of food, but the German Army would still be as strong as ever on the western front.

"I have never considered bomb-dropping as the most important function of the airplane, and I have no reason to change this opinion now that we have entered the war. The situation shows that, as a result of the flying machines' activities, every opposing General knows precisely the strength of his enemy and precisely what he is going to do. Thus surprise attacks, which for thousands of years have determined the event of war, are no longer possible. When the United States sends enough airplanes abroad to bring down every German airplane that attempts to ascertain the disposition of the armies of the Allies—literally sweeps from the heavens every German flying machine—the war will be won, because it will mean that the eyes of the German gunners have been put out.

"It is probable that Germany can be whipped without airplanes if we take time enough. But in that case five years would find us still at the job. To accomplish the desired end as soon as possible, the United States must be able to equip the Allies, between now and a year from now, with a vast air fleet. It is, by the way, the one thing that the United States can do and do quickly. If, for instance, we could have 10,000 machines at the front tomorrow morning it would be far more effective than sending, if we were able, 1,000,000 men. If we could drop 1,000 airplanes and aviators over there today, everybody in Germany would know before night that we were there.

"We are bringing over to this country foreign motors which have stood up against the rigors of war usage, and these will be duplicated here. Our plants, when the proper adjustments are made, will be able to make quickly the motors needed for our battleplanes.

"Another encouraging feature of the entire situation is that there are men from this country now at work in foreign motor factories obtaining the required experience and information based on the accurate knowledge obtained by the Allies in actual conflict under all conditions.

"One of our biggest tasks in this country is going to be the taking over of the business of schooling aviators assigned to the battle fronts. This will enable the foreign factories to give their full time to manufacturing airplanes. Teaching aviators will not interfere with the work of our Government in assembling the machine for which the money will be appropriated.

"When I was in Europe in 1907 military authorities told me that when an airplane was three thousand feet up there was no anti-aircraft gun in existence that could reach it. Now machines at eighteen thousand feet—about three and one-half miles—make successful targets. This is one example of the great advance which the war has made in the development of both airplanes and guns."

"Do you think that with such a large fleet of flying machines as it is contemplated for this country to send abroad it will be possible to devastate Germany by flying over it?" Mr. Wright was asked.

"When this country has sent abroad an immense air fleet it may not be practicable, even though it were possible, to cover the entire German nation and destroy it with dynamite bombs. This would mean flights of at least five hundred miles, or one thousand miles counting the return trip. This, of course, would require a great quantity of ammunition and equipment. I mean by this that when the end of the journey was reached there would scarcely be enough ammunition aboard to justify the long flight.

"But there is one thing that could be done to the very great disadvantage of the German Government. Essen, the site of the Krupp Gun Works, is only about 150 miles from the present line of battle. This could be reached, bombarded, and put out of business. Raids could be conducted against other business and population centres in Western Germany, producing upon her irreparable injury.

"I am convinced that while, under existing conditions, the German line is practically impregnable, if once you give the Allies unchallenged supremacy in the air, a way will be found to break through the Teuton lines and get in behind them. Because, don't you see, by doing this the Allies will have made the German gunfire ineffective? It is the accuracy of aim now possible to both sides that results in such widespread destruction. Gunners on both sides now hit the mark because of the presence of airplanes to direct the fire. Take from Germany her aerial aids, and immediately they would begin to do what most hurts the feelings of a German; that is, they would begin to waste ammunition and time. The war is being run absolutely from above.

"France and England have spent millions in experimental work and with satisfactory results. Naturally, with such an incentive as they have had since August, 1914, they have made improvements, especially in the building of motors, and are far ahead of us at the present moment. One foreign motor in particular weighs only 374 pounds, has developed 150 horse power, and has the important quality of durability. This motor has given certain war airplanes a speed of 125 miles an hour, and with it the aviator can climb 10,000 feet in ten minutes.

"Germany all along has been conservative both of men and airplanes. She has not taken nearly so many chances as the Allies. Nobody seems to know how many machines she has in operation, but it is fair to say that, needing munitions and other supplies as badly as she does, she cannot manufacture flying machines any faster, at least, than France and England. I think it is conceded that the Central Powers cannot any more than compete with their opponents in the manufacture of airplanes. Therefore, the United States in this regard holds the balance of power.

"There are many things for us to learn in addition to the industrial problem of standardizing parts, speeding up production, and seeing that the flying machines reach the other side after they are built. Training aviators to endure the vicissitudes of flight under such abnormal conditions is, next to supplying our allies with the machines themselves, the greatest work of all. This phase of our cooperation will be carried on, with success I am sure, in the large training fields which are being laid out and developed as rapidly as possible by the War Department."

The largest of these training fields to be established by the United States War Department lies about eight miles northeast of Dayton. It contains four square miles of territory, beautifully situated. A bit of sentiment is found in the circumstance that it includes the original testing grounds of the Wright Brothers at what was then known as Simms Station. The old airplane shed is to be left standing in this cow pasture.[8] A mile and a half away 3,000 men, under the supervision of Captain Warring, of the United States Army Signal Corps, are employed in erecting forty hangars, which will house 240 flying machines, barracks for officers and men, mess halls, and so on, and in tearing down houses, barns, fences, and other obstructions on the 2,500-acre field. This training ground has been named the Wilbur Wright Field.

The Government has just started the construction of an airplane supply depot on that field to cost $700,000. It is authoritatively asserted that Dayton, which gave the flying machine to the world, will in the greatest war of the world be the centre of the flying-machine development from the point of view of supplying aircraft to the Allies, training soldiers and civilians to fly, and in research work, at which Orville Wright is engaged without interruption and in entire sympathy with the aims of the members of the Aircraft Production Board.

In addition to the Wilbur Wright Field, there is also, northeast of Dayton, about a mile and a half from the centre of the town, another aviation ground known as Wright Field, where civilians are to be trained.[9] Two other training grounds are south of Dayton, so that four large flying fields are in the immediate vicinity of the city. The visitor is impressed with the fact that things in this region will make appear all the more strange in the near future the figures of United States aeronautical activity for the eight years preceding the war, when the army ordered fifty-nine airplanes and received fifty-four. In 1916 it ordered 366 planes and received 64. Nine factories produced this output. It is believed in some quarters that we need forty to fifty aeronautical centres. We have at this writing four. Great Britain has 107.

As to what would be his contribution to the work of helping get together the flying machines which he thought would solve the whole problem for the Allies, Mr. Wright said:

"Several months before the United States entered the war I built, at my own expense, the experimental laboratory, fully equipped with machinery and the necessary testing devices, in order to do what I had long wished—spend my whole time in my own way, subject to nobody's rightful interference, in research work. For years after my brother and I invented the airplane we were both too busy demonstrating and perfecting it, and in the actual business of manufacturing, to devote much time to original research in aeronautics.

"The laboratory is amply large for the kind of experiments I wish to continue to make. I am rather of the opinion that the type of measuring instrument used by Wilbur and myself in 1901 gave results as accurate as those in the possession of any laboratories today. I have peculiarly good reasons for thinking that this is true.

"I will work in hearty co-operation with the members of the Aircraft Production Board. Already I am on terms of intimate confidential relations with these men who have undertaken the gigantic problem of putting the airplanes over on the other side. I am hopeful that in this way, and by giving free of all cost any information in my possession to all applicants who are behind the Government in doing this work, I may be of help. The laboratory will make any tests free of charge. The data which we have obtained in all experimental and practical work are at the service of the United States Government."

---

1. *New York Times Magazine*, July 1, 1917, 1–2.
2. After the United States declared war in April 1917, the Aircraft Production Board was formed on May 16 to assist and advise the military services and manufacturers on design and production of aircraft and engines. On July 24 Congress approved an appropriation

of $639,241,258 for military aviation. Approximately half of this amount was for aircraft and engine manufacture. The rest was for other types of support equipment and facilities, training, armament, and other overhead.

3. See document 53, note 10.
4. See document 10, note 3.
5. Taylor was employed by the Wrights in June 1901, not 1900.
6. In light of the obvious U.S. potential for mass production, many observers, including Orville Wright, forecast that a rapidly created air armada built in the United States would reach Europe in a short time. Because of the complexity of aircraft design and construction, underestimation of the demands of retooling American automobile manufacturing plants and expanding the existing small aircraft plants, and problems of bureaucracy and corruption, however, the actual U.S. output during the war was far below the optimistic estimates. Moreover, of those aircraft that were produced, few were advanced designs. For details on U.S. aircraft production during World War I, see Edgar S. Gorell, *The Measure of America's World War Aeronautical Effort* (Burlington, Vt.: Lane Press, 1941), and R. M. McFarland, *History of the Bureau of Aircraft Production* (Maxwell AFB, Ala.: Historical Studies Office, Air Material Command, Maxwell Air Force Base, 1951).
7. Howard Coffin and Edward Deeds of the Aircraft Production Board were not the disinterested parties that Orville Wright suggested. Both had major industrial manufacturing and business interests and stood to benefit enormously from the large government wartime investment in aviation. Carefully arranged holding companies obfuscated any obvious conflict of interest, enabling Coffin and Deeds to administer government aircraft contracts with one hand and receive the profits with another. Troubled over the low production output in light of the huge expenditures, after the war Congress investigated the aircraft industry, including the personal roles of Coffin and Deeds. See U.S. Justice Department, "Report of Aircraft Inquiry," in *Hughes Report,* 1918. Although his involvement amounted to little more than lending his famous name, Orville Wright was a partner with Deeds and others in the Dayton-Wright Airplane Company, which did receive government contracts during the war. Orville was never implicated in any wrongdoing.
8. The Wrights began flying at Simms Station, or Huffman Prairie as it was also known, in 1904. They built a hangar on the field at that time. In 1910, when they began training pilots at Huffman Prairie for the Wright exhibition team, a larger hangar was built on a different spot. This is the hangar to which the interviewer is referring here. It was finally torn down in the late 1930s or early 1940s as part of a renovation project of Wright-Patterson Air Force Base, on whose premises the brothers' old flying field lies. The precise location of the hangar is unknown. Huffman Prairie, the site of the brothers' flying experiments in 1904, 1905, and 1910, remains largely undeveloped. It is the only Wright brothers' site that still appears much as it did in the Wrights' time. For further details on the field, see Dwain K. Butler, Janet E. Simms, and Daryl S. Cook, "Archaeological Geophysics Investigation of the Wright Brothers' 1910 Hangar Site," *Geoarchaeology: An International Journal* 9, no. 6 (1994): 437–66.
9. In 1948 Wilbur Wright Field was merged with Wright Field, Huffman Prairie, the Fairfield Air Depot, and Patterson Field to form the expansive Wright-Patterson Air Force Base, one of the largest military and aerospace research installations in the world.

57 • SAYS AIRCRAFT WILL WIN WAR[1]
Interview with Orville Wright

When Orville and Wilbur Wright built and flew the first man-carrying flying machine, they believed they were making wars impossible. Now, with the greatest war in history at a deadlock because of the equality of aerial equipment, a great increase in the allied aerial forces is the one way to end it, Orville Wright asserts. In indorsing the program of the aircraft production board,[2] Mr. Wright declares that "if the Allies' armies are equipped with such a number of airplanes as to keep the enemy planes entirely back of the line, so that they are unable to direct gunfire or to observe the movement of the allied troops it will be possible to end the war."

"When my brother and I built and flew the first man-carrying machine," said Mr. Wright, "we thought that we were introducing into the world an invention which would make further wars practically impossible. Nevertheless, the world finds itself in the greatest war in history. Neither side has been able to win on account of the part the airplane has played. Both sides know exactly what the other is doing. The two sides are apparently nearly equal in aerial equipment, and unless present conditions can be changed the war will continue for years.

"However, if the Allies' armies are equipped with such a number of aeroplanes as to keep the enemy planes entirely back of the line, so that they are unable to direct gunfire or to observe the movement of the allied troops—in other words, if the enemy's eyes can be put out—it will be possible to end the war. This is not taking into account what might be done by bombing German sources of munition supplies, such as Essen, which is only about 150 miles behind the fighting lines. But to end the war quickly and cheaply, the supremacy in the air must be so complete as to entirely blind the enemy.

"The program laid down by the aircraft production board, if carried out, will obtain this result. The business organization and manufacturing equipment of our country offer the facilities for carrying out this program, and I believe that by no other method can the war be ended with so little loss of life and property."

1. *Aerial Age Weekly,* July 9, 1917, 563.
2. See document 56, notes 2 and 6.

58 • WRIGHT TO MAKE AEROS FOR COMMERCIAL USE[1]
Interview with Orville Wright

Dayton, O.

Orville Wright is ready to announce an invention that will revolutionize the manufacture of aeroplanes and make them cheap as "flivvers,"[2] it was reported here recently.

"I'm experimenting with wing models to increase the efficiency of plane surfaces," Wright told an interviewer. "Big battle planes don't interest me very much, except that I know they are needed to end the war, so we may tackle the aeroplane for the uses of peace.

"What is wanted is a comparatively low powered machine, say, of 100 horsepower, whose wing surfaces are so efficient and whose inherent stability is so high it will not require a big field to alight in.

"After the war flying will become safe, popular and comparatively cheap. As soon as the war is over I expect to see the whole country mapped out with air highways. Along these routes, say every seven miles, there will be alighting stations and hangars.

"With these airdromes so near to each other as this, it always will be easy for an aviator to make a safe landing in case of engine trouble. While flying a half to a mile above ground—a modest altitude nowadays—it will be easy to glide to safety if you are stalled midway between stations.

"We already have an air route between here and Indianapolis, with airdromes seven miles apart, and I am looking forward to the rapid extension of this system as soon as the war is over."

1. *Aerial Age Weekly,* October 29, 1917, 280.
2. This was a nickname for the Ford Model T automobile.

59 • THE FUTURE OF CIVIL FLYING[1]
Orville Wright

Fifteen years have passed on Dec. 17, 1918, since Orville Wright and his late brother Wilbur startled an incredulous world with the announcement that they had achieved the conquest of the air by the invention of a heavier-than-air craft, the airplane. That forever memorable day which, for the first time in history of the world, saw a machine heavier than air, and carrying a human pilot, raise itself from the ground, fly under full control, and land again at the will of the pilot, today appears almost shrouded in the dim past of history, so common has the sight of an airplane become to the public. The fact that the airplane proved one of the most effectual weapons in the defense of Civilization should compensate for the sorrow that may be felt at the airplane being used for destruction before it could demonstrate its usefulness in peaceful pursuits.

Now that the din of arms has ceased and a rightful peace is soon to be established, the airplane promises to soon enter a new era of its development, which will be characterized by the advent of commercial aviation and civil

flying. The following article, written especially for *Aviation and Aeronautical Engineering,* is of exceptional interest as expressing the views the Dean of Aviation holds with respect to the principal problems which confront the establishment of civil aeronautics.

Although it is now fifteen years since the first flight was made with a heavier-than-air machine, the use of the airplane for commerce and sport has developed but little. This failure has been accounted for in several ways. It has been said that the expense of owning and maintaining a flying machine is too great. This possibly has been true so far as the commercial use was concerned, but it certainly does not account for the small amount of use for sport. While the first cost of the airplane is slightly greater, and its upkeep a good deal greater, than that of the automobile, yet its cost in both of these respects is very much less than that of a yacht. It really is no greater than the expense of a comparatively small motor boat. We have thousands of young men in the country who easily have been able to afford that expense.

The failure of the airplane for sport really has been due, in my opinion, to the fact that it was not sufficiently safe for the purposes for which the sportsman wished to use it. For many years the structure and control of the airplane have been such as to make it thoroughly safe while in flight. So long as one did not venture away from the flying field, there was no danger. However, the sportsman is not content to fly round and round over his flying field. He wants to get about and see the country; and one who has never been up in a flying machine or balloon has little idea how beautiful this earth really is. He wants to travel from city to city. Flying over a single field, although incomparably more exhilarating and pleasant, is somewhat like driving an automobile on a race track only; in time it becomes more or less monotonous.

In order to create a real sport it will be necessary to provide means for flying cross-country without risk. There are several ways in which this can be accomplished:

1. The perfection of the flying machine and motor to that degree where forced landings will never be necessary.

2. The establishment of distinctly marked and carefully prepared landing places at such frequent intervals that one could always be reached in case of the sudden stoppage of the motor.

3. The development of airplanes of such design as to permit of landing in any ordinary field encountered in cross-country flying.

The first of these methods can hardly be utilized at the present time. Perfection in design and construction can only be arrived at through long experience and use, and experience and use can only be secured through perfection in design and construction.

The second method, while in many respects the more desirable of the three, is not easy of accomplishment on account of the expense involved. When flying at a height of one mile one can glide a distance of six to eight miles in any direction after the motor has stopped, to reach a landing place. Therefore, to make flying perfectly safe, good landing places must be provided every ten or twelve miles. For the high speed machines, such as are generally used today, these fields would have to be very smooth and measure at least a half mile on each side. The preparing of the surface of reasonably flat ground is an expensive undertaking, as has been shown in the preparation of the several training fields established by the Government. The improvement costs more than the land itself. There also would be a continuous expense for upkeep.

But when these landing places are once provided then flying will become common, not only for sport but for commercial purposes as well. Several times lately the trip from Dayton, Ohio, to Washington, D.C., has been made by airplane in three hours. The best time from Dayton to Washington by rail is sixteen hours. And a few days ago a flight was made from Dayton to New York in four hours and ten minutes—less than one-fourth the best time by rail. Such flights would be exceedingly common if it were not for the danger involved in flying over ground where, if the motor should stop suddenly, no safe landing place would be within reach. Fields sufficiently large and smooth for our present high speed machines are exceedingly rare. But with the excellent motors and planes which have been developed as a result of the war forced landings would probably not occur once in a hundred such trips; yet one chance in a hundred is entirely too big a risk to take, if one expects to continue flying for long.

More and more landing places will, no doubt, be provided as the use of the airplane increases, but its use is heavily handicapped until these landing places are provided. In fact, unless undertaken by the Government, they cannot be realized for many years. For this reason the third plan seems the more feasible for the immediate future.

To land safely in ordinary fields a machine must either be able to fly at very low speeds or it must have some provision of coming to stop quickly after it once touches the ground. The space required to stop after touching the ground is approximately in proportion to the square of the landing speed. An airplane which can fly and land with a speed as low as 30 miles an hour will run approximately only one-fourth as far on the ground as if it were to land at a speed of 60 miles an hour. For landing at 30 miles an hour a field eight or nine hundred feet square is sufficient; for landing at 60 miles an hour a field three or four thousand feet on a side would be necessary. The area of the field for the higher speed would be sixteen times that of the field for the lower speed. A fifteen acre field would be sufficient for the slow speed machine, while a 240 acre field would be needed for the higher. Clear fields one-half mile or more square are exceedingly rare.

Not only does the high-speed machine require a large field, but it also requires a very smooth surface for landing. The shock of landing increases with the square of the speed. A bump on the ground will produce a strain four times as great when landing at 60 miles as it does when the landing is made at 30 miles an hour. This advantage in favor of the slow machine is even greater than that due to the difference in the size of the fields required.

There are several ways in which the space required for landing may be reduced. One would be by using machines of large wing area and very low flying speeds. Another would be by providing some kind of brake to check the speed of the machine after it touches the ground. This has been attempted a number of times but usually with rather disastrous results. When a brake is applied to the wheels, a little more pressure on one wheel than the other causes the machine to swerve from its course, often breaking the wings or the landing gear. Checking the speed by means of a reversible propeller has been suggested, but this has several serious drawbacks. In the first place no reversible propeller of practical construction has as yet been produced, and in the second place such a propeller would be of no use in forced landings after the motor had stopped. A third and much more difficult method would be by means of a machine that would rise and descend vertically. Experienced engineers look upon this method with the least favor on account of its many difficulties.

The airplane has already been made abundantly safe for flight. The problem before the engineer today is that of providing for safe landing.

---

1. *Aviation and Aeronautical Engineering*, January 1, 1919, 676.

60 • SPORTING FUTURE OF THE AIRPLANE: REDUCED LANDING SPEEDS AN ESSENTIAL FACTOR[1]

Orville Wright

The use of the airplane for sport has fallen short of the predictions made for it ten years ago by its most conservative adherents. I believe this has been mostly due to the craze for speed. There were more fliers who flew merely for sport in 1909 and 1910 than there are today, although the present machines are more controllable, better constructed and more reliable in almost every way. The design of the present-day machines provides for greater comfort, and also for greater safety in rough landings.

On the other hand the fields on which our present fast machines can land without some kind of a smash are extremely rare. The size of the field required now is approximately fifteen times what it was in 1910. This is due to the higher landing speeds today. In fact, there is always a pretty good chance of an accident, though not necessarily a serious one, in nearly every landing now, unless the landing is made upon a specially prepared field. The fast machines are perfectly safe when flown over specially prepared fields, but there are only a small number of such fields in the entire country. It is this uneasiness about safe landings that has spoiled flying as a sport.

The same craze for speed possessed the automobilist in the early days. But the automobile did not come into much use for sport until that craze had subsided. We now have the same problem in the flying sport. If we can be satisfied with speeds from thirty to seventy-five miles an hour for a few years, I believe there is no question about a big use being developed. It is true that the high speed machine possesses a number of advantages over the low speed. But the high speed machine as designed today is dangerous in landing; and landing is almost the only dangerous thing about ordinary flying. Increased speed will gradually come with use.

There are a number of ways in which slower speeds may be attained. The simplest way is to increase the area of the planes so that sufficient lift can be obtained at slow speeds. It takes a great increase in area of wings per pound of weight carried to have much effect on the landing speed. Increasing the wing area four times, without any increase in total weight, would reduce the landing speed only to one-half. At the same time the landing speed of the machine is being reduced, the maximum speed is also reduced and in the same proportion. The maximum speed of an airplane is but little more than twice its minimum speed, excepting in machines of very high power in proportion to weight.

If the wing area could be varied while in flight, a large area could be used in starting and landing, and a smaller area when flying at high speeds. This would give a greater variation between the minimum and maximum speeds. No good mechanical means have as yet been discovered for varying the wing area, since it is essential that the general efficiency of the wing be not impaired by the device through which the area variation is accomplished.

A changeable wing camber[2] would also be advantageous; but the maximum reduction in speed to be had in this way is not more than twenty or twenty-five per cent.

If the machine could be lifted vertically by means of lifting screws, landings could be made in extremely small areas. However, this is a most difficult problem. Besides, in case the motor should stop this system would be useless. Moreover the weight that can be lifted in this way is very small in comparison with the power used. One hundred pounds of thrust of the propeller will sustain about eight hundred pounds in the ordinary type machine. But the same propeller giving a thrust of one hundred pounds in a vertical direction would lift only one hundred pounds weight. Lifting screws must be of greater diameter and slow speed to be at all efficient. Since the weight of the propeller increases approximately with the cube of its diameter, not to mention the difficulties of gearing down, etc., the use of the propeller for lifting vertically is greatly handicapped.

Another course that is open to development is that of providing some means of checking the speed after the machine touches the ground. This possibly can be accomplished in a number of ways, although up to date nothing good has been designed. Brakes on the landing wheels have been tried, but not with success. A pressure slightly more on one wheel than on the other causes the machine to spin in a circle, often making it roll over on one wing.

Flaps, which can be turned so as to present large areas to the air in the forward direction in landing, have been proposed. But these have but little effect because the flaps require a high velocity in order to present any considerable resistance. Their resistance would vary with the square of the speed.

It has been proposed to release a large parachute in landing, and allow the machine to settle gently to the ground. An airplane weighing two thousand pounds would require a parachute of about eight thousand square feet to enable it to settle with a velocity of ten feet per second. Few airplanes can withstand a fall of ten feet per second without damage. This method appears so impracticable in many ways as to seem hardly worth consideration.

A propeller which would furnish a thrust in the reverse direction, after the machine had touched the ground, would be effective. Here the difficulties are mechanical. No one has as yet succeeded in making a reversible propeller which will stand use. Most of the reversible or variable pitch propellers have been made of metal. The metal quickly crystallizes.

Attempts have also been made to use the tail skid as a brake. The load carried on the tail skid is so slight that sufficient traction is not easily secured.

If enough landing places were available, present types of airplanes would be practicable both for sport and for commerce. But on account of the great cost involved we can hardly hope for them in the near future. It, therefore, seems more feasible to modify the machines, so that they can be landed on almost any ordinary field that one would encounter in the course of an extended cross-country flight.

---

1. *U.S. Air Service,* February 1919, 4–5.
2. "Camber" refers to the curvature of a wing profile.

61 • THE COMMERCIAL AIRPLANE[1]

Orville Wright

The last year has seen unusual activity in Aeronautics. With the close of the war the inventor and engineer turned his thoughts to the development of machines suitable for commerce and pleasure.

The war did a great service in the refinement of details of airplane construction, which is of permanent value. It also did wonders in the production of reliable motors of light weight; but the powers used in military airplanes were so great that not all of these motors are useful for commercial machines in the immediate future.

Airplanes developed for military use naturally are not well adapted for ordinary use. The requirements for war and peace are so different. In war, certain risks must be taken; in peace these risks will not be tolerated. In the military machine, high speed is a prime consideration, though it adds greatly to the danger of landing; in the machine of commerce, safety is of first importance, even if speed must be sacrificed to obtain it. If large, smooth landing fields were to be had at frequent intervals, landings could be made with safety at high speed; but until these fields are provided, the airplane must be built to land in the ordinary fields now available.

A great deal has been done in the past year toward the development of commercial machines. In some cases the high maximum speed has been sacrificed to allow of a low landing speed. In others the machines are provided with wings of variable camber in order to obtain large lifts at slow speeds for landing, and small drifts at high speeds. Such wing surfaces give a greater range between the minimum and the maximum speeds.[2] Ordinarily, the landing speed is not much less than one-half of the maximum speed of the machine. Experiments are being made in an endeavor to develop a reliable reversible propeller, so that the speed of the machine can be checked in steep descents for getting into a field, and the machine stopped after a short run on the ground.

A combination of some of these devices will no doubt permit of landings at speeds less than one-third of the maximum speed. In other words, flights can be made at one hundred miles an hour and landings at a speed of only thirty miles, a speed necessitating no special preparation or smoothing of the surface of the field, and requiring but a short run on the ground after landing. The shock of landing at thirty miles is barely over one-third of that at fifty miles, and requires a field of less than one-fourth the area of that for landing at fifty miles. These developments for safety in landing, I believe, are the most important contribution to the commercial use of airplanes made in the past year. The slower machines may be flown over ordinary country with perfect safety.

The last year has also witnessed a great development in the finish of the machine and in the luxuriousness of the accommodations furnished for travel by airplane. Probably the most important along this line is in the enclosed machines, which provide protection against oil and noise from the motor, and at the same time, give a better view of the landscape than has been possible heretofore.

Considerable advance has been made in the speed of airplanes, some of which are today travelling at nearly two hundred miles an hour. But this advance is not of so great importance commercially, because these fast machines have such high landing speeds, and cannot be used safely in even ordinary cross-country flying.

The distance that can be travelled in a single flight is likewise gradually increasing. Flights of five hundred to a thousand miles, without landing, are not uncommon. Much longer flights have been made, notably in the successful flights across the Atlantic.[3]

I think it can be safely said that the last year has seen the greatest advance yet made in the use of the airplane for pleasure and commerce.

---

1. *New York Aero Show Program,* March 1920 (clipping in Wright Papers, Manuscript Division, Library of Congress, Washington, D.C.).
2. The reference is to the development of the wing flap, a movable surface on the trailing edge of the wing; when deployed, the wing flap increases lift and allows for lower landing and diving speeds. In the early 1920s Orville Wright and James Jacobs, his old friend and colleague from the Wright Company, devised and patented an improved flap called the "split flap." The idea proved to be somewhat ahead of its time, however. In January 1922 the Navy Bureau of Aeronautics published a report on the innovation, "Air Force and Moment for Dayton-Wright Split-Flap Aerofoil," dismissing it as having no value. Orville was vindicated years later, however, when the navy was among the first to adopt the split flap. During World War II, the feature contributed greatly to the effectiveness of the famed Douglas SBD Dauntless dive-bomber and numerous other aircraft. The split flap was Orville's last significant technical contribution to aeronautics.
3. On May 31, 1919, the U.S. Navy–Curtiss Flying Boat NC-4, commanded by Lieutenant Commander Albert Read, completed the first transatlantic crossing by air. The flight was made in stages, with stops in Halifax, Nova Scotia; Trepassy Bay, Newfoundland; Horta and Ponta Delgada in the Azores; Lisbon, Portugal; and Ferrol del Caudiullo, Spain. Total flying time was 57 hours and 16 minutes. Later that year, on June 14 and 15, John Alcock and Arthur Whitten Brown made the first nonstop crossing of the Atlantic in a Vickers Vimy bomber, flying from St. John's, Newfoundland, to Clifden, County Galway, Ireland, in 16 hours and 27 minutes.

62 • LOW-SPEED LANDING IS FIRST NEED OF AVIATION[1]

Orville Wright

A machine capable of landing at such low speed as to make landing in small, fenced-in areas safe is the greatest need in practical aviation.

It is well known that this could be accomplished if some method were provided of changing the area of airplane wings while in flight without injuring their efficiency.

On the other hand, some of the advantages of a variable-area wing may be partly secured through more scientific knowledge of air flow about airplane wings, from which it might be possible to design wings of higher efficiency when flying at high speeds and of greater lift, per unit of area, at low speeds, so as to permit of slow landings. Another need is more accurate data for calculating the pressures on airplane wings when moving through the air at high speed.

---

1. *Popular Science Monthly,* February 1922, 68. Reprinted with the permission of *Popular Science,* Times Mirror Magazines, New York, N.Y.

63 • INVENTOR OF THE AIRPLANE DETAILS SOME OF EARLY EXPERIENCES IN RADIO MESSAGE TO WORLD[1]

Published transcription of message by Orville Wright

Twenty years' progress in the science of aviation formed the basis of a message given to the world by radio by Orville Wright, one of the inventors of the airplane, on the evening preceding the 20th anniversary of the conquering of the air by Mr. Wright and his brother, Wilbur.

The message was broadcasted from Station WLW, Cincinnati, and was heard by thousands of persons who had tuned in, in various sections of the country.

His talk was filled with reminiscences of the most interesting character while his review of the accomplishments of the airplane and its possibilities for the future formed a decidedly unusual lesson of instruction as well as one which did not lack of entertainment. He also made an appeal for support of the N.A.A.[2]

The text of his message follows:

"After several centuries of endeavor, just twenty years ago on the 17th of December, 1903, man for the first time succeeded in rising in free flight from the ground in a motored aeroplane.

"I shall not here attempt to enter into an account of the many causes of this long delay nor into a description of the manner in which this first flight was accomplished; but will confine myself to a consideration of some of the more important developments which have been achieved since that first flight, and to some speculations as to what may reasonably be expected of the aeroplane in the near future.

"The 1903 machine with operator weighed 750 pounds and was pushed by two propellers driven in opposite direction by automobile chains from a four-cylinder gasoline motor of twelve horse power. More than sixty pounds were carried per horse power. The standard machines of today weigh from two to four thousand pounds, and are driven by motors of one-hundred to five-hundred horse power.

First Air "Records"

"A single tractor propeller attached directly to the motor is now used. The weight carried per horse power in the modern aeroplane is usually between ten and twenty-five pounds, but recent contests in Europe have brought out several light planes which are reported to carry more than seventy-five pounds to the horse power.

"Four flights were made on the 17th of December, 1903, with this first plane. The longest flight in point of duration was of fifty-nine seconds. The greatest distance traversed was 852 feet, and the greatest altitude attained was between fifteen and twenty feet. A speed of thirty miles an hour, with reference to the air, was made in all of the flights, but the speed over the ground was only six to ten miles an hour, as the flights were all made against winds of more than twenty miles velocity.

"Today flights of over thirty-six hours' duration are on record, and a distance of over 2,500 miles has been covered in a single flight. Recently a speed of 265 miles an hour was attained; and the record of altitude, I believe, now stands at a little more than 36,000 feet.

"This comparison, however, is not an exact measure of the progress that has been made in the perfection of the aeroplane in the last twenty years, for it must be taken into consideration that at the same time my brother and I were trying out this first machine to see whether it would fly at all, we were also trying to learn to fly.

Were Inexperienced Flyers

"The termination of these first flights was brought about entirely by our inexperience as operators and not through any failure of the machine itself to perform. Speaking conservatively, the 1903 machine in the hands of an experienced operator was capable of a flight of 20 minutes or more, and of reaching an altitude of more than a thousand feet.[3] Thirty miles an hour, however, was practically its limit in speed.

"In our inexperienced hands that first machine resembled something between a bucking bronco and a roller coaster. We intended to fly it at a uniform height of about six feet from the ground, which we thought would be safest, but in some of its antics, in spite of all our efforts to keep it down it made its altitude record of a little more than fifteen feet.

"If the machine which Macready and Kelly used this year in making their endurance and distance records[4] had existed twenty years ago, when there were no trained pilots, and had been in the hands of a novice, I suspect it never would have left the ground at all, so much of its success depended upon the skill of the pilot; and there would have been another demonstration of the impossibility of flight.

"And if the racing plane used by Williams last October in making his speed record of 265 miles an hour[5] had been in the hands of a novice taking his first lesson in flight all by himself, any one can make a guess for himself whether he would have broken the 1903 record of fifty-nine seconds.

Improvement Has Been General

"The improvement in aeroplanes has been general. But probably in no respect has progress been so rapid as in the perfection of the mechanical and structural details of both motor and plane. This was bound to come as a result of practical experience and of the fine work of the thousands of engineering minds engaged in the designing and building of motors and planes during the war. To this improvement mostly is due the safety of flight of today.

"Progress along scientific lines has likewise been rapid. The establishment of aeronautical laboratories in many countries throughout the world has greatly contributed to the advancement of the science of aerodynamics. The result of this research has been a great reduction in the resistance encountered by the aeroplane in traveling through the air and a consequent reduction in the power required from the motor.

"Aviation offers little opportunity to the inventor with a happy idea. The improvement of the aeroplane is now the product of highly specialized work, and is becoming more so year by year.

Little Chance for Layman

"Of the thousands of suggestions offered in the last twenty years by the layman, I cannot think of one which has contributed materially to the improvement of the plane. I do not mean to discourage invention, but am merely trying to point out to the man on the street that however original and brilliant he may be, he has practically no chance of making any contribution of value in the field of aviation without first preparing himself by a thorough study of the general principles of aerodynamics.

"When one compares the uses of the aeroplane as imagined twenty years ago with the uses actually realized today, one hesitates to predict what its future may bring forth. Twenty years ago my brother and I thought that its use would be principally scouting in warfare, carrying mail, and other light loads to places inaccessible by rail or water, and sport. But the wildest stretch of the imagination of that time would not have permitted us to believe that within a space of fifteen years actually thousands of these machines would be in the air engaged in deadly combat.

"Our expectation of its value in scouting has been fulfilled. Surprise attacks which formerly won battles are now impossible. But we did not foresee the extent to which the aeroplane might be used in carrying the battle line to the industrial centers and into the midst of non-combatants, though we did think it might be used in dropping an occasional bomb about the heads of the rulers who declared war and stayed at home.

"The possibilities of the aeroplane for destruction by bomb and poison gas have been so increased since the last war, that the mind is staggered in attempting to picture the horrors of the next one. The aeroplane, in forcing upon governments a realization of the possibilities for destruction, has actually become a powerful instrument for peace.[6]

Warfare Revolutionized

"Not only has warfare on land been revolutionized by the aeroplane, but on water as well. Bombing tests have been conducted in the past two years at sea sixty miles off the Atlantic coast. Powerfully armored battleships were sunk with bombs dropped from the air into the water about them. These tests have demonstrated that direct hits are not necessary, and that no battleship, however armored, can be safe from attack from above unless a fleet of aeroplanes more powerful than the enemy's is provided to protect it.[7]

"For several years we have had an air mail service between New York and San Francisco. This service is operated the year round under every condition of wind and weather. For the period of twelve months ending June last over ninety-six per cent of the trips scheduled were carried out. In this service the flying is suspended during the hours of darkness, so that the advantage of the aeroplane over the railroad train in speed is partly lost.

"The train runs day and night. But a four-day test of carrying through mail by air between New York and San Francisco, utilizing twenty-four hours of the day, was carried out successfully last August. The test was purely experimental to determine the feasibility of night flying. Although the planes used were the regular day-service ones specially equipped, the night flying came through without a failure.

Men Kept in Training

"In the last three days of the test the mail was carried from coast to coast with an average of twenty-eight hours to the trip. The work being done by the Post Office Department in carrying mail by aeroplane serves not only a useful civil purpose, but at the same time is keeping a large number of aviators and air mechanics in training—a great asset in our national preparedness.

"The aeroplane is now also extensively used in regular passenger air lines, competing more or less with rail and water lines. In Europe there are a large number of these lines connecting all the principal centers of population. In America we have only one. Up to date these passenger lines have not been financially profitable to the operating companies except where the profit is derived from governmental help in the form of subsidies. Until greater confidence in the safety of flight is inspired in the public mind the patronage of these passenger lines will be too limited for profit.

"A bill known as the Winslow Bill to establish in the Department of Commerce a Bureau of Aeronautics which would have complete supervision of civil aviation, was introduced in the last Congress, but too late to receive consideration. A similar bill will come before the present Congress.[8]

"The bill is supported by all interested in aeronautical progress, including such organizations as the National Advisory Committee for Aeronautics, the National Aeronautic Association, and the Aeronautical Chamber of Commerce.

Believes in N.A.A.

"In closing, I wish to say a few words in regard to the National Aeronautic Association. At a Congress in Detroit in October, 1922, the National Aeronautic Association was organized. Delegates from every part of the country to the number of 350 were present. Prior to that time there was no organization in America which adequately represented the aeronautic interests as a whole.

"Some of the objects of the association are these: To encourage and advance the science and art of aeronautics; to aid and encourage the establishment of uniform and proper state and national laws to regulate aerial navigation; to supervise aeronautical sports, to establish the authenticity of air records; and to organize into a patriotic body the national sentiment supporting a comprehensive, definite, and orderly commercial and military-naval aeronautic program. The National Aeronautic Association is the American representative of the Federated Aeronautique Internationale.

"A nation-wide campaign for membership is now being inaugurated. If you are interested in the sport, art, or science of aeronautics, or in keeping our country's air program abreast of our economic and national activities for purposes of national security, you will be welcomed as a member."

---

1. *National Aeronautic Association Review,* January 1, 1924, 3. Reprinted with the permission of the National Aeronautic Association, Arlington, Va.
2. "N.A.A." was the National Aeronautic Association.
3. Orville was being overly optimistic here. The original 1903 powered airplane was highly unstable in pitch and very difficult to fly. As a measure of this difficulty it is useful to note that the Wrights did not match their best 1903 flight of fifty-nine seconds until the *forty-ninth* flight of their second powered airplane in 1904. Further, flights by accurate modern reproductions of the 1903 airplane in the hands of experienced pilots have thus far failed to come even close to the one long flight of the Wrights on December 17, 1903.
4. This "machine" was the Fokker T-2 aircraft in which the U.S. Army Air Service pilots Lieutenant John A. Macready and Lieutenant Oakley G. Kelly made the first nonstop fight across the United States on May 2 and 3, 1923, in 26 hours and 50 minutes. This airplane is in the collection of the National Air and Space Museum, Smithsonian Institution, Washington, D.C.
5. This was the Curtiss R2C-1 racing aircraft in which U.S. Navy Lieutenant Al Williams set a new world speed record in 1923. The actual date was November 4 (not October), and the precise speed was 266.5 mph.

6. See document 53, note 2.
7. The most significant of these tests to demonstrate the efficacy of airpower against naval vessels came on July 21, 1921, when Brigadier General William "Billy" Mitchell commanded a highly publicized mock bombing experiment using the anchored and unmanned ex-German battleship *Ostfriesland* as the target. Mitchell's airplanes sank the *Ostfriesland,* to much public acclaim. But critics suggested that the tests were not conclusive because the raid was not conducted under true combat conditions. For details on the Mitchell bombing tests, see Alfred F. Hurley, *Billy Mitchell: Crusader for Air Power* (Bloomington: Indiana University Press, 1975), 56–72.
8. The Winslow bill was reintroduced, but it died amid fierce congressional debate over government regulation of aviation. It was not until the passage of the Air Commerce Act in 1926 that broad-scale federal regulation of aviation began. For a history of federal aviation regulation in this period, see Nick A. Komons, *Bonfires to Beacons: Federal Civil Aviation Policy under the Air Commerce Act, 1926–1938* (Washington, D.C.: Smithsonian Institution Press, 1989).

64 • ORVILLE WRIGHT FORECASTS AIRCRAFT EXPANSION[1]

Testimony by Orville Wright before the Morrow Board[2]

Orville Wright, with his brother Wilbur inventor of the airplane and himself the first man in the world to fly, testified before the President's air commission on October 12. Chairman Dwight Morrow said to him: "We have asked you to appear before the Board because you, in a sense, are responsible for the whole problem. You and your brother taught men to fly. It will not be necessary to ask for your record. The work of your brother and yourself is known wherever men fly. It will be known in the future as long as men fly."

MR. WRIGHT: Not being a student of naval or military affairs, I shall not presume to make any suggestions as to the use of aircraft in warfare. I offer only a few suggestions, and none of them new, along the lines of civil aviation, in which I believe the National Government can and should take part immediately.

There are many other ways in which the Government can eventually participate, but I do not venture to make suggestions far in the future.

The promotion of civil aviation will serve two purposes: It will contribute to the happiness and welfare of the people and at the same time will build up a reserve for our national defense. The large body of skilled mechanics, of experienced aeronautical engineers, as well as the factories experienced and equipped for rapid output, which will be in existence, can be turned quickly to military uses in the emergency of war. Government money spent in building up such a reserve for national defense will not be wasted should war never occur. The greatest present drawback to the use of aircraft for civil purposes, such as commerce, mail, travel, and sport, is the lack of suitable air ports and suitable emergency landing fields.

Several of the larger cities now have the benefit of landing fields and a few others are planning to build and maintain fields at the expense of the municipalities. But it will be necessary to provide intermediate fields, to make flying between the larger cities safe. The smaller cities can not now afford to provide these intermediate fields. Money spent by the National Government in helping to provide these fields; in the equipping of the air ports properly; in marking and lighting the airways; in providing radio or other means of directing the course; and in furnishing meteorological reports to as many of the fields as is necessary, will be money well spent and will some day bring large returns.

The commercial use of aircraft brings out the need of regulations for the protection of the public. It is clear that this regulation should be uniform throughout the country and therefore should be by the National Government rather than by the States. I think this can be done best through one of the present governmental departments. The Department of Commerce is well suited to this. But some congressional legislation will be necessary to put the control of aerial transportation in that department.

I believe the examination and licensing of every pilot who engages in the transportation of passengers or merchandise, for pay, should be required. I also believe that proper precautions must be taken to insure the safe condition of the planes so used. If this is done by Government inspection the cost of such inspection should be at the expense of the public, which is being protected, so that it can not work a hardship on the small manufacturer or operator. For, it seems, everything should be done to encourage these small manufacturers and operators. I do not believe that the licensing of pilots or the inspection of planes should be required of any excepting those dealing with the public. I think it essential that Government regulation should not go too far at first. Further regulation can be added as experience demonstrates its necessity. What we need now is the beginning.

The success of our air mail, operating in every kind of weather, twenty-four hours of the day, demonstrates the practicability and usefulness of the airplane in peaceful pursuits in the future. Government aid, such as is now given to maritime commerce, will greatly hasten that day.

THE CHAIRMAN: Are there any questions of Mr. Wright?

SENATOR BINGHAM: Mr. Wright, what do you think of the statement that has been made that aeronautical engineering has become standardized?

MR. WRIGHT: I think it is changing every day.

THE CHAIRMAN: Do you think that the state of aeronautics is such as to require very considerable experimentation still to go on?

MR. WRIGHT: Oh, yes, indeed. I think that will be required for years and years. There has been a very rapid advance in the last five years, since the war.

SENATOR BINGHAM: It has just been recommended to this committee that money be spent for the purchase of planes and for the training of pilots and that the engineering field, McCook Field, for the Army, and the Naval Aircraft Factory be closed down.[3] Do you think that such a procedure would tend to better aeronautics?

MR. WRIGHT: I do not.

SENATOR BINGHAM: What do you think of the work being done by the engineering division of the Army?

MR. WRIGHT: I think it has been very good, all that could be expected.

SENATOR BINGHAM: You are satisfied that they have spent their money properly and made real advances?

MR. WRIGHT: I think so, as far as I have observed it.

SENATOR BINGHAM: What do you think of the value of racing and some of these other so-called stunts, such as flying across the Pacific and into the northern regions?

MR. WRIGHT: All attempts of that kind lead to the perfection of the machine. Each competitor does his best to improve the existing models. So that while some of them have no immediate use excepting in making a record, the development that has occurred in designing the machine, in producing such a machine, is used in civil aviation and, I suppose, in the branches of military aviation.

SENATOR BINGHAM: You feel, then, that it has been worth while to promote the national air races and similar things?

MR. WRIGHT: I believe heartily in them.

SENATOR BINGHAM: You spoke of the importance of the Government doing something for meteorology. How far do you think we ought to carry this?

MR. WRIGHT: I think that should be carried as it is found necessary. In flying cross-country the pilot is going out of one area possibly to another and storm area. He should have advice in advance as to what is ahead of him so that he can avoid the danger. I think at the present this could be provided for by having stations at some of the principal airports and furnishing charts to the intermediate stations, so that the pilot can pick up the information as he travels along.

THE CHAIRMAN: Any further questions?

MR. COFFIN: One question, Mr. Wright: In the commercial tour which finished in Detroit on Sunday afternoon a week ago in a driving rainstorm after covering 2,000 miles, eighteen started, as I remember it, and seventeen finished; what do you think of that sort of contest?

MR. WRIGHT: I believe in that also; very useful.

MR. COFFIN: Only one other thing, Mr. Chairman. We are hearing and have for years heard of the Wright brothers and their accomplishments, but we hear very little of Miss Katharine Wright, who, after all, was just as instrumental in developing the airplane as were the brothers.[4] I think we ought to at least be introduced to her. She is in the room.

THE CHAIRMAN: The Chairman apologizes to Mr. Wright for not recognizing the most valuable member of the family.

MR. WRIGHT: The apology is accepted.

THE CHAIRMAN: Are there any further questions?

MR. DURAND: Mr. Wright, I want to ask a little question: What, in your view, may be looked for in the near future along the line of advances in weight-carrying-capacity and radius of operation?

MR. WRIGHT: That has been gradually extending for the last six or seven years. I see no reason why it should not go on for some time to come, at least, at the same rate that it has been progressing.

MR. DURAND: That is, you look for a continuous development?

MR. WRIGHT: Up to a limit. There will be an ultimate limit. There will be a limit, but I do not feel that we have nearly reached that.

MR. DURAND: You would not feel like attempting to specify that limit?

MR. WRIGHT: No, I have not made a calculation of that kind and therefore would not wish to express a definite figure.

REPRESENTATIVE PARKER: Mr. Wright, you heard Mr. Madden's[5] testimony. Now, if we should stop the Government experimentation and leave it all in the hands of the industry, do you suppose we would progress as fast as we would—I mean, having the Government specify what they want in the plane and leaving the experimentation in the hands of the industry; do you suppose we would progress as fast as we would under the present system?

MR. WRIGHT: I think we would progress faster under a system in which both the industry and the Government carry on experimentation. I do not believe in concentrating all of it in any one place.

REPRESENTATIVE PARKER: In the industry?

MR. WRIGHT: Yes; [I do not believe in concentrating all of it either in the industry or in the Government, nor in just one division of the Government,] for instance, at McCook Field. [I believe in having an engineering division in the Army and one also in the Navy. I believe friendly competition between these divisions is for the public good.][6]

REPRESENTATIVE PARKER: I wanted your opinion on that.

THE CHAIRMAN: We are very much indebted to you, Mr. Wright.

---

1. *U.S. Air Services*, November 1925, 20–22.
2. The official name of this committee was the President's Aircraft Board. It was more commonly known as the Morrow Board after its chairman, Dwight W. Morrow.
3. McCook Field was the site of the U.S. Army Air Service's engineering experiment station, an aeronautical research and test facility hastily set up just outside Dayton, Ohio, in 1917 when the United States entered World War I. By the mid-1920s the activities of the station were outgrowing the facility. In 1927 the operations of McCook Field were moved

several miles down the road to Wright Field, which became part of the expansive Wright-Patterson Air Force Base in 1948. Although McCook itself was closed, the engineering function continued and grew at Wright Field, and then at Wright-Patterson, making McCook the origin of one of the most important aerospace research centers in the world. See Peter L. Jakab, "Aerospace in Adolescence: McCook Field and the Beginnings of Modern Aerospace Research," in Peter Galison and Alex Roland, eds., *Atmospheric Flight* (Dordrecht, Netherlands: Kluwer Academic Publishers, 2000, forthcoming), and Maurer Maurer, "McCook Field, 1917–1927," *Ohio Historical Quarterly* 67 (1958): 21–34.

Also created in 1917, the Naval Aircraft Factory (NAF) at Philadelphia was the U.S. Navy's counterpart to McCook Field, although the NAF manufactured aircraft in addition to carrying out research and engineering functions. The NAF was reorganized into various naval-aviation research entities after World War II. Naval research and development finally left Philadelphia altogether in 1974, but all ongoing naval research centers have their roots in the NAF. See William F. Trimble, *Wings for the Navy: A History of the Naval Aircraft Factory, 1917–1956* (Annapolis, Md.: Naval Institute Press, 1990).

4. Wilbur and Orville's younger sister, Katharine, was born three years to the day after Orville, on August 19, 1874. She was fifteen when their mother, Susan Koerner Wright, died of tuberculosis in 1889. She had taken over the responsibility of running the household and caring for the family when her mother became ill a few years earlier, and she formally adopted that role after her mother's death. Katharine assisted her brothers by looking after the bicycle shop while they were away experimenting at Kitty Hawk and by helping them prepare for the trips, but she made no technical or material contribution to building the aircraft. She was the only member of the Wright family to graduate from college. After receiving her degree from Oberlin College in 1898, she taught classics at Steele High School in Dayton.
5. "Mr. Madden" refers to Representative Martin B. Madden, chairman of the House Committee on Appropriations.
6. The words in brackets appeared in the original transcript of the President's Aircraft Board hearings and were deleted from the *U.S. Air Services* published version. Otherwise, the *U.S. Air Services* version is identical to the hearings transcript.

65 • WHAT IS AHEAD IN AVIATION: AMERICA'S FOREMOST LEADERS IN MANY BRANCHES OF FLYING GIVE REMARKABLE FORECASTS OF THE FUTURE[1]

Interview with Orville Wright[2]

"Aviation has gone beyond my dreams."—Orville Wright

AMAZING RECORDS

No one could have foreseen, and I myself never expected, the tremendous development of aviation at the present time. Airplanes are safer than ever before; they are finding applications beyond my most hopeful dreams; and the new records that are daily established are an outstanding tribute to the performance of the modern plane.

By way of example, I recall an altitude flight that I made in Germany not so many years ago. Flying over a captive balloon tethered on a steel cord—barographs then were unknown—I made a mark of something less than 600 feet. Today the altitude record is more than seven miles!

Flying today, I miss the thrill of the rickety planes we used to use—but I am convinced that the cabin type of plane is best suited to the high speeds of modern aviation. No air traveler today is anxious to put up with the inconvenience of a stinging wind in an open cockpit.

I do not believe, despite aviation's great advance, that the day of the "flivver" plane for every family is immediately at hand,[3] if for no other reason than the considerable space that airplanes require to land and to take off.

1. *Popular Science Monthly,* June 1929, 18–19, 124–29. Reprinted with the permission of *Popular Science,* Times Mirror Magazines, New York, N.Y.
2. Also included in this article were statements from nineteen other leading aviation authorities of the day: Grover Loening, Glenn H. Curtiss, C. E. Rosendahl, J. E. Fechet, William A. Moffett, William E. Boeing, Charles L. Lawrence, Alexander Klemin, Edward A. Stinson, C. S. Jones, Igor I. Sikorsky, Edward P. Warner, J. H. Dellinger, John F. O'Ryan, C. M. Keys, Harris M. Hanshue, F. B. Rentschler, Sherman M. Fairchild, and Giuseppe M. Bellanca.
3. "Flivver" was the nickname for the Ford Model T automobile. Belief in the feasibility of the concept of the "every man's airplane"—analogous to the simple, inexpensive Ford Model T—persisted for decades. Even after World War II, with thousands of military pilots returning to civilian life, the cost, the required skills, and the complexity of operation of aircraft precluded a democratization of flying, along the same lines as had developed with the automobile. Henry Ford, incidentally, who had expanded into aircraft manufacture after World War I, did produce a prototype of a small, single-engine, light aircraft, called the Ford Flivver, in 1926, but it was never commercially manufactured.

66 • SUN POWER MOTOR[1]

Orville Wright

I will not attempt to predict what will be the next "great invention," but as man's physical well-being depends largely upon the amount of power at his command I would say that "the most needed invention" is a motor which economically converts the latent energy in matter into motive power, or economically derives power directly from the rays of the sun.

1. *Science News Letter,* April 16, 1932, 239. Orville Wright's response to the question: "The next great invention: what does the world need most?," posed by the organization Science Service. Orville Wright was one of eleven eminent Ameri-

can inventors queried. Reprinted with the permission of *Science News*, the weekly newsmagazine of science, copyright 1932 by Science Service, Washington, D.C.

67 • ORVILLE WRIGHT FORESEES GREAT PROGRESS IN NEXT DECADE[1]

Interviews with Orville Wright

When attending a celebration in his honor on the 34th anniversary of the first flight, Orville Wright made one of his infrequent statements to the press. This was on December 17th, at Columbia University, New York, where he attended the first of a series of annual Wright Brothers' Lectures, under the auspices of the Institute of the Aeronautical Sciences. Mr. Wright is quoted in *The New York Times* as follows:

> Proposals for flying machines weighing 250,000 pounds tax the imagination, but no more than today's accomplishments taxed the imagination ten years ago. I would not be surprised if developments of the next ten years will be as great.

He was asked what he considered the outstanding development in aeronautics in 1937. He replied that there had been so many it would be difficult to pick just one. From the standpoint of outstanding flights, however, he believed the Russian flights over the North Pole to the United States worthy of mention,[2] but no more so than the regular passenger and mail service across the Pacific. He mentioned the Martin flying boat built at Baltimore for Russia as an outstanding piece of new construction,[3] and he observed that aeronautics was advancing about evenly in all fields, including research, manufacture and performance.

In greeting Mr. Wright and about 200 engineers, scientists and aviation industrial leaders, Dr. Nicholas Murray Butler, president of Columbia University, said:

"We have lived to see world communication transformed by the science of aeronautics under the leadership of the great pioneer (Orville Wright) whom we welcome here this afternoon."

Prof. B. Melvill Jones, Francis Mond professor of aeronautical engineering at Cambridge University, England, spoke on "Boundary Layer Experiments in Flight." He preceded his lecture with a brief tribute to the Wright brothers.

"It is not new to some of you, but not everybody knows the art and science of flight was accomplished by the research work of the Wright brothers," Professor Jones said. "The name of the Wrights will endure forever."

After the lecture members of the Institute attended a private dinner at the Hotel Biltmore. There they were joined by Col. Charles A. Lindbergh, who sat with Mr. Wright and Professor Jones.

Following the dinner the Institute made its annual awards for outstanding achievements in the aeronautical sciences. The Daniel Guggenheim Medal was awarded to Dr. Hugo Eckener, "for notable contributions to transoceanic air transport and to international cooperation in aeronautics." The medal was accepted by Comdr. Charles E. Rosendahl on behalf of Dr. Eckener, who was unable to attend.[4]

Eastman N. Jacobs, aeronautical engineer of the National Advisory Committee for Aeronautics, was given the Sylvanus Albert Reed Award "for his contribution to the aerodynamic improvement of airfoils used in modern military and commercial aircraft."

The Lawrence Sperry Award for "important improvement of aeronautical design of high-speed commercial aircraft" was presented to Clarence L. Johnson, research engineer of the Lockheed Aircraft Corporation.[5]

Honorary fellowships in the Institute were presented to Professor Jones and Glenn L. Martin.[6] Only one American and one foreign Honorary Fellow are elected each year.

The nation observed the 34th anniversary of the first flight by sending every available aircraft into the air at 10:30 in the morning,[7] the hour the airplane was born. Naval and military stations joined with civilian organizations by holding open houses, aircraft displays, aerial reviews and exhibitions, luncheons, dinners and radio broadcasts. A squadron of the Army's Boeing bombers and airplanes from the aircraft carriers *Yorktown, Enterprise,* and *Wasp* flew from Norfolk, Va., to Kitty Hawk, N.C., where they dipped in salute above the Wright Memorial[8] which stands on the spot where Wilbur and Orville Wright first left the earth in a mechanically propelled plane.

On December 16th Orville Wright attended a meeting of the National Advisory Committee for Aeronautics in Washington. On the 17th appeared the following interview in *The Washington Herald:*

"When 34 years ago you first flew, did you conceive the airplane as the weapon it is now?" he was asked. For a moment he seemed startled, and then he said, slowly and carefully:

"I thought the airplane would bring peace. I thought it would bring war home to the people of every nation. I thought that an airplane could fly over an enemy capital, and that no nation would dare go to war with such a weapon in existence. We didn't dream that airplanes would he developed as they have. We didn't dream that there would be such defensive equipment as anti-aircraft guns."

"If you had known what the plane would be, would you have gone forward with your invention?" he was asked.

"We didn't think of it at the time. We had no idea. It was to us an interesting experiment, purely a matter of science. And we didn't know the world would go crazy."

"To what point do you think airplanes will be developed?"

"There is no way of telling. Things are moving too fast. No one can predict where it will end."

Mr. Wright was then asked what aviation needed next to foster its progress. He said:

"Speed has progressed faster than navigation. I might say that the speed of planes has outrun the facilities for guiding and landing them. We need practical blind flying instruments, better radio equipment, so that planes can fly anywhere in all weather. When we get those, these crashes in the mountains will be ended."

In a radio address delivered over NBC, at 7:45 P.M., December 17th, The Honorable Louis Johnson, Assistant Secretary of War, paid tribute to the Wright brothers by saying:

To the living Orville Wright, who still devotes his strength and his energy to perfect and to develop the flying machine, the Army, in behalf of all friends of aviation extends best wishes for continued success and happiness. In memory of Wilbur, the mighty air armada of the United States Army which rules the skies, proudly proclaims his handiwork. To his skill and to his ingenuity, the Army Air Corps stands as a living monument. The Wright brothers and the Army Air Corps owe much of their success to each other. Aviation is deeply indebted to both.

---

1. *U.S. Air Services*, January 1938, 14–15.
2. On June 18–20, 1937, Valery Chkalov, Georgiy Baidukov, and A. V. Belyakov made the first nonstop flight from Moscow to the United States via the North Pole. See Georgiy Baidukov, *Russian Lindbergh: The Life of Valery Chkalov* (Washington, D.C.: Smithsonian Institution Press, 1991).
3. This "flying boat" was the Martin Model 156, also known as the "Russia Clipper."
4. Dr. Hugo Eckener began his professional life as a journalist, and early on he was critical of the viability of lighter-than-air travel. But after meeting the famed airship pioneer Count Ferdinand von Zeppelin in 1904 and making his first flight, Eckener was immediately converted and joined the Zeppelin firm. During World War I he held the position of flight instructor for the company, and after the war he became the world's leading promoter and expert on airship navigation. Eckener piloted the famous *Graf Zeppelin* on 104 transatlantic crossings and on a round-the-world fight in 1929. He also piloted the *Hindenburg* on its maiden Atlantic crossing in 1936. Eckener was selected to receive the Guggenheim Medal several months before the *Hindenburg* was destroyed in a fiery crash over Lakehurst, New Jersey, on May 6, 1937. The board of the Guggenheim Medal Fund made the public announcement of Eckener's selection on May 17 to convey their continued confidence in airship travel and in Eckener's ability in the wake of the disaster. Despite this gesture, the loss of the *Hindenburg* signaled the end of the great airship era.
5. Clarence L. "Kelly" Johnson would go on to develop some of the most significant and famous aircraft in history, with designs such as the Lockheed U-2 and SR-71 high-altitude reconnaissance aircraft, among many others. Johnson won the Lawrence Sperry Award in 1937 for his work on the fowler flap on the Lockheed Model 14 Electra. See Clarence L.

Johnson, *Kelly: More Than My Share of It All* (Washington, D.C.: Smithsonian Institution Press, 1985).

6. See document 55, note 5.
7. The precise time at which Orville lifted off at Kitty Hawk on December 17, 1903, was 10:35 A.M.
8. On March 2, 1927, President Calvin Coolidge signed into law a $50,000 appropriation bill for the creation of a permanent national monument to the Wrights and their achievement at Kitty Hawk. After the largest of the great sand dunes at Kill Devil Hills was stabilized with artificial topsoil and hardy imported grasses, a beautiful, sixty-foot granite shaft with feathered wings sculpted into the sides was erected upon a five-point star base. Placed on top was an aeronautical beacon, which can be seen for miles in every direction at night. The structure was completed and dedicated in 1932 (see photo 52).

68 • ORVILLE WRIGHT TAKES LOOK BACK ON 40 YEARS SINCE FIRST FLIGHT; DESPITE AIR WAR, HAS NO REGRETS[1]

Interview with Orville Wright by Fred C. Kelly

Inventor, at 72, Says He and Brother at Kitty Hawk Foresaw Some of Developments but of Course Not All—Likens Aviation to Fire, Useful as Well as Destructive.

Dayton, O., Nov. 6.

With the memorable date of December 17 approaching, the fortieth anniversary of the first airplane flight, Orville Wright, who made this flight, in a machine of his and his brother Wilbur's invention, consented to answer a number of questions for publication.

He was at his office and laboratory, at 15 North Broadway, on the West Side of Dayton, a short walk from the site of the bicycle shop in which the Wrights built the first plane. He had arrived, as he always does, punctually at 8:30 a.m., as if he had to punch a time clock.

Sitting so erect at times that he hardly touched the back of his chair, with arms folded in front of his chest, eyes alert, Orville Wright did not look his 72 years. There are few lines in his face except little smile wrinkles at the corners of his eyes and mouth.

My first question was: "What is your feeling about the use of the airplane as an instrument of wholesale destruction and human slaughter? Do you ever wish you had never invented it?"

"No," Wright replied promptly. "I don't have any regrets about my part in the invention of the airplane, though no one could deplore more than I do the destruction it has caused.

"I feel about the airplane much the same as I do in regard to fire. That is, I regret all the terrible damage caused by fire. But I think it is good for the human race that someone discovered how to start fires and that we have learned how to put fire to thousands of important uses."

Not Thinking about War

"How much did you and Wilbur foresee of the uses of the airplane for war purposes?"

"At the time we first flew our power-plane at Kitty Hawk, N.C., we were not thinking of any practical uses for it at all. We just wanted to show that it was possible to fly. But after our experiments at a field near Dayton in the summer of 1904 we saw that the machine could be useful for military purposes, especially for scouting.

"As early as January 1905 we had enough faith in its military uses to offer it to the United States Government, but our War Department did not then show any interest in it.[2] We thought observations from scouting planes could prevent surprise attack by an enemy.

"We saw, too, that it would be possible to drop bombs on enemy territory. And we hoped that no government would want to risk starting a war and subjecting its people to the kind of devastation the airplane could inflict.

"One thing we particularly believed might prevent wars was the opportunity the airplane provided promptly to drop bombs on the buildings occupied by the members of parliament and highest government officials, or rulers, of the country that declared war. We thought the plane might thus make war so inadvisable that no government would dare to start one."[3]

"But did you ever think the plane would create the world revolution it has, or that there would be night bombings from bases hundreds or even thousands of miles away?"

"No, we didn't even suppose anyone would ever fly or make landings at night. Nor did we reckon with the amount of punishment human beings seem able to endure.

Hitler Undreamed Of

"It never occurred to us that if a fanatical leader, for purposes of personal aggrandizement, should start a war, his people would put up with terrible suffering year after year without mass protest.

"Of course, the German people were doubtless led to accept the assurance of their leaders that the war would be fought on foreign soil with no bombings on their own cities. Perhaps the danger of bombings may cause even Germans to think twice before getting into another war."

"What do you consider the greatest single contribution of the Wright brothers toward successful flight? You were the first, I believe, to think of devising a mechanism to present the right and left wings at different angles to the wind, to get sidewise balance, and your wind-tunnel experiments provided the first accurate knowledge about air pressures on wing surfaces. Which of these contributions proved to be the more important?"

Important Contribution

Wright tilted back his chair and looked at me reflectively for a moment before replying:

"First of all, it was necessary to have a machine that would lift itself. There was no need of a system of control until one was able to get a machine into the air. Indeed, it would have been possible in 1903 for us to build a machine and fly it in calm air without our system of control, though, of course, such a machine could not have had any practical use. But without knowledge of how to build wings of the right shape—that is, of a shape to give more lift for the amount of power expended than had been possible before—we could not have flown at all.

"Except for what we learned from our wind-tunnel experiments in 1901, we never could have built wings that would lift the machine and a pilot with the amount of motor power then available.

"So, answering your question, for the first flight the system of control was less important than the knowledge of how to build wings of the right shape. But today, for the practical airplane, the two are about equally important. To try to distinguish between the value of these two features now would be like trying to determine whether the chicken or the egg should have precedence."

"Was there any time during your experiments when you felt greatly discouraged?"

"When we discovered in 1901 that tables of air pressures prepared by our predecessors were not accurate or dependable, that was discouraging, in a way, and disappointing. For it meant that instead of starting from where others had left off, as we had expected to do, we must start from scratch.

Thrill of Discovery

"But, on the other hand, the fact that these data which others had considered accurate now turned out to be inaccurate was interesting. One gets a certain thrill from discovering something others have not known. From one way of looking at it, you might even have called it encouraging, that the data others had used could not be relied upon. It suggested that maybe the reason others had failed to fly was not because the thing couldn't be done."

"And the moment of greatest elation? Was it when the plane first left the ground in successful flight on Dec. 17, or after the flight was over and you could think about what you had achieved?"

Wright smiled as he said:

"Oh, neither of us felt any great elation over what we did that day. You see, we had faith in our calculations and had felt so sure we were going to fly that when we succeeded we were not surprised. In fact, I had got more kick out of flying before I had ever been in the air—while lying in bed thinking of how exciting it would be to fly."

"By the way, how much gasoline did that first Kitty Hawk plane carry?"

"Only about half a gallon. The tank was just a foot long by three inches in diameter."

"It was that small to keep down the weight?"

"No, it could have been much larger as far as weight was concerned. But it was all we needed. It contained enough fuel to last about 15 minutes and take us 9 to 10 miles, and that was farther than we had any intention of going."

Not Interested in Distance

"You weren't interested then in making a distance record?"

"Well, of course, we knew it would be a record if we lifted into the air at all, because no one had ever done even that with a power machine before. But we weren't concerned about going any great distance or at high speed.

"We just wanted to make a clear demonstration that the machine was capable of sustained flight.

"The distance was not important as long as it was enough to prove that we had made a real flight—not a mere hop. As to speed, it would have been much easier to fly if we had built the machine for greater speed, as we could have done; but we wanted it to fly at as low speed as possible to give greater ease and safety in landing."

"Now, about military aviation today. Do you think our Government should have a department of the air, as some have suggested, headed by a Cabinet member, just as we have for the Army and the Navy?"

"No," Wright replied emphatically. "There should not be a separate air department. There should not be a separate Army and Navy, either. I think there should be a single department of national defense, with air forces, ground forces, and naval forces all parts of the whole. None of the branches of national defense should have any rivalry with another, but only co-operation.

Pearl Harbor and Crete

"Both at Pearl Harbor and Crete were examples of what may happen when there is too much separation and independence in the different branches of a country's armed forces.

"If we had an air force, treated as a separate department, our situation would be made worse than it is. Each department would try to outdo the others. Each would be jealous of its prestige and be always trying to convince Congress that it, rather than another department, should have the larger increase in appropriations. I have had enough dealing with our Government to know how undesirable that sort of thing can be.

"I don't think there is much rivalry between, say, the artillery, cavalry, or engineers, and the infantry branches of the Army, because the men in those parts of the Army all think of themselves as belonging to the same team.

"But there has always been an unfortunate rivalry and competition between the Army and the Navy. That wouldn't exist if they weren't separated into different departments. And why should they be separated? Why should one be competing with the other for either appropriations or glory?

"One of the best things President Roosevelt has done since the present war started, it seems to me, is having the Army and Navy and air forces in certain areas under the command of one man, as, for example, Gen. [Douglas] MacArthur in the Southwest Pacific, and under Gen. [George H.] Brett of the Army Air Force, at Panama. That same principle of unified command should be applied on a still broader scale."

For Same Basic Training

"And you would not have aviators trained separately for work with land forces and to fly from ships at sea?"

"Naturally there would be some specialization, but the basic training should be all the same. And no flyer would think of himself as permanently assigned to land forces or sea forces. Every flyer would know that he was simply part of the national defense for assignment wherever needed."

"You wouldn't have one branch of the national defense trained at Annapolis and another at West Point?"

"No. Those places should not be separate institutions. If we were properly organized, students would go from one to the other to receive training. Having one place for training of ground troops exclusively and the other for sea forces only helps to create a kind of rivalry that does harm. Such feeling of rivalry should never be allowed to start.

"Men who are drafted today go to perhaps half a dozen places for training and don't feel themselves bound to loyalties for any one training center. It should be the same in regard to West Point and Annapolis. Men being trained for officers could go to both."

"But wouldn't you have to separate the training of a man who is to be, say, an ocean navigator, or who will handle naval guns, and one who will direct ground troops?"

"Certainly. Just as we now separate the training of those who are to specialize in field artillery or cavalry. But such specialization doesn't need to be done in rival or competing institutions.

Flying Is Flying

"And the basic training could all be the same. A man trained to be an airplane navigator operates over both land and sea, and not much separate training should be needed for him to become a navigator on a battleship. Signal corps training would be much the same whether for use by ground, sea or air forces.

"When a man starts to learn to fly it doesn't matter whether he is later to fly from the deck of a plane carrier or from an airfield. Most of the more fundamental training today at West Point and Annapolis is mathematics, languages, history, engineering, drilling and so on, presumably must be about the same, or should be.

"Every officer in the national defense forces should have been educated broadly enough to know problems and difficulties of the different branches of the national defense. It should be so organized that the high command could assign men to the land, sea or air forces and transfer them from one to another, wherever most needed."

"Then you wouldn't have Army and Navy teams competing at football each year and showing bitter rivalry?"

"Surely it would be better," replied Wright with a chuckle, "if they had a football team made up of students from both West Point and Annapolis. Then they could be learning co-operation. They could doubtless find some other good teams to play against."

Future of Aviation

"What about the future of aviation after the war?" I asked. "What developments do you look for in the way of new uses for the airplane?"

"Well, I'm not one of those who think the plane is going to supplant railroads, ships, trucks and automobiles right away.

"Uses of airplanes will increase, of course. But it may be some time before they can carry freight as cheaply as railroads or ships can. There will be trans-Atlantic passenger service, much more passenger service of all kinds. And I shouldn't be surprised if passenger service by plane across the Atlantic may be lower priced, almost immediately after the war, than first-class fares on boats have been.

"It will be some time, though, before cargo planes can compete in price with big boats for carrying heavy freight. However, cargo planes will do more and more carrying of perishable goods.

"Perhaps letters sent to any considerable distance in the United States will regularly go by air at the same postage rate as those sent to nearby points by train or truck.

"There will be an increase in use of privately owned planes, but I don't think this increase will be enough for a few years yet, to be at all revolutionary."

"Do you look for great advances in the speed, carrying power, and range of bombers?"

"I hope," replied Wright solemnly, "that after this war is over it will be possible to avoid building any more bombers of any kind.

"If, because of failure of international co-operation, it is still considered necessary to go on building up big fleets of bombers, then we'll be right back where we were and the sacrifices of this war will have been pretty much in vain. We shall have lost the war."

---

1. *St. Louis Post-Dispatch,* November 7, 1943, 1D, 4D. Reprinted with the permission of the Pulitzer Publishing Company, St. Louis, Mo., copyright 1943.
2. By January 1905 the Wrights were confident that their invention had reached an acceptable level of practicality to offer it for sale. Wanting to give their own country the first opportunity to develop this important new technology, the Wrights called on their local congressman, Robert M. Nevin, for advice on how to proceed with opening negotiations with the U.S. government. Nevin suggested they prepare a letter describing the airplane's performance capabilities and the terms for its sale, and he would present it personally to the secretary of war, William Howard Taft. Unfortunately, Nevin was ill when the letter arrived in his office. Unaware of the Wrights' prearrangement with Nevin, a clerk simply forwarded the letter as routine correspondence to the U.S. Army Board of Ordnance and Fortification. Having received numerous hollow offers promising a practical flying machine before, the board was skeptical of the Wrights' claims and simply responded with a form reply rejecting the brothers' offer. Wilbur and Orville were affronted that these government officials did not take them at their word and dropped the matter. They then felt free to pursue foreign contracts with a clear conscience. To be fair, the board had received many obviously frivolous proposals in recent years, and the Wrights provided no photographs of their airplane in flight or any other concrete proof of their credibility beyond their basic assertion that they had a practical flying machine. Given the circumstances and the Wrights' somewhat naive approach to dealing with government bureaucracy, this initial false start was not terribly surprising.
3. See document 53, note 2.

69 • WRIGHT FAVORS FREE COMPETITION ON POSTWAR FOREIGN AIR ROUTES[1]

Interview with Orville Wright by Alexander McSurely

Notables of aviation world pay tribute this week to co-inventor of airplane at dinner in Washington on 40th anniversary of Kitty Hawk flight.

The co-inventor of the airplane and the first man to fly it believes that international air routes in the postwar period should not be limited to any one company or to any one country.

Orville Wright, 72-year-old scientist, who will receive tributes of the aviation world, Dec. 17, at Washington, on the 40th anniversary of the first motor-powered airplane flights at Kitty Hawk, N.C., in 1903, voiced his opinion in an interview at his secluded laboratory in Dayton, shortly before leaving for Washington to attend a dinner given in his honor.

Anniversary Dinner. "Aviation in Peace" will be the theme of the anniversary dinner, which will be attended by many of the country's aviation leaders. Jesse Jones, Secretary of Commerce, will preside.

Wright foresees a serious crisis in the aviation industry in the postwar period, paralleling the "dark age" of American aviation following World War I, unless intelligent and cooperative handling by government and industry are able to avert it.

World Trade Factor. "International air commerce will play an important role undoubtedly in future development of aviation," the white-haired inventor said, "but I do not think any one company or any one country should have a monopoly. Government subsidy paid for a large part of the expansion of our international air routes, before the war, and certainly the operations now going on would not be possible except for government financing. It does not seem fair that the companies, who have had the advantage of this government financing, should claim a right to monopolize the world's air routes because of this."

Opposes Cutthroat Competition. On the other hand, Mr. Wright does not favor a wide-open cutthroat competition between all airlines.

"If all our airlines which have signified their intention of operating foreign routes, do so, however, there won't be any business for anybody," he continued. "There must be some reasonable arrangement worked out."

Advancements in science may make some aviation procedures obsolete, he predicted, referring particularly to rocket propulsion for aircraft and to development of some more efficient method of landing and launching airplanes than the present bulky, heavy landing gears. He believes the helicopter will have practical value in short trips, although he does not consider it as likely to approach the conventional airplane in efficiency for longer hauls.

Private Flying. He is conservative on the development of private flying after the war, while admitting its great potentialities for widening the sphere of aviation.

The interviewer lit a cigarette and blew a fat lazy smoke-ring.

Mr. Wright watched it rolling through the air and grinned.

"Do you know the scientific principle involved in making that ring?" he asked. "The rolling motion that your tongue gives to it creates a centrifugal force that holds the smoke together."

Smoke Tunnels. From this tangent he began a discussion of smoke tunnels and their use in testing aircraft structures by making visible the airflow over a wing or other air foil. A representative of the Griswold smoke tunnel in Connecticut recently visited him in Dayton to consult about some early smoke tunnel experiments in his laboratory here in 1919.

"We used a very small smoke tunnel, and used the blower from our regular wind tunnel. At one time we tried tobacco smoke provided by a man who sat there smoking and puffing it in, but it wasn't very successful. Later, we tried a mixture of chemicals to provide the smoke and it worked better. If conditions are right, the smoke shows little eddies and vortices in the air currents over an airfoil which offer a key to many of your design problems."

Kitty Hawk Flights. Naturally the conversation turned back to the Kitty Hawk flights, and the years of practical testing and experiments which led up to them.

Orville Wright receives all tributes in the name of the famous Wright Brothers team, rather than accepting individual credit for his own work. He credits that remarkable cooperative association between his brother Wilbur, who died of typhoid fever in 1912, and himself, as the most important single factor in their discovery of the principles which made power airplane flight possible.

Still Eager Aeronautics Student. Four decades after that wintry day when he crouched on the lower wing of the flimsy biplane and launched into space at Kitty Hawk, his hair is thinner and whiter, he is a little stouter, but he is still in excellent physical condition, and his gray-blue eyes sparkle as he discusses aeronautical theories or research in which he is presently engaged.

As Orville Wright goes to Washington for the anniversary observance, the original Kitty Hawk plane still remains in England, where it was sent in 1928 as the result of the long-standing controversy between the Smithsonian Institution and the Wrights.[2]

A year ago, however, Dr. Charles G. Abbot, secretary of the Institution, published a statement giving full credit to the Wrights.[3]

May Bring Plane to U.S. Mr. Wright indicated recently that he was considering bringing the plane back, but that he would take no action while the war continued because of possible hazard to the historic aircraft during its passage back to this country.[4]

---

1. *Aviation News,* December 13, 1943, 10–11. Reprinted with the permission of *Aviation Week & Space Technology,* Washington, D.C.
2. See articles regarding the Wright/Smithsonian controversy and the loan of the 1903 Wright airplane to the Science Museum in London: documents 17, 19, 20, and 24.
3. See C. G. Abbot, "The 1914 Tests of the Langley 'Aerodrome,'" *Annual Report of the Board of Regents of the Smithsonian Institution, 1942* (Washington, D.C.: U.S. Government Printing Office, 1943), 111–18.
4. See document 20, note 2, and document 24: "Orville Wright Ordered Return to America of Original Airplane."

WITNESSES TO THE BIRTH OF FLIGHT

WHEN WILBUR AND ORVILLE WRIGHT made their historic first powered airplane flights on December 17, 1903, there were only five people present to witness the epic moment. All were local residents. Three were members of the Kill Devil Hills Lifesaving Station, near Kitty Hawk, which worked the dangerous shores of the North Carolina Outer Banks. Also on hand were W. C. Brinkley, a lumber buyer from nearby Manteo, who was there to inspect planks from a wrecked boat, and Johnny Moore, a boy from Nags Head. Two other crew of the lifesaving station observed from their distant posts through spyglasses.

One prominent Kitty Hawk resident, William Tate, was noticeably absent. When the Wrights had begun searching for a place to test their first glider in 1900, they had contacted the National Weather Bureau in Washington, D.C., seeking locales of suitable terrain and wind conditions to conduct their experiments. Among the sites that seemed promising was Kitty Hawk, a spot located on an isolated strip of beach off the coast of North Carolina. The brothers looked no further after receiving a welcoming response to an inquiry Wilbur made with the local weather station. Wilbur's letter was answered by Tate, a local inhabitant considered the best-educated person in this modest little fishing village. "If you decide to try your machine here & come I will take pleasure in doing all I can for your convenience & success & pleasure," Tate wrote, "& I assure you you will find a hospitable people when you come among us."[1] True to his word, Tate put Wilbur up in his home until Orville reached Kitty Hawk with their camping equipment and supplies a few days later. It was the beginning of a lifelong friendship between Tate and the two polite strangers from Dayton.

Tate played an important role in the Wrights' flying experiments leading up to their success in 1903. In addition to helping Wilbur and Orville make do in the spare environs of Kitty Hawk, he, and especially his half-brother Dan Tate, frequently provided the needed third pair of hands to launch the gliders when one or the other of the Wrights was on board piloting. Tate had planned to be there for the test of the powered airplane. But despite the signal flag the brothers raised to alert the village of a trial, Tate thought it was too windy that morning to launch the Flyer. He intended to stop by the Wright camp later that day after his chores were finished.

Having been with Wilbur and Orville through so many of their earlier experiments and frustrations, Tate always regretted missing their triumph. In future years, he was typically on hand for the periodic ceremonies commemorating the Wrights' great achievement. He very much wanted to be present at Kill Devil Hills on December 17, 1953, to observe the planned fiftieth-anniversary celebration of the first flights. Sadly, William Tate died, at the age of eighty-four, six months short of the golden anniversary of flight.

Fortunately, Tate had put his reminiscences of the Wrights' time at Kitty Hawk on paper. On two occasions—the twenty-fifth and the fortieth anniversaries of the first flight—Tate published articles sharing his memories of Wilbur and Orville and his view of the significance of their accomplishment (documents 71 and 72). Though not published writings by the Wright brothers, they merit inclusion in this book because of the unique perspective they bring. Tate, a witness to and a participant in the Wrights' glider trials, was a historical player in critical aspects of the Wright story. His publications are thus an interesting and useful supplement to the core material of this collection.

A few other publications fall into this special category and are included as well. Charles E. Taylor was a mechanic and machinist the Wrights hired in 1901 to help with their bicycle-manufacturing business. Most significant, it was Taylor who performed the majority of the work in fabricating the twelve-horsepower engine used in the 1903 Kitty Hawk airplane. He remained in the Wrights' employ until 1911. In 1948 he published "My Story of the Wright Brothers," detailing his relationship with them and the making of the world's first successful airplane power plant (document 73).

Another person who played a notable role at Kitty Hawk on December 17, 1903, also left a published account of his experiences with the Wrights. John T. Daniels, one of the lifesaving crew on hand that day, assisted the brothers in handling the Flyer that morning and shared in the celebration of the success. W. O. Saunders's "Then We Quit Laughing" is an extensive interview with Daniels (document 70). Surprisingly, Daniels makes no reference in the article to what turned out to be his most historically significant act that day. He had been enlisted by the brothers to man the camera that they positioned at the foot of the launching rail to take a photograph of the "moment of triumph." Daniels snapped the shutter just as Orville lifted the Flyer off the rail, capturing one of the most famous and widely reproduced images ever taken (see photo 23).

Mabel Beck, the author of the final piece in the appendix, was not a witness at Kitty Hawk, but she wrote a key documentary article concerning the subsequent history of the 1903 Wright airplane (document 74). Mabel joined the Wright Company in 1910 and went on to serve as Orville's personal secretary until his death in 1948. She was curt and abrasive and literally acted as gatekeeper to Orville's private domain. No one, not even Orville's few close friends, got to him without going through Mabel. Even the other family members, especially the brothers' sister, Katharine, regarded her with unveiled disdain because of her aggressive possessiveness of Orville. Any person or group wanting Orville's counsel or participation had to deal with Mabel. She also knew the Wright story as well as her employer and was quite capable of answering any inquiries. In 1954 she wrote a short, but very important, summary of what had happened to the Wright Flyer after December 17, 1903, until the loan of the aircraft to the Science Museum in London in 1928. This is the only source for certain details concerning the material history of the Flyer after its one and only day in the air in 1903.

This appendix of publications by the Wrights' associates is limited to those involved with the epic events of December 17, 1903, and with the brothers' historic airplane. Numerous other reminiscences were written by people whose paths crossed the Wrights' over the years, but to include them would be beyond the scope of this book. After all, this is a collection of the published writings of the *Wrights.* Nevertheless, the perspectives of those who were part of the defining act of the brothers' lives present a special case. To revive at least these few historically muted voices seemed a worthy and meaningful addition to this assembly of Wright material.

Mention should be made of one other article written by a Wright contemporary living on the Outer Banks at the turn of the century. Alpheus W. Drinkwater was a local telegrapher and line repairman for the U.S. Weather Bureau. In 1956 he published his recollections of the events on and around December 17, 1903, in which he claimed to have forwarded the Wrights' famous telegram informing members of their family of their successful flights (see photo 26). In fact, the telegraph operator on duty at Kitty Hawk that day was Joseph J. Dosher, the same person who had received Wilbur Wright's initial letter in 1900 inquiring about the suitability of Kitty Hawk for conducting flying experiments. Dosher, not Drinkwater, sent the Wrights' brief message home on December 17. In a 1937 letter to a journalist with the *Dallas Morning News,* Orville Wright recounted the news coverage of the first flights and specifically noted that the frequently repeated Drinkwater story was untrue. Drinkwater did send out a number of telegrams for reporters who had come to Kitty Hawk to cover the Wrights' activities in 1908, when the brothers had returned to the Outer Banks to practice flying with one of their later powered aircraft. But he was not a participant in the events five years earlier. Since this aspect of Drinkwater's article is apocryphal, it does not meet the criteria for the appendix. However, the account, entitled "I *Knew* Those Wright Brothers Were Crazy," is listed in the bibliography, along with other personal reminiscences about the Wrights.

1. William J. Tate to W. Wright, August 18, 1900, in Fred C. Kelly, ed., *Miracle at Kitty Hawk: The Letters of Wilbur and Orville Wright* (New York: Farrar, Straus, and Young, 1951), 25–26.

70 • THEN WE QUIT LAUGHING[1]

Interview with John T. Daniels by W. O. Saunders

The man who was in the first airplane wreck tells of those days when Wilbur and Orville Wright were "just a pair of poor nuts" playing with kites and watching the gulls fly on the North Carolina coast.

I found him at the wheel of a clumsy old ferryboat plying between the towns of Morehead City and Beaufort on the North Carolina coast—a rugged, bronzed, gray-eyed, gray-haired son of Neptune, steering his craft cunningly through the tortuous channel of a harbor beset by the conflicting currents of many inland waters where they meet and mingle with the tides and currents of the open sea.

"I rather expected to find you piloting aircraft by this time," I said to him by the way of opening conversation.

"Who, me?" replied the ferryman. "No, sir, the only way they'll ever get me in one of them airplanes again will be to put me in irons and strap me in. I reckon I'm the proudest man in the world today because I was the first man ever wrecked in an airplane, but I've had all the thrill I ever want in an airplane; I wouldn't take a million now for that first thrill, but you couldn't give me a million to risk another."

Captain John T. Daniels, America's first airplane casualty, figured in the wreck of the first power-driven heavier-than-air flying machine ever flown, at Kill Devil Hills on Virginia Dare Shores, North Carolina, on that epochal morning of December 17, 1903.

John Daniels was one of a little group of natives of the North Carolina coastland who stood by at Kill Devil Hills that morning when Wilbur and Orville Wright prepared to try out their first power-driven airplane. The brothers Wright had to have help in handling that first plane, and Captain Daniels, then a patrolman on duty at the Kill Devil Hills Coast Guard Station, volunteered as one of their helpers.

"It's just like yesterday to me," said Captain Daniels. "The Wrights got their machine out of its shed that morning, and we helped them roll it up to the top of the highest hill, on a monorail.[2]

"That first plane had only one wheel to roll on,[3] not like the planes now that have two wheels. It couldn't stand up without somebody supporting it at each end, and I had hold of one of the wings on one end.

"It was a sad time, I'm telling you. We'd been watching them Wright boys from our station for three years and visiting them at their camp.

"When they first came down to Kill Devil Hills in the summer of 1900 and begun to experiment with their funny-looking kites we just thought they were a pair of crazy fools. We laughed about 'em among ourselves for a while, but we soon quit laughing and just felt sorry for 'em, because they were as nice boys as you'd ever hope to see. "They didn't put themselves out to get acquainted with anybody, just stuck to themselves, and we had to get acquainted with them. They were two of the workingest boys I ever saw, and when they worked *they worked.*

The Dayton Gannets

"I never saw men so wrapped up in their work in my life. They had their whole heart and soul in what they were doing, and when they were working we could come around and stand right over them and they wouldn't pay any more attention to us than if we weren't there at all. After their day's work was over they were different; then they were the nicest fellows you ever saw and treated us fine.

"The Wrights came down to Kill Devil Hills, where they could find a good elevation for trying out their glider, where there were good winds almost all the time, where they would have a soft place to land almost anywhere when their glider came down, and where they wouldn't be bothered by outsiders. They didn't seem to mind us natives.

"Well, they hadn't been down there long before we just naturally learned to love 'em—such nice boys wasting their time playing with kites and watching the gulls fly. They were such smart boys—natural-born mechanics—and could do anything they put their hands to. They built their own camp; they took an old carbide can and made a stove of it; they took a bicycle and geared the thing up so that they could ride it on the sand. They did their own cooking and washing; and they were good cooks too.

"But we couldn't help thinking they were just a pair of poor nuts. We'd watch them from the windows of our station. They'd stand on the beach for hours at a time just looking at the gulls flying, soaring, dipping. They seemed to be interested mostly in gannets. Gannets are big gulls with a wing spread of five or six feet. They would watch gannets for hours.

"They would watch the gannets and imitate the movements of their wings with their arms and hands. They could imitate every movement of the wings of those gannets; we thought they were crazy, but we just had to admire the way they could move their arms this way and that and bend their elbows and wrist bones up and down and which a way, just like the gannets moved their wings.

"But they were a long way from being fools. We began to see that when they got their glider working so that they could jump off into a wind off that hill and stay in the air for several minutes, gradually gliding down to the beach almost as graceful as a gannet could have done it.

"We knew they were going to fly, but we didn't know what was going to happen when they did. We had watched them for several years and seen how they figured everything out before they attempted it.

My First Flight—and Last

"We had seen the glider fly without an engine, and when those boys put an engine in it we knew that they knew exactly what they were doing.

"Adam Etheridge, Will Dough, W. C. Brinkley, Johnny Moore and myself were there on the morning of December 17th. We were a serious lot. Nobody felt like talking.

"Wilbur and Orville walked off from us and stood close together on the beach, talking low to each other for some time. After a while they shook hands, and we couldn't help notice how they held on to each other's hand, sort o' like they hated to let go; like two folks parting who weren't sure they'd ever see each other again.

"Wilbur came over to us and told us not to look sad, but to laugh and hollo and clap our hands and try to cheer Orville up when he started.

"We tried to shout and hollo, but it was mighty weak shouting, with no heart in it.

"Orville climbed into the machine, the engine was started up and we helped steady it down the monorail until it got under way. The thing went off with a rush and left the rail as pretty as you please, going straight out into the air maybe 120 feet when one of its wings tilted and caught in the sand, and the thing stopped.

"We got it back up on the hill again, and this time Wilbur got in. The machine got a better start this time and went off like a bird. It flew near about a quarter of a mile, but was flying low, and Wilbur must have miscalculated the height of a sand ridge just where he expected to turn, and the rudder hit the sand. He brought the plane down, and we dragged it back to the hill again.[4]

"They were going to fix the rudder and try another flight when I got my first—and, God help me—my last flight.

"A breeze that had been blowing about twenty-five miles an hour suddenly jumped to thirty-five miles or more, caught the wings of the plane, and swept it across the beach just like you've seen an umbrella turned inside out and loose in the wind. I had hold of an upright of one of the wings when the wind caught it, and I got tangled up in the wires that held the thing together.

"I can't tell to save my life how it all happened, but I found myself caught in them wires and the machine blowing across the beach, heading for the ocean, landing first on one end and then on the other, rolling over and over, and me getting more tangled up in it all the time. I tell you, I was plumb scared. When the thing did stop for half a second I nearly broke up every wire and upright getting out of it.

They Thought It Was a Fake

"I wasn't hurt much; I got a good many bruises and scratches and was so scared I couldn't walk straight for a few minutes. But the Wright boys ran up to me, pulled my legs and arms, felt of my ribs and told me there were no bones broken. They looked scared too.

"The machine was a total wreck. The Wrights took it to pieces, packed it up in boxes and shipped it back to their home in Dayton. They gave us a few pieces for souvenirs, and I have a piece of the upright that I had hold of when it caught me up and blew away with me.

"We didn't see anything more of the Wright boys until the spring of 1908. You see, they had to do a lot of work back in Dayton to fix that machine up with wings that would take advantage of shiftin' winds instead o' keeling over to 'em.[5]

"When they finally came back, the newspaper fellows got onto them. A man named Salley came down from Norfolk, hid out in a marsh about a mile away from the camp, and sent out the first newspaper story.

"I remember a lot of papers wouldn't print it and thought Salley was faking.

"But some of the papers printed the telegram, and then the newspaper men from up North began to flock down to Kill Devil Hills to see for themselves.

"But none of those newspaper men ever got close enough to the machine to tell the truth about it, and none of 'em talked to the Wrights. The Wrights wouldn't even take the machine out of its shed when they discovered the newspaper men around. It was funny the way those New York newspaper men hid around in the bushes a mile or more away from the Wright's camp and wrote interviews with Wilbur and Orville. But I reckon they had to earn their money somehow."

Captain Daniels warped the Morehead City–Beaufort ferryboat into its dock at Beaufort and rested on his wheel while his eyes scanned the horizon far out on the open sea.

"That little rascal Lindbergh, who flew from New York to Paris, is telling it that running a flying machine is safe as running an automobile and a whole lot easier. Maybe so; I'm not denying it. As for me, I want the deck of good old boat or the solid earth under my feet. I got caught up in an airplane once, and that was enough for me.

"I like to think about it now; I like to think about that first airplane the way it sailed off in the air at Kill Devil Hills that morning, as pretty as any bird you ever laid your eyes on. I don't think I ever saw a prettier sight in my life. Its wings and uprights were braced with new and shiny copper piano wires. The sun was shining bright that morning, and the wires just blazed in the sunlight like gold. The machine looked like some big, graceful golden bird sailing off into the wind.

"I think it made us all feel kind o' meek and prayerful like. It might have been a circus for some folks, but it wasn't any circus for us who had lived close by those Wright boys during all the months until we were as much wrapped up in the fate of the thing as they were.

"It wasn't luck that made them fly; it was hard work and hard common sense; they put their whole heart and soul and all their energy into an idea and they had the faith. Good Lord, I'm a-wondering what all of us could do if we had faith in our ideas and put all our heart and mind and energy into them like those Wright boys did!"

---

1. *Collier's Weekly,* September 17, 1927, 24, 56.
2. The Wrights' powered airplane was larger and much heavier than their earlier gliders. It measured 40 feet, 4 inches, in span and weighed 605 pounds without the pilot, so it could not be easily carried and hand launched like the gliders. To accommodate the more substantial craft, the Wrights set up a simple 60-foot launching rail to support the airplane during its takeoff run. The rail was made from four 15-foot two-by-fours laid end to end and sheathed with a metal strip. The Flyer rode down this track on a small, wheeled dolly, or "truck" as the Wrights called it. The brothers humorously referred to the launching rail as "the Grand Junction Railroad."
3. Daniels is referring to the one-wheeled dolly the airplane sat upon when being moved and when taking off, not an actual wheel mounted on the aircraft itself.
4. This was actually the fourth flight. Wilbur and Orville took turns piloting the Flyer. Wilbur made the second flight, covering 175 feet. Orville was back at the controls for the third flight, traveling approximately 200 feet for a duration of 15 seconds. On the fourth and final flight, Wilbur was in the air 59 seconds and traveled a distance of 852 feet.
5. The Wrights returned to Kitty Hawk in 1908 with a modified version of their third powered airplane, first flown in 1905. The 1903 airplane was never flown again after the history-making first flights on December 17, 1903.

71 • WITH THE WRIGHTS AT KITTY HAWK: ANNIVERSARY OF FIRST FLIGHT TWENTY-FIVE YEARS AGO[1]

Captain William J. Tate

Captain William J. Tate, keeper of the Light House Depot at Coinjock, N.C., was born sixty-eight years ago in Kitty Hawk, N.C., and in his home Wilbur Wright stayed on his arrival there in September 1900, until joined by Orville Wright; in his yard the first Wright glider was assembled. As a member of the National Aeronautic Association, Captain Tate has given the Review a share of his many recollections of the early efforts of the Wrights.

In this year of our Lord 1928, when the world has become air-minded; when we speak of altitudes of nearly eight miles as mere nothings; when dawn to sunset flights are being made across the continent without creating much comment; after the world has been air-girdled; the Pacific spanned in single bullseye shots thousands of miles in length but accurate to the dot in the hitting of small islands; when the transatlantic passenger airships actually are carrying passengers for so much per ticket, it has been thought by some (not I) that it would be well for the writer to contribute an article relative to the impressions upon the natives of that lonely coast line strip of North Carolina where the Wrights chose to conduct their first experiments.

The writer would have to be versatile even to hope to make the average reader see those early days twenty-five years ago as we natives saw them at the time of the advent of the Wrights. You first must firmly fix in your mind some facts regarding the section to which they came, and you must fully understand the viewpoint of the average man there, his surroundings and his contact with the outside world before you can begin to appreciate how he felt about those "two crazy nuts" who thought that they could fly.

This coast strip of country is peopled by a hardy race of men who are principally the descendants of shipwrecked forefathers. Nearly all of us can trace our ancestry to a shipwreck on the bleak coast harking back to the days when navigation was not aided by the many safety devices that now are in vogue, and when the coast was unprotected by Coast Guard service. The writer is the son of a shipwrecked Scotsman.

Denied the advantages of good schools, subsisting upon the fruits of a battle with the sea, having little or no transportation, and being out of touch with the outside world, the average man had become immune to the fact that there was anything new. It is true that at the time the Wrights found us, we had a telegraph line running down the coast, and we had a daily mail, but these innovations were of recent date, and as there was no use for the telegraph line other than for the Weather Bureau's purpose of sending observations of the weather, it had just as well not existed.

Therefore at the time the Wrights arrived in our community, we were set in our ways. We believed in a good God, a bad Devil, and a hot Hell, and more than anything else we believed that the same good God did not intend man should ever fly. Our reasoning was to the effect, that nearly, if not everything, was mapped out, and finally decided upon "in the beginning", and that if it had been intended that man should fly, he would already be flying, or at least wing feathers would have been growing on his shoulders. "No Sirree", was the average logical way that it was frequently summed up, "God didn't intend that man should fly, and what God didn't intend won't ever be done".

I am a native of this coast section myself, and while I am putting down here the true mental attitude of the average coast man at the advent of the Wrights, I want it understood that I make no apology for this. I will not plead our isolation, the result of viewpoints arrived at on account of the lives we led, or the lack of surrounding environments calculated to make a person more progressive mentally. It is a fact that certain eminent scientific men before, and even after Orville Wright had made the first flight, had proven mathematically that it was impossible to fly. Therefore we were upheld in our opinions both before and after the first flight by minds more brilliant than ours.

The first news of the Wrights at Kitty Hawk, was the receipt of a letter by the postmaster, which in terse and plain phraseology, asked the postmaster for a description of the beach, stating that he and his brother were thinking of carrying on experiments in scientific kite flying during their vacation. The postmaster was Mrs. Addie M. Tate, wife of Captain W. J. Tate. Captain Tate was assistant postmaster, and upon him devolved the duties of the office, and it was he who answered the letter boosting Kitty Hawk as such a spot, giving a good description of the beach, the Kill Devil Hills, etc. In his letter Wilbur Wright said: "An ideal location would be some place with a level plain free from trees and shrubbery. If there were some prominent elevation such as a high hill without trees it would add very much to the desirability."

In reply I wrote: "At Kitty Hawk there is a strip of bald sand beach, free from trees, with practically nothing growing on it except an occasional bunch of buffalo grass. This strip of beach is about 1500 yards wide from ocean to bay, and extends many miles down the coast. The average elevation is from 8 to 20 feet above sea level, but at certain places drifting sand hills have been piled up by the wind until some of them (the Kill Devil Hill) have reached an elevation of 75 to 100 feet above the plain. The prevailing winds are from the northeast, and these hills are very steep on the southwest side, but not so steep on the northeast side. I would say that they average from 20 to 45 degrees on the south side." I did not say a word about transportation facilities, neither did I give a word of direction about how to get to Kitty Hawk. Mr. Wright never forgot to joke me about this lack of information, which no doubt was impressed on him during the wearisome trip from Elizabeth City to Kitty Hawk. Wilbur Wright must have been thoroughly sold on Kitty Hawk as a glider resort. He never went to the trouble to write further, but made his preparations and left Dayton for Kitty Hawk.

On the morning of September 12th, 1900, I answered a knock at the door of my humble domicile, and found a neighbor's boy, Elijah W. Baum, and a strange gentleman who took off his cap and introduced himself as Wilbur Wright of Dayton, Ohio, "To whom you wrote concerning this section". He was invited in and asked to be seated and we began a conversation.

There and then Wilbur Wright proceeded to unfold a tale of hardship on his trip from Elizabeth City to Kitty Hawk, stating that he had been some 48 or more hours on the way. He told me of how the miserable little boat had to run for harbor in a blow, and how he could not eat the provender cooked by the two men on the boat, and how consequently he had been without food for 48 hours. His account of the trip really amused me, I had heard the same before by others not accustomed to small boats in crossing our North Carolina Sounds. He was a tenderfoot and of course had a tale of woe to tell. His graphic description of the rolling of the boat and his story that the muscles of his arms ached from holding on, were interesting, but when he said that he had fasted for 48 hours that was a condition that called for a remedy at once.[2] Therefore we soon had him seated to a good breakfast of fresh eggs, ham and coffee, and I assure you he did his duty by them.

A day or two of rest put him back to normal, and I went with him to the Kill Devil Hills and to the Coast Guard Station, where he met and talked with many of our citizens. The weekly freight boat having made a trip to Elizabeth City, his paraphernalia was brought to our home and on September 17th, he began to first work on assembling the 1900 glider. Then we natives got curious and began to discuss him and his darn fool contraption that he was sewing, glueing, and tying together with string. In the meantime it had been drawn out of him by adroit questioning that his brother would be down in a couple of weeks, they were going to live in a tent and were going to make some experiments with their contraption in the art of flying. Immediately it became public information that he was inventing a flying machine, and of course all the various and sundry comments were indulged in whenever two or more natives were gathered together. If comment and criticism had been a helping factor the Wrights would have flown soon after their arrival at Kitty Hawk.

September 28th, Orville arrived, and the brothers went into a tent to live over on the beach. I made a trip to the city for them and purchased various articles, such as dishes, an oil stove, and gasoline, and when they left in the autumn I purchased these new innovations from them. They also gave me the remains of the 1900 glider and I brought it back where it was first assembled and took the frame apart. Mrs. Tate salvaged the sateen coverings and that is why our two little girls, aged three and four, wore dresses made from the wing coverings of the 1900 glider.

Of their return to Kitty Hawk, in 1901, 1902 and 1903; of their persistent efforts and experiments which led to that first successful flight, all of which is known to the ordinary school boy; of their return to the Hills in 1908 when the news broke over a dense world that the Wrights were actually flying, a volume could be written. Much also could be written concerning their return again in 1911.[3] That has all been told by others more capable of giving the account than the writer of this simple tale, but from the many articles that have been written some things have not been stressed.

At this writing the world is preparing to do honor to the Wrights by the erection of a Federal memorial on the top of Kill Devil Hills,[4] and the National Aeronautic

Association is also preparing to erect a Boulder at the spot where the first flight was made. Care has been taken by this Association to have a majority of the living eye witnesses assemble at the site and agree upon, and mark the actual spot of the first flight.

With the whole world vying with itself to do honor to the genius of the Wrights, and with many of our prominent citizens here in eastern North Carolina trying to make the impression that "they knew the Wrights would fly", I am telling the world that 99 per cent. and .99 of the other per cent. of the world back in 1900 to 1903 simply believed them to be a pair of harmless nuts, not dangerous, but simply crazy on the subject of flying like an over-ardent or enthusiastic person will sometimes become over something new.

I believe I am the first man to advocate a monument or a memorial at Kitty Hawk in honor of the Wrights. As far back as in 1912 after the death of Wilbur Wright, in a letter to the Custodian of the Hall of History, Raleigh, North Carolina, and also in another letter to a school mate who is very interested in local historical events, I said:

"I want to put myself on record by saying that we North Carolinians are lacking in civic pride. We are prone to pass unnoticed historical events that are momentus, remember them later and do nothing about it. If Virginia Dare had been born in Massachusetts instead of North Carolina, a shaft piercing the sky would mark the spot instead of the simple monument that now exists. If Wilbur Wright had begun the assembly of that first 1900 experimental glider which led to man's conquest of the air on the front yard of some citizen in California, as he began it in my front yard here in North Carolina, tons of printers ink would have been spread over the event, a monument would have marked the spot, and tourists would have come from thousands of miles, just to see and stand on the spot. Verily, we Tar Heels are very much lacking along the lines of the preservation of our epoch-making events of history."

---

1. *Aeronautic Review,* December 1928, 188–92. Reprinted with the permission of the National Aeronautic Association, Arlington, Va.
2. The only thing Wilbur had had to eat during the previous forty-eight hours was a small jar of jelly that his sister, Katharine, had slipped into his suitcase.
3. See document 33, note 2.
4. See document 67, note 7.

72 • I WAS HOST TO WRIGHT BROTHERS AT KITTY HAWK[1]

Captain W. J. Tate

December 17th, 1903—December 17th, 1943. What an era! Has any man ever lived with an imagination elastic enough, if he had been standing on the bleak sand dunes of the North Carolina coast when Orville Wright first lifted himself into the air on that epochal morning, to have predicted one-half what has happened since?

No. Imagination is an elastic article, but no such imagination has ever existed.

As the fortieth anniversary of flight approaches, the Governor of North Carolina, the State in which this feat was performed, has declared that December 17th shall be known as Kitty Hawk Day. He has appointed a committee, composed of: Congressman of the First District of North Carolina, the Ex-Secretary of the Navy under Woodrow Wilson, and Ex-Ambassador to Mexico, to formulate plans for a celebration, with Gen. H. H. Arnold among the speakers. The people of the coast section are preparing to outdo themselves. Fighters, scouters, and bombers will participate. The writer has had the temerity to believe that a word or two from him, who was North Carolina's first contact with Wilbur and Orville Wright, might find their way into print and add his mite to the memorable occasion.

On other occasions I have had the pleasure of relating in detail how Wilbur Wright knocked on the door of my home one evening, introduced himself, and inquired whether he and his brother, who was still in Ohio, might arrange to stay with my family until they could pitch camp. One of the most memorable episodes in anyone's life would be the honor of having in his home Wilbur and Orville Wright at the very beginning of their experiments which resulted in their immortal achievement.

With all oceans spanned; round-the-world flights in a few days a common procedure; with our bombers and fighter planes carrying death, destruction and devastation to the enemies of the Allies; with no place on earth farther than sixty hours from your nearest airport; with the prospects of commerce by air after peace to astound all of us who can read or dream, I thought it would be well to hark back to the 1900–1903 era and just say, "What fools we mortals be!"

It's not in my power to make the average reader realize the world's attitude towards the two men from Dayton who appeared on the scene at Kitty Hawk in August, 1900. The latent curiosity of the natives of Kitty Hawk was aroused when word got out that they were here to experiment with the invention of a flying machine. The community of Kitty Hawk at that time was a hardy race, chiefly the descendants of shipwrecked sailors whom storm and misfortune had cast upon the shores of the North Carolina coast. (I am the descendent of a shipwrecked father born in Scotland.)

The natives were isolated, having little communication with the outside world. While it is true that the old Life Saving Service gave employment to some, and there was a Government telegraph line and a telegraph office, this telegraph service was used for observations of the weather and tracing the track of tropical hurricanes which sometimes swept the coast and brought destruction to shipping. There was little commercial use made of this telegraph line.

I have said that we were isolated. In the phrasing of today, brother, you can say *that* again. It was double-barreled ISOLATION. Few strangers from other parts entered our midst. The annual and semi-annual visits of the higher officials of the Life Saving Service were monumental events in our lives. Being ISOLATED meant that we were narrow in viewpoint; our yardstick in the measurement of world affairs was more than a few inches short; our horizon was strictly limited. A lack of the proper school facilities contributed largely to our cramped existence.

This is admitted, not to belittle the citizenship, but in a horse-sense way to show why we, in 1900, thought the Wrights were a couple of nuts; harmless, but definitely wearing bats in their belfries.

I do not want to apologize for this attitude. History has shown since that we were in eminent company. Because outside of a few scientists and students of aerodynamics in this Nation and the rest of the world, every one thought the same thing about anyone who would think seriously about flying. I exclude from this category the several intrepid characters who had carried on diverse gliding experiments. I wish to make my meaning plain by saying that I refer to the average run-of-mine human being, who had a living to make, at that time. The whole darn world thought the same way we citizens of Kitty Hawk did on the subject of flying. Again we were in excellent company, because, if I am right in my history, a distinguished scientist in March, 1904, some three months after the Wrights had made those four flights at Kitty Hawk, read a paper before an imposing body of deep thinkers, proving scientifically, mathematically, theoretically, and morally, that flight with a heavier-than-air contraption was impossible until the Law of Gravitation had been repealed.

This one thing, if nothing else, would preclude the necessity for making apology for the mental attitude of the people of our community towards the Wrights and their ideas when they first appeared on the scene at Kitty Hawk.

Time went on. The Wrights, in the face of ridicule, continued their experments during the summers and autumns of 1900–1901–1902–1903, making four separate seasons of practical demonstration.

They were familiar to most of the natives. Their uniform courtesy to everyone had built up a respect and regard "for the two nuts," which tempered very greatly the attitude which prevailed at first. Time and association, that great leveler, had brought about this attitude, and parents began naming their boys Wilbur and Orville.

Prior to the first flight a few of our people had persuaded themselves that there was a remote chance that the Wrights might succeed, and it was laughable to note how many skeptics were converted to devout believers just as soon as the first flight had been made. There was many a I TOLD YOU SO after that first flight.

This was not the case throughout the rest of the world, and it took many years, or up to about 1908, before mankind accepted the fact that the Wrights had flown in a heavier-than-air machine.[2] Europe, I might say, accepted the fact and began to outstrip us in airmindedness—a fact which I hate to acknowledge.

The airplane of today is accepted as being the greatest instrument of destruction to life and property the world has ever seen; but in the face of that fact, I have a hope and belief that we will see it, after peace is declared, as the greatest preserver of peace the world has ever seen. It is an instrument with which we can map whole countries in a short while. It can penetrate the camouflage of any warlike nation which thinks it has a divine right to perpetrate such atrocious crimes as the world has experienced in the present war, and to prevent all such nations from committing the indescribable crimes now being perpetrated.

May God speed that day, is my prayer!

1. *U.S. Air Services,* December 1943, 29–30.
2. Although news of the Wrights' achievement had filtered out through press accounts and witnesses to the Wrights' continued experimenting in Dayton, Ohio, in 1904 and 1905, the brothers did not make their first major public flights until the summer of 1908. With those flights all doubt about what the brothers had achieved was erased.

73 • MY STORY OF THE WRIGHT BROTHERS[1]

Charles E. Taylor, as told to Robert S. Ball

When the boys flew at Kitty Hawk, I thought their success was pretty nice. But there weren't any jig steps. They were quite matter-of-fact about things.

It was a hot June night in Dayton. It must have been a Saturday because I was at the Wright Cycle Company gassing with Wilbur and Orville. They used to stay open Saturday nights to take care of the folks who worked all week and couldn't get around any other time.

One of the brothers, I forget which, asked me how would I like to go to work for them. There were just the two of them in the shop and they said they needed another hand. They offered me $18 a week. That was pretty good money; it figured to 30 cents an hour. I was making 25 cents at the Dayton Electric Company, which was about the same as all skilled machinists were getting.

The Wright shop was only six blocks from where I lived—at Calm and Gale streets—and I could bicycle to lunch. Besides, I liked the Wrights. So I said all right and I reported in on June 15th. That was in 1901.

I was a machinist and had done job work for the boys in my own shop. Once I made up a coaster brake they had invented but they dropped it later. I knew they were interested in box kites and gliders, and that they had gone South to Kitty Hawk, North Carolina, in 1900 with a glider. I didn't know anything about that stuff but I did know something about the bicycle business.

Three weeks after I went to work for the Wrights they took off for the South with another glider and I was alone in charge of their bicycle company. They trusted me to handle not only their customers but their money.

When they returned that year they decided to build a small wind tunnel to test out some of their theories on wings and control surfaces. We made a rectangular-shaped box with a fan at one end powered by the stationary gas engine they had built to drive the lathe, drill press and band saw. I ground down some old hack-saw blades for them to use in making balances for the tunnel. Nowadays, wind tunnels run into the millions of dollars and some are big enough to hold full-scale airplanes.[2]

That was the first work they asked me to do in connection with their flying experiments. For a long while, though, I was kept busy enough repairing bicycles and waiting on customers. The Wrights did most of their experimenting upstairs where they had a small office and workroom. I worked in the shop in the back room on the first floor.

It was part of my job to open up at 7:00 a.m. They would get in a little later, between eight and nine o'clock. We all stayed until closing time at six. We went home for lunch, but at different times so we didn't have to close the shop. Their father, Milton Wright, was a bishop in the United Brethren Church and the boys never worked on Sunday.

My wife's people had lived in Dayton years before and had become acquainted with Bishop Wright. He even visited them after they moved to Nebraska where I met and married Mrs. Taylor. And her uncle owned the building the Wright Brothers rented for their bicycle business. But I had never heard of the Wrights until I moved to Dayton and met them in the course of some work they brought into my shop around 1898.

So far as I can figure out, Will and Orv hired me to worry about their bicycle business so they could concentrate on their flying studies and experiments. I suppose the more of the routine work I shouldered, the faster they were able to get on with their pet project—and I must have satisfied them for they didn't hire anyone else for eight years. If they had any idea in June of 1901 that someday they'd be making a gasoline internal-combustion engine for an airplane and would need some first-rate machinework for it, they sure didn't say anything about it to me.

But when they returned from the South in 1902, they said they were through with gliders and were going to try a powered machine. They figured they'd need a larger machine to carry the motor and they started work on the new biplane right away. At the same time they tried to locate a motor. They wrote to a dozen companies, some of them in the automobile business, requesting one that would produce 12 horsepower but wouldn't weigh too much. Nothing turned up.

So they decided to build one of their own. They figured on four cylinders and estimated the bore and stroke at four inches. While the boys were handy with tools, they had never done much machinework and anyway they were busy on the air frame. It was up to me. My only experience with a gasoline engine was an attempt to repair one in an automobile in 1901.

We didn't make any drawings. One of us would sketch out the part we were talking about on a piece of scratch paper and I'd spike the sketch over my bench.

It took me six weeks to make that engine. The only metal-working machines we had were a lathe and a drill press, run by belts from the stationary gas engine. The crankshaft was made out of a block of machine steel 6 by 31 inches and one and five-eighths inches thick. I traced the outline on the slab, then drilled through with the drill press until I could knock out the surplus pieces with a hammer and chisel. Then I put it in the lathe and turned it down to size and smoothness. It weighed 19 pounds finished and she balanced up perfectly, too.

The completed engine weighed 180 pounds and developed 12 horsepower at 1,025 revolutions per minute.

And that reminds me: The engine in the Kitty Hawk machine that's been in England for the last 20 years isn't the original motor entirely. Somebody got away with the original crankshaft and flywheel at an Eastern air show,[3] and I had to make new parts to complete the original engine.

Data on the First Engine

The body of the first engine was of cast aluminum, and was bored out on the lathe for independent cylinders. The pistons were cast iron, and these were turned down and grooved for piston rings. The rings were cast iron, too. While I was doing all this work on the engine, Will and Orv were busy upstairs working on the air frame. They asked me to make the metal parts, such as the small fittings where the wooden struts joined the spars and the truss wires were attached. There weren't any turnbuckles in the truss wires, so the fit had to be just so. It was so tight we had to force the struts into position.

The fuel system was simple. A one-gallon fuel tank was suspended from a wing strut, and the gasoline fed by gravity down a tube to the engine. The fuel valve was an ordinary gaslight pet cock. There was no carburetor as we know it today. The fuel was fed into a shallow chamber in the manifold. Raw gas blended with air in this chamber, which was next to the cylinders and heated up rather quickly, thus helping to vaporize the mixture. The engine was started by priming each cylinder with a few drops of raw gas.

The ignition was the make-and-break type. No spark plugs. The spark was made by the opening and closing of two contact points inside the combustion chamber. These were operated by shafts and cams geared to the main camshaft. The ignition switch was an ordinary single-throw knife switch we bought at the hardware store. Dry batteries were used for starting the engine and then we switched onto a magneto bought from the Dayton Electric Company. There was no battery on the plane.

Several lengths of speaking tube, such as you find in apartment houses, were used in the radiator.

The chains to drive the propeller shafts were specially made by the Indianapolis Chain Company, but the sprockets came ready-made. Roebling wire was used for the trusses.[4]

I think the hardest job Will and Orv had was with the propellers. I don't believe they ever were given enough credit for that development. They had read up on all that was published about boat propellers, but they couldn't find any formula for what they needed. So they had to develop their own, and this they did in the wind tunnel.

They concluded that an air propeller was really just a rotating wing, and by experimenting in the wind box they arrived at the design they wanted. They made the propellers out of three lengths of wood, glued together at staggered intervals. Then they cut them down to the right size and shape with a hatchet and drawshave. They were good propellers.[5]

We never did assemble the whole machine at Dayton. There wasn't room enough in the shop. When the center section was assembled, it blocked the passage between the front and back rooms, and the boys had to go out the side door and around to the front to wait on the customers.

We still had bicycle customers. The Wright Brothers had to keep that business going to pay for the flying experiments. There wasn't any other money.

While the boys always worked hard, and there never was any horseplay around the shop, they always seemed to find time to stop and talk with a customer or humor the neighborhood children who wandered in. Sometimes I think the kids were the only ones who really believed that Will and Orv would fly. They hadn't learned enough to say it couldn't be done.

We block-tested the motor before crating it for shipment to Kitty Hawk. We rigged up a resistance fan with blades an inch and a half wide and five feet two inches long. The boys figured out the horsepower by counting the revolutions per minute. Those two sure knew their physics. I guess that's why they always knew what they were doing and hardly ever guessed at anything.

We finally got everything crated and on the train. There was no ceremony about it, even among ourselves. The boys had been making these trips for four years, and this was the third time I had been left to run the shop. If there was any worry about the flying machine not working, they never showed it and I never felt it.

You know, it's a funny thing, but I'm not sure just how or when I learned that Will and Orv had actually flown the machine. They sent a telegram to the bishop saying they had made four successful powered flights that day—December 17, 1903—and would be home for Christmas.

I suppose their sister Katharine or maybe the bishop came over and told me about it. I know I thought it was pretty nice that they had done what they set out to do; and I was glad to hear that the motor ran all right. But I don't remember doing any jig steps. The boys were always so matter-of-fact about things; and they never made any effort to get me excited.

Even when they got home there was no special celebration in the shop. Of course they were pleased with the flight. But their first word with me, as I remember, was about the motor being damaged when the wind picked up the machine and turned it topsy-turvy after Wilbur had completed the fourth flight. They wanted a new one built right away. And they were concerned with making improvements in the controls. They were always thinking of the next thing to do; they didn't waste much time worrying about the past.

The Wrights didn't go into the airplane experiment with the idea of making a lot of money. They just seemed to be curious about the problems involved—I suppose you would call it a challenge—and they determined to find out why they couldn't make it work. It was not a game with them or a sport. It may have been a hobby at the start, but now it was a serious business.

I was happy, working for Will and Orv, and I know they were pleased with my work. They showed it in many ways. Orville even left me an $800 annuity in his will. When I finally left his employ in 1919 he could have forgotten about me then and there. But the fact he did not helps me believe he appreciated that I had a part in giving the airplane to the world, though nobody made any fuss about it and I didn't either.

Will and Orv were always thoughtful at Christmastime. The second year I was with them they gave me a two-inch micrometer. Another year it was a one-foot scale. And one Christmas they gave me a $10 gold piece.

People have asked me if I knew why neither Wilbur nor Orville ever married, particularly since their older brothers Reuchlin and Lorin and their sister Katharine did. I'm sure I never asked them, but I remember that Orv used to say it was up to Will to marry first because he was the older of the two. And Will kept saying he didn't have time for a wife. But I think he was just woman-shy—young women, at least.

He would get awfully nervous when young women were around. When we began operating at Simms Station on the outskirts of Dayton in 1904, we always went out on the traction cars. If an older woman sat down beside him, before you knew it they would be talking and if she got off at our stop he'd carry her packages and you'd think he had known her all his life. But if a young woman sat next to him he would begin to fidget and pretty soon he would get up and go stand on the platform until it was time to leave the car.

I don't recall that Orville was that shy, but after Wilbur died I guess he just didn't feel like getting married. I think both the boys were mentally flying all the time and simply didn't think about girls.

They were both fond of children, though. Orville, especially, was quite a hand with kids. He used to make toys there in the shop and give them away. Later, he designed a little wooden man on a flying trapeze and licensed some company to make it.

The Wrights didn't drink or smoke, but they never objected too much to my cigar smoking. I used to smoke around 25 cigars a day. Once I walked down the street with three cigars going at once—you know how a young fellow does crazy things once in a while.

Both the boys had tempers, but no matter how angry they ever got, I never heard them use a profane word. I never swore, myself, and to this day I can't think of a time I ever let go with anything stronger than heckety-hoo. The boys were working out a lot of theory in those days, and occasionally they would get into terrific arguments. They'd shout at each other something terrible. I don't think they really got mad, but they sure got awfully hot.

Both Admitted Being Wrong

One morning following the worst argument I ever heard, Orv came in and said he guessed he'd been wrong and they ought to do it Will's way. A few minutes later Will came in and said he'd been thinking it over and perhaps Orv was right. First thing I knew they were arguing the thing all over again, only this time they had switched ideas. When they were through though, they knew where they were and could go ahead with the job.

It was Orville who gave me my first flight. He first offered me a hop in 1908 at Fort Myer, Virginia, when we were demonstrating the Wright airplane for the first Army contract (which it later won). I was in the passenger's seat and we were preparing to take off when a high-ranking officer asked Orville if he would mind taking along an Army observer instead.

Naturally I got out and Lieutenant Thomas E. Selfridge took my place. The machine crashed shortly after the takeoff. Lieutenant Selfridge was killed and Orville was seriously injured. Lieutenant Selfridge was the first military air casualty, and a big Air Force fighter base at Mount Clemens, Michigan, is named for him. Since then, a lot of people say they have narrowly avoided being killed in airplanes by a last-minute switch in plans. Maybe I was the first, though.

In May, 1910, Orv finally took me up. It was at Simms Station,[6] and he did what a lot of pilots have done in later years with their first-flight passengers. He tried to give me a scare. We were flying around over the field when suddenly the plane began to pitch violently. I grabbed hold of a strut and looked over at Orv. He didn't seem upset, although he appeared to be having a hard time controlling the machine. Pretty soon the pitching stopped and we landed. Orv asked me if I were scared. I said, "No, if you weren't, why should I be?" He thought it was very funny.

I always wanted to learn to fly, but I never did. The Wrights refused to teach me and tried to discourage the idea. They said they needed me in the shop and to service their machines, and if I learned to fly I'd be gadding about the country and maybe become an exhibition pilot, and then they'd never see me again.

One of my jobs that summer of 1904 was as sort of airport manager at Simms Station. I suppose it was the first airport in the country, with all due respect to the sands of Kitty Hawk. It was a small pasture the boys had arranged to use. We built a shed for the machine and a catapult to assist in the take-offs,[7] because the field was small and rough.

It was made up of a wooden track and a tower at the starting end. We drew heavy weights to the top of the tower on ropes which were rigged through pulleys to the bottom of the tower, out to the take-off end of the track, and back to the airplane. When the weights were released, the machine would dart forward. Now people are fooling around with assisted take-offs again for big planes.

We were all very busy out at Simms Station that summer testing out the new airplane we built to replace the Kitty Hawk machine. We scarcely had time to keep the bicycle business going, and by the following summer the boys gave it up entirely.

I must have built half-a-dozen engines for the boys before the airplane company was formed in 1909 and they took on additional help.

They also had me doing repair work on the air frames, and as they began to travel around to demonstrate the machines it was up to me to help with the crating, uncrating and assembling.

A Futile Visit to France

I went to France in 1907 to be with Wilbur and Orville although we never did get around to uncrating the machine we shipped over on that trip. Some mix-up in the contract negotiations. Then I was at Governor's Island, New York with Wilbur for the Hudson-Fulton flight,[8] and at Montgomery, Alabama, with Orville to help set up the first flying school.[9]

After the company was started in 1909 the place was expanded, more men were hired, and I was put in charge of the engine shop with men working under me. Some of the personal feeling of the old days, when there were just the three of us, was gone. It was beginning to be big business. We had lots of orders and the first plane sold for private use was to Robert J. Collier. He was a close friend of Wilbur and Orville and owned stock in the company.

Then Calbraith Perry Rodgers came down to Dayton in 1911 to see about the machine he had ordered for his proposed transcontinental flight, and offered me $10 a day plus expenses to be his mechanic on the trip. At the time my wages were $25 a week. I told him I'd go; then I told Orv about it. He asked me not to quit. I told him I had already given my word to Rodgers and couldn't very well back out. He told me to make it a sort of leave of absence, and to be sure and come back.

Rodgers left the race track at Sheepshead Bay, Long Island, on September 17th, and reached Long Beach, California, 47 days later.[10] It was my job to care for the plane every night, and make re pairs after every mishap. I traveled on a special train that accompanied the flight. Rodgers failed to win the $50,000 prize posted by William Randolph Hearst because he took longer than 30 days to make the crossing. But it was the first coast-to-coast flight.

I didn't get in on the finish in California. My wife, with our three children—a boy sixteen, a girl fourteen and our five-week-old baby daughter—had preceded me to California. She was taken ill soon after their arrival, so I passed up the last two days of the flight to be with her.

Because of Mrs. Taylor's condition, I stayed on in California for nearly a year, working first for Roy Knabenshue, who was then the Wright exhibition manager,[11] and later for Glenn L. Martin.[12] Martin began building airplanes in 1909[13] in Los Angeles, and is still at it in Baltimore.

In the fall of 1912 I took my family back to Dayton, but left the baby in Los Angeles in the care of Mrs. I. C. Shafer. We had known her family for many years back in Ohio. Mrs. Taylor was again hospitalized and she remained so until her death in 1930.[14]

Back East, it wasn't like old times. Wilbur had died on May 30th, from typhoid fever and there were a lot of new faces around the Wright plant. The pioneering days seemed about over for me.

Maybe that's why that Christmas of 1912 stands out in my memory. It wasn't going to be a very happy one, for either the Wrights or the Taylors. Christmas Eve there came a knock at the door, and there was Orville with a big basket filled with everything for a big Christmas dinner. He just handed me the basket, wished us a "Merry Christmas," and went away. It was the first time he had ever come to our house.

I stayed on with Orville, after he sold the company in 1915 and retired to his laboratory.[15] I helped out with some of his inventions and experiments, and kept his car in good running order. But there was less and less work to do, and finally I got restless and took a job downtown with the Dayton-Wright Company in 1919.

In 1916 we took the Kitty Hawk plane out of storage and fixed it up for its first exhibition, at the Massachusetts Institute of Technology in Cambridge, Massachusetts.[16] If it hadn't been for Knabenshue, there might not have been the historic relic to exhibit there or in Washington, now. Roy tells how he approached Wilbur early in 1912 and asked him what he was going to do with the Kitty Hawk and Wilbur told him, "Oh, I guess we'll burn it; it's worthless." Roy argued it was historic and finally talked him out of destroying the plane.

It was then forgotten until Orville got this request to show it in Massachusetts. It came from Lester D. Gardner (then publisher of *Aviation* magazine, later an officer in the Army Air Service in the first World War and founder of the Institute of the Aeronautical Sciences) who was in charge of the aeronautical part of the dedication program of the new buildings of MIT at Cambridge. Orville was reluctant at first, but consented when Gardner and Roy convinced him how interesting it would be to the public.

Orville and I continued to see each other frequently after 1919. He used to bring odd jobs to me at the plant where I was working, and I would visit him at his laboratory. Then in 1928 I moved to California, and I didn't see him again until 1937. That was when Henry Ford hired me to help restore the original Wright home and shop when he moved them to his Greenfield Village museum at Dearborn, Michigan. They were installed on the grounds near the first Ford workshop and Thomas Edison's original laboratory.[17]

I helped Fred Black, the director of the project, track down the original machinery and furniture, and then I built a replica of the first Wright engine. The home and shop were dedicated in April, 1938, with all the big names in aviation on hand.

I met Orville often during this period, both in Dayton and in Dearborn. When I left the Village to return to California in 1941, I called on him in Dayton. That was the last time I saw him, but he wrote to me regularly about his work and I kept him posted on what I did. He wrote every December 17th. It was sort of a personal anniversary with us and it was also a Christmas message.

An epidemic of hog cholera was responsible for my career as a machinist and the honor of being the "third hand" of the Wright Brothers in the most important years of their lives.

I was born on a little farm on the banks of the Wabash near Cerro Gordo, Illinois, not far from Decatur, on May 24, 1868. I probably would have grown up to be a farmer but the cholera wiped us out and my father moved to Lincoln, Nebraska, to work with his brother in a bakery. I quit school at the end of the seventh grade and, though twelve years old, started work as errand boy on the *Nebraska State Journal*. Later I got a job in the *Journal*'s bindery and that's where I got my first chance to work with tools and machines. That kind of work just seemed to come natural to me, and I liked it.

I was doing business at Kearney, Nebraska, making all the metal house numbers in town, when I met Henrietta Webbert at the Jolly Young Men and Girls Club in 1892. Two years later we were married. Her family, as I've said, had lived in Dayton. They had returned there from Kearney when the depression hit early in the nineties. I was having a hard time finding work in Nebraska so when my wife's brother wrote there were jobs to be had in Dayton, we went there, too, in 1896.

In Dayton I went to work for the Stoddard Manufacturing Company. Stoddard made farm machinery but had gone into bicycle production and when I had spent two years on the production line and in the toolroom, I decided to open my own shop. It was here that Wilbur and Orville used to bring in special jobs, but by the time they asked me to work for them I had sold my place at a profit and was working at Dayton Electric Company. I never was much of a hand for that executive stuff and felt a lot happier just being around tools.

When I came out here to California in 1928 I got work in a machine shop in Los Angeles and then the big depression hit us. I was out of work but had saved some money. I invested this in 336 lots in a new land development on the edge of the Salton Sea, down in the southern California desert. I built a little house and sat around waiting for something to happen. Nothing did.

Job Hunting at Sixty-Seven

By 1935 I was down to my last nickel. So I sold the house and went to San Diego looking for a job. I was sixty-seven then but in fine shape. At the old Consolidated Aircraft Corporation, they told me they couldn't possibly hire anybody sixty-seven years old. I didn't tell them about working for the Wright Brothers. What difference should that make?

But up at North American Aviation in Los Angeles they didn't seem to care about my age and in a few weeks I was doing special work in the toolroom and the experimental shop. They gave me three raises in four weeks. I stayed there until Mr. Ford sent for me in 1937 to help out with the Wright restoration project.

That Greenfield Village thing was supposed to be sort of a lifetime job but there wasn't anything to do around the old shop so I left in 1941 and came back to Los Angeles. The war was on and I got a job at O'Keefe & Merritt Company, working on cartridge cases and electrical stuff. I worked 60 hours a week beside men half my age all through the war.

Then right after V-J Day I had a heart attack and had to stop working. I was seventy-seven then and had worked for 65 years.

There isn't much to do now. My hearing isn't as good and lately my eyes have begun to bother me. My family is scattered and I don't get to see much of them. I never kept in touch with the old aviation crowd—except Orville—and never went or was invited to any of the big celebrations they would hold every now and then in honor of the Wright Brothers and the advancement of aviation. I guess people didn't know where to find me.

I always wanted to go back into the laboratory with Orville. He hinted at it in some of his letters—saying he needed expert workmanship on his projects—but he never came right out and asked me. I had intended to go back East this past summer if my old pump would let me, but Orville died on January 30th.

In the last note I got from him, shortly before he died, he wrote: "I hope you are well and enjoying life; but that's hard to imagine when you haven't much work to do." It was signed "Orv." He knew me pretty well.

Shortly after he told the foregoing story, Mr. Taylor received an invitation from Paul Edward Garber, the Smithsonian Institution's Curator of Aeronautics, to serve as Superintendent of Inspection and Assembly of the Kitty Hawk plane prior to its formal exhibition in the National Museum in Washington on December 17th. Although assured that all arrangements for a journey from Los Angeles to Washington would be handled jointly by the Smithsonian and *Collier's* and that every provision would be made for his comfort and convenience, Mr. Taylor's physician advised it would be unwise for him to attempt the trip.[18]

1. *Collier's Weekly*, December 25, 1948, 27, 68, 70.
2. See document 5, note 15.
3. The crankshaft and the flywheel of the original 1903 engine were on display at a New York aeronautical exhibition in 1906. The items disappeared at the close of the show and have never been seen since. See also document 74, note 4.
4. See document 30, note 2.
5. See document 5, note 16.
6. The field itself was known as Huffman Prairie, a cow pasture eight miles outside of Dayton where the brothers did much of their experimental flying after 1903. The local interurban railway had a stop near the field called Simms Station.
7. See document 43, note 3.
8. See document 47, notes 2 and 3.
9. See document 33, note 5.
10. Rodgers actually reached Pasadena, California, in forty-nine days, on November 5, 1911, officially completing the coast-to-coast flight. On arrival he was offered $5,000 by the Long Beach Chamber of Commerce to fly on to their oceanfront community. Rodgers left for Long Beach on November 12. After a brief stop in Covina Junction because of an engine problem, he took off again for Long Beach. Over Compton the engine sputtered again. In his attempt to land, Rodgers crashed and was severely injured. On December 10, still not fully recovered from his injuries, Rodgers took off from Compton in his rebuilt Wright aircraft, dubbed the *Vin Fiz*. Finally, eighty-four days after beginning his

journey in New York, Cal Rodgers reached the Pacific Ocean at Long Beach. For a full account of Rodgers's transcontinental flight, see Eileen F. LeBow, *Cal Rodgers and the Vin Fiz: The First Transcontinental Flight* (Washington, D.C.: Smithsonian Institution Press, 1989), and E. P. Stein, *Flight of the Vin Fiz* (New York: Arbor House, 1985).

11. See document 36, note 2.
12. See document 55, note 5.
13. Recent research has demonstrated that Glenn L. Martin actually flew his first aircraft in 1910, not 1909, which has heretofore been given as the date in standard biographical accounts. See John R. Breihan, "From Amusements to Weapons: The Glenn L. Martin Aircraft Company of California, 1910–1917," *Journal of the West* 36 (July 1997): 30.
14. According to her death certificate, Charlie Taylor's wife, Henrietta Webbert Taylor, died on January 7, 1935, not in 1930. Her extended hospitalization was the result of what appeared to be mental illness. Her stated diagnosis was "psychosis." Actually, she had a condition known as Banti's syndrome, a disease of the spleen that constricts blood flow and that can cause symptoms that appear to be associated with a mental disorder. Banti's syndrome was not identified until after Henrietta became ill. After her death, an autopsy confirmed the presence of Banti's syndrome, unfortunately too late for Henrietta to have avoided living a life with the stigma of mental illness.
15. See document 53, note 10.
16. See Mabel Beck, "The First Airplane—After 1903" (document 74).
17. After being laid off during the Great Depression, Taylor lost his life's savings in a real estate venture. He was working for North American Aviation and making 37½ cents an hour when Ford found him and hired him to man the historic Wright bicycle shop that Ford had recently purchased and moved to Greenfield Village, Ford's museum of American ingenuity and achievement, in Dearborn, Michigan. See also document 74, note 3.
18. Charlie Taylor died in 1956 at age eighty-eight.

74 • THE FIRST AIRPLANE—AFTER 1903[1]

Mabel Beck

This account by Miss Beck, who joined The Wright Company in 1910 and served as secretary first to Wilbur Wright and then to Orville Wright until the latter's death in 1948, was written at the request of this magazine following the return of the first airplane from England to the United States and its deposit in the Smithsonian Institution on the forty-fifth anniversary of the first flight. Although it was never intended for publication, and is not in the form and style that the author might wish, we believe it is a document of great historical interest, first because of its subject, and second because Miss Beck is the only person still living who can state these particular facts with the authority of a participant.

James M. H. Jacobs, referred to in the text, died about ten years ago. He was one of The Wright Company's first employees, was foreman in the woodwork-

ing shop, and collaborated with Orville Wright from time to time in experimental work. He was co-inventor with Mr. Wright of the split flap.[2]

Miss Beck's statement, with slight editorial interpolations, is here printed for the first time.—Editor's Note

After the last flight on December 17, 1903, while the machine was left standing unguarded on the ground, it was struck by a sudden gust of wind which lifted it from the ground and rolled it over and over. The rudders [i.e., the elevators, in front, and vertical rudder, at the rear] were badly damaged, and some other parts broken.

When it was returned to Dayton, in 1903, the machine, in boxes, was stored in a shed in the rear of the old Wright workshop at 1127 W. Third Street. In December of 1910 the old workshop was remodeled, and the Wright offices were moved to the second floor at this address.[3]

The machine suffered most from going through the Dayton flood of March 1913. The greater part of the machine, still in the boxes in which it was shipped from Kitty Hawk to Dayton, lay several weeks in the water and mud. The water at the place of storage was ten to eleven feet deep in the street.

Not long afterwards, the shed in the rear [of 1127 W. Third Street] was torn down, and the boxes containing the 1903 plane were stored in a barn on the site of 15 N. Broadway. In the late summer of 1916 this barn was torn down and Mr. Wright put up his laboratory, which he still occupied at the time of his death.

In May 1916, Orville Wright was asked to exhibit the 1903 machine at the Massachusetts Institute of Technology at the time of the dedication of the new Institute buildings. The first week of June, the machine was taken from the barn to the Wright factory, where it was assembled by the factory workmen. The front and rear rudders had to be almost entirely rebuilt. The cloth and the main cross-spars of the upper and lower center sections of the wings also had to be made new. A number of other parts, such as ribs, had to be repaired.

All parts, except those mentioned and the motor, were the original parts of the 1903 machine. The motor now in the machine is a close copy of the 1903 motor but was built about a year later [for the 1904 machine in which it was used in the flights of that season]. The parts of the original 1903 motor were still at hand in 1948, except the crankshaft and flywheel. These were lent in 1906 to the Aero Club of America for exhibition at the aero show in that year and were not returned. They have never been found.[4]

Jim Jacobs, Wright Company mechanic, who in 1916 was at the Wright Company School at Mineola, L.I., was ordered to go to Boston to set up the machine at M.I.T. This was the first time the 1903 machine had been exhibited since the historic flights in December 1903. It was subsequently exhibited at the New York Aero

Show, February 1917, at the Society of Automotive Engineers Summer Meeting at Dayton in June 1918, at the New York Aero Show, February 1919, and for the last time in the United States at the National Air Races at Dayton in October 1924, after which it was returned to the laboratory at 15 N. Broadway for storage. Jim Jacobs had charge of assembling the machine at all of these exhibits.

In January 1921, it was set up at South Field, Dayton, which was owned by the Dayton-Wright Company, for purposes of obtaining testimony in the Montgomery *vs.* the United States & Wright-Martin Company suit. It had no motor installed in it. It was only up for a week or two and was then crated and returned to the laboratory at 15 N. Broadway for storage.

There the machine remained until it left Dayton for England on January 28, 1928. It was in place in the new section at the Science Museum, South Kensington, England, when that section was dedicated by King George V and Queen Mary on March 20, 1928.[5]

When, in December 1925, the decision was made to send the machine to England, the original cloth was in bad shape, very frail, dirty and badly worn from having been handled so much in setting up the machine at various exhibitions. Mr. Wright therefore decided to recover the entire machine with new cloth. The original cloth was "Pride of the West" muslin, not treated, and was purchased in 1903 from a Dayton dry goods store, the Rike-Kumler Company. In 1925 this particular muslin was not available in Dayton. Upon inquiry, we found "Pride of the West" in 1903 was made by the Slater Cotton Company. A letter was directed to this company, but, we learned, the Slater mill had been absorbed by the American Bleached Goods Company. This company, fortunately, was able to furnish "Pride of the West" and Mr. Wright ordered 125 yards. With this, the entire machine was recovered, wings, center sections, elevators, and rudder. (The 1904 and 1905 machines were also covered with "Pride of the West" muslin, not treated.)

Actual work on the machine was not started until December 1926. Jim Jacobs was hired to do the woodwork and assembly, and Mr. Wright and I laid out and cut all the cloth, and I did the sewing. Jacobs later did the crating. Only the three of us had anything to do with the final work on this machine. I arranged for the transportation from Dayton to London.

The machine was completely set up by March 1927. It stood in the laboratory until January 1928, when it was torn down and crated. I was custodian, and during Mr. Wright's summer vacation in Canada I went to the laboratory every day to see that everything was all right.

In June 1927, several weeks after his historic flight from New York to Paris, Col. Charles A. Lindbergh was in Dayton on a private visit to Mr. Wright. Very early one morning, in order to avoid the crowds that were pursuing him everywhere, Colonel Lindbergh, in company with Mr. Wright and General Gillmore, the commanding officer of Wright Field, came out to the laboratory to see the machine. Mr. Wright called me at my home about 6:30 a.m., saying they were coming out and for me to be there. I met Colonel Lindbergh at that time.

---

1. *U.S. Air Services,* December 1954, 9–10.
2. See document 61, note 2.
3. This was the last of several locations of the Wright Cycle Company in Dayton, where most of the research and building of the Wrights' experimental aircraft took place. The brothers moved into this shop in 1897. Although the Wrights were out of the bicycle business by 1905, the space at 1127 West Third Street was leased until 1916, when Orville moved into a new laboratory he had built near by. In 1936 Henry Ford purchased the shop at 1127 West Third Street for $13,000 and in 1937 moved it, along with the Wright brothers' home at 7 Hawthorn Street, to his museum of historic structures called Greenfield Village in Dearborn, Michigan. For further details on the Wrights' bicycle business, see Fred C. Fisk and Marlin W. Todd, *The Wright Brothers: From Bicycle to Biplane* (Dayton, Ohio: Toddfisk, 1995). See also document 53, note 10.
4. The article is slightly inaccurate in the statement that the motor mounted on the Wright Flyer when it was restored for display at MIT in 1916 was a *copy* of the one used in 1903. In fact, many of the internal components of the display motor did come from the original 1903 engine flown at Kitty Hawk—including three of the four cylinders and pistons, connecting rods, and other pieces. Further, the crankcase was built in 1904, as Beck states, but it was not part of the engine that powered the 1904 and 1905 aircraft. Two motors were made in 1904—one of four-inch bore like the 1903 engine, and one of four-and-one-eighth-inch bore. The latter was the engine flown in 1904 and 1905. The four-inch bore engine of 1904 was experimented with in the Wrights' workshop in 1904, 1905, and 1906, but it was never flown on an aircraft. The engine mounted on the Wright Flyer when it was prepared for public display in 1916 was composed of parts of the 1904 *test* engine, combined with the remaining original 1903 engine parts that were still on hand. The statement that the 1903 crankshaft and flywheel were never found after the 1906 Aero Club exhibition is accurate. The 1904 crankshaft was modified to the 1903 configuration when it was fitted to the display engine in 1916. For further details on the history of the Wright Flyer engine after 1903, see Rick Leyes, "The 1903 Wright Flyer Engine: A Summary of Research," in *National Air and Space Museum: Research Report, 1986* (Washington, D.C.: Smithsonian Institution Press, 1986), 185–97, and Marvin W. McFarland, ed., *The Papers of Wilbur and Orville Wright,* 2 vols. (New York: McGraw-Hill, 1953), appendix 5, "Aeroplanes and Motors," 2:1210–15.
5. See documents 17, 19, 20, and 24 regarding the Wright/Smithsonian controversy and the loan of the 1903 Wright airplane to the Science Museum in London.

BIBLIOGRAPHY

The historical literature on the story of Wilbur and Orville Wright is vast. *The Published Writings of Wilbur and Orville Wright* seeks to complement the many biographies, monographs, articles, reminiscences, technical analyses, and other treatments of the brothers' fascinating and accomplished lives. What follows is a selection of references and readings that add further detail and context to the Wrights' published writings gathered in this book.

Beyond published sources, there is a significant body of original manuscript material related to the Wright brothers. The majority of the primary documentation is held in two repositories: the Manuscript Division of the Library of Congress, Washington, D.C.; and the Wright State University Archives, Dayton, Ohio. Most of the correspondence, notebooks, and diaries focusing on the invention of the airplane are in the Library of Congress. The Wright State collection is made up largely of material concerning family history and legal documents pertaining to the patenting and sale of the airplane. Both of these archives also contain large photographic collections. An additional source of existing photographs related to the Wright brothers is the Archives Division, National Air and Space Museum, Smithsonian Institution, Washington, D.C. Lastly, a small amount of original Wright material is located at the Franklin Institute, Philadelphia, Pennsylvania.

Reference Works and Published Papers

Andrews, A. S. *The Andrews, Clapp, Stokes, Wright, Van Cleve Genealogies.* Fort Lauderdale, Fla.: Privately printed, 1984.

Kelly, Fred C., ed. *Miracle at Kitty Hawk: The Letters of Wilbur and Orville Wright.* New York: Farrar, Straus, and Young, 1951.

McFarland, Marvin W., ed. *The Papers of Wilbur and Orville Wright.* 2 vols. New York: McGraw-Hill, 1953.

Nolan, Patrick A., and Zamonski, John. *The Wright Brothers Collection: A Guide to the Technical, Business and Legal, Genealogical, Photographic, and Other Archives at Wright State University.* New York: Garland Publishing, 1977.

Renstrom, Arthur G. *Wilbur and Orville Wright: A Bibliography Commemorating the Hundredth Anniversary of the Birth of Wilbur Wright, April 16, 1867.* Washington, D.C.: Library of Congress, 1968.

———. *Wilbur and Orville Wright: A Chronology Commemorating the Hundredth Anniversary of the Birth of Orville Wright, August 19, 1871.* Washington, D.C.: Library of Congress, 1975.

———. *Wilbur and Orville Wright: Pictorial Materials, a Documentary Guide.* Washington, D.C.: Library of Congress, 1982.

Biographies

Combs, Harry. *Kill Devil Hill: Discovering the Secret of the Wright Brothers.* Englewood, Colo.: TernStyle Press, 1979.

Crouch, Tom D. *The Bishop's Boys: A Life of Wilbur and Orville Wright.* New York: W. W. Norton and Co., 1989.

Fitzgerald, Catharine, and Young, Rosamond. *Twelve Seconds to the Moon: A Story of the Wright Brothers.* Dayton, Ohio: Journal Herald, 1978.

Freudenthal, Elsbeth E. *Flight into History: The Wright Brothers and the Air Age.* Norman: University of Oklahoma Press, 1949.

Howard, Fred. *Wilbur and Orville: A Biography of the Wright Brothers.* New York: Knopf, 1987.

Kelly, Fred C. *The Wright Brothers: A Biography Authorized by Orville Wright.* New York: Harcourt, Brace and Co., 1943.

McMahon, John R. *The Wright Brothers: Fathers of Flight.* Boston: Little, Brown and Co., 1930.

Walsh, John Evangelist. *One Day at Kitty Hawk: The Untold Story of the Wright Brothers and the Airplane.* New York: Crowell, 1975.

Personal Reminiscences of the Wrights

Bauer, Charles J. "Ed Sines, Pal of the Wrights." *Popular Aviation,* June 1938, 40, 78.

Boston, Grace. "Wright Boys Interested in Aviation When They Were School Boys in This City." *Cedar Rapids Evening Gazette,* September 19, 1928.

Brewer, Griffith. "With the Wrights in America." *Flight,* September 3, 1910, 706–8.

———. "Wilbur Wright, Gold Medalist of the Society." *Aeronautical Journal* 16 (July 1912): 148–53.

Brookins, Walter R. "Early Days with the Wright Brothers." *Chirp,* June 1936, 3.

Claudy, Carl H. "With the Wright Brothers at Fort Myer." *World Today,* September 1909, 929–36.

Coffyn, Frank T. "Flying with the Wrights." *World's Work,* December 1929, 80–86, and January 1930, 76–82.

———. "Flying as It Was: Early Days at the Wrights' School." *Sportsman Pilot,* May 15, 1939, 14–15, 30–34.

Coffyn, Frank T., as told to W. B. Courtney. "I Got Up Early." *Collier's,* December 15, 1934, 25, 55–57.

Cox, James. "The Wright Brothers." In *Journey Through My Years,* 81–84. New York: Simon and Schuster, 1946.

de Lambert, Charles M. "My Memories of Wilbur Wright." *U.S. Air Services,* March 1935, 13–15.

Drinkwater, Alpheus W. "I *Knew* Those Wright Brothers Were Crazy." *Reader's Digest,* November 1956, 188–89, 192, 194.

Findley, Earl N. "The Wright Brothers and the Reporter." *Beehive* 28 (spring 1953): 25–29.

Kelly Fred C. "For the Wright Record." *Technology Review* 47 (June 1945): 484–85.

———. "Traits of the Wright Brothers." *Technology Review* 51 (June 1949): 504–7.

———. "At Home with the Wrights." *New York Times,* October 11, 1953, sec. 10, pp. 4.

Lahm, Frank S. "Flying with Wilbur Wright." *American Aeronaut,* August 1909, 19–22.

———. "Wilbur Wright's First Flights in France." *U.S. Air Services,* August 1924, 29–31.

———. "Training the Airplane Pilot." *Journal of the Royal Aeronautical Society* 37 (October 1933): 916–42.

———. "The Wright Brothers as I Knew Them." *U.S.A. Recruiting News,* May 1938, 4–7.

Loening, Grover. "First Flyer in More Ways Than One." *U.S. Air Services,* December 1943, 20.

Miller, Ivonette Wright. *Wright Reminiscences.* Dayton, Ohio: Ivonette Wright Miller, 1978.

Newton, Byron. "Watching the Wright Brothers Fly." *Aeronautics,* June 1908, 8.

Root, Amos I. "My Flying-Machine Story." *Gleanings in Bee Culture,* January 1, 1905, 36–39, 48.

Rouchier, Maurice. "Le premiers élèves de l'homme-oiseau." *La Vie au grand air,* March 13, 1909, 66–67.

Werthner, William. "Personal Recollections of the Wrights." *Aero Club of America Bulletin,* July 1912, 13.

Other Published Sources on the Wright Brothers and the Early History of the Airplane

Aero Club of America. *Navigating the Air: A Scientific Statement of the Progress of Aëronautical Science up to the Present Time.* New York: Doubleday, Page, and Co., 1907.

Bilstein, Roger E. *Flight Patterns: Trends of Aeronautical Development in the United States, 1918–1929.* Athens: University of Georgia Press, 1983.

Brewer, Griffith. "The Life and Work of Wilbur Wright," and "Wilbur Wright." *Aeronautical Journal* 20 (July-September 1916): 68–84, 128–35.

Brunsman, August E., and Charlotte K. Brunsman. "Wright & Wright, Printers: The 'Other' Career of Wilbur and Orville." *Printing History* 10, no. 1 (1988): 1–19.

Cayley, Elizabeth, and Gerard Fairlie. *The Life of a Genius.* London: Hodder and Stoughton, 1965.

Chandler, Charles deForest, and Frank P. Lahm. *How Our Army Grew Wings: Airmen and Aircraft before 1914.* New York: Ronald Press, 1943.

Chanute, Octave. *Progress in Flying Machines.* New York, 1894. Reprint, Long Beach, Calif.: Lorenz and Herweg, 1976.

———. "Gliding Experiments." *Journal of the Western Society of Engineers,* November 1897, 593–628.

———. "Experiments in Flying." *McClure's Magazine,* June 1900, 127–33.

Crouch, Tom D. *A Dream of Wings: Americans and the Airplane, 1875–1905.* New York: W. W. Norton and Co., 1981.

———. "The 1905 Wright Flyer: A Machine of Practical Utility." *Timeline,* August-September 1985, 24–37.

———. "How the Bicycle Took Wing." *American Heritage of Invention and Technology,* summer 1986, 10–16.

———. "Capable of Flight: The Feud between the Wright Brothers and the Smithsonian." *American Heritage of Invention and Technology,* spring 1987, 34–46.

———. "Capable of Flight: The Saga of the 1903 Wright Airplane." In *Exhibiting Dilemmas: Issues of Representation at the Smithsonian.* Ed. Amy Henderson and Adrienne Kaeppler. Washington, D.C.: Smithsonian Institution Press, 1997.

Davy, M. J. B. *Henson and Stringfellow: Their Work in Aeronautics.* London: His Majesty's Stationery Office, 1931.

DuFour, Howard R., and Peter J. Unitt. *Charles E. Taylor: The Wright Brothers Mechanician, 1868–1956.* Dayton, Ohio: Howard R. DuFour, 1997.

Fetters, Paul H. *Trials and Triumphs: A History of the Church of the United Brethren in Christ.* Huntington, Ind.: Church of the United Brethren in Christ, Department of Church Services, 1984.

Fisk, Fred C. "The Wright Brothers' Bicycles." *Wheelmen,* November 1980, 2–15.

Fisk, Fred C., and Marlin W. Todd. *The Wright Brothers: From Bicycle to Biplane.* Dayton, Ohio: Toddfisk, 1995.

Frost, Robert. "A Trip to Currituck, Elizabeth City, and Kitty Hawk." *North Carolina Folklore* 16 (May 1968): 3–9.

Gibbs-Smith, Charles Harvard. *Sir George Cayley's Aeronautics, 1796–1855.* London: Her Majesty's Stationery Office, 1962.

———. *The Invention of the Aeroplane, 1799–1909.* New York: Taplinger Publishing Co., 1965.

———. *Clément Ader: His Flight-Claims and His Place in History.* London: Her Majesty's Stationery Office, 1968.

———. *The Aeroplane: An Historical Survey from Its Origins to the End of World War II.* 2d ed. London: Her Majesty's Stationery Office, 1970.

———. *The Rebirth of European Aviation, 1902–1908: A Study of the Wright Brothers' Influence.* London: Her Majesty's Stationery Office, 1974.

Gollin, Alfred. *No Longer an Island: Britain and the Wright Brothers, 1902–1909.* Stanford, Calif.: Stanford University Press, 1984.

Hallion, Richard P. *Legacy of Flight: The Guggenheim Contribution to American Aviation.* Seattle: University of Washington Press, 1977.

———, ed. *The Wright Brothers: Heirs of Prometheus.* Washington, D.C.: Smithsonian Institution Press, 1978.

Harris, Sherwood. *The First to Fly: Aviation's Pioneer Days.* New York: Simon and Schuster, 1970.

Hart, Clive. *The Dream of Flight: Aeronautics from Classical Times to the Renaissance.* New York: Winchester Press, 1972.

———. *The Prehistory of Flight.* Berkeley: University of California Press, 1985.

Hart, Ivor B. *The Mechanical Investigations of Leonardo da Vinci.* London: Chapman and Hall, 1925.

Hayward, Charles B. *Practical Aviation: An Understandable Presentation of Interesting and Essential Facts in Aeronautical Science.* Chicago: American Technical Society, 1919.

Hildebrandt, Captain Alfred. "The Wright Brothers' Flying Machine." *American Magazine of Aeronautics,* January 1918, 13–16.

Hobbs, Leonard S. *The Wright Brothers' Engines and Their Design.* Washington, D.C.: Smithsonian Institution Press, 1971.

Hodgins, Eric. "Heavier Than Air." *New Yorker,* December 13, 1930, 29–32.

Jakab, Peter L. *Visions of a Flying Machine: The Wright Brothers and the Process of Invention.* Washington, D.C.: Smithsonian Institution Press, 1990.

———. "Otto Lilienthal: 'The Greatest of the Precursors.'" *AIAA Journal* 35 (April 1997): 601–7.

Jarrett, Philip. *Another Icarus: Percy Pilcher and the Quest for Flight.* Washington, D.C.: Smithsonian Institution Press, 1987.

Kinnane, Adrian. "A House United: Morality and Invention in the Wright Brothers Home." *Psychohistory Review,* spring 1988, 367–97.

Koontz, Paul R., and Walter Edwin Roush. *The Bishops: Church of the United Brethren in Christ.* 2 vols. Dayton, Ohio: Otterbein Press, 1950.

Langley, Samuel P. *Experiments in Aerodynamics.* Washington, D.C.: Smithsonian Institution, 1891.

———. *The Internal Work of the Wind.* Washington, D.C.: Smithsonian Institution, 1893.

———. *Langley Memoir on Mechanical Flight.* Washington, D.C.: Smithsonian Institution, 1911.

Lilienthal, Otto. *Birdflight as the Basis of Aviation,* trans. A. W. Isenthal. New York: Longmans Green, 1911.

Loening, Grover C. *Our Wings Grow Faster.* New York: Doubleday, Doran, and Co., 1935.

———. *Takeoff into Greatness: How American Aviation Grew So Big So Fast.* New York: G. P. Putnam's Sons, 1968.

Lougheed, Victor. *Vehicles of the Air: A Popular Exposition of Modern Aeronautics with Working Drawings.* Chicago: Reilly and Britton, 1910.

Maxim, Hiram S. *Artificial and Natural Flight.* London: Whittaker and Co., 1909.

McFarland, Marvin W. "The Gentlemen and the Press." *Boeing Magazine,* December 1953, 8–11.

———. "Orville Wright and Friend." *U.S. Air Services,* August 1956, 5–7.

Means, James, ed. *The Aeronautical Annual.* Boston: W. B. Clarke and Co., 1895–97.

Means, James Howard. *James Means and the Problem of Manflight.* Washington, D.C.: Smithsonian Institution, 1964.

Moedebeck, Hermann W. L. *Pocket-Book of Aeronautics,* trans. W. Mansergh Varley. London: Whittaker and Co., 1907.

Moolman, Valerie. *The Road to Kitty Hawk.* Alexandria, Va.: Time-Life Books, 1980.

O'Dwyer, William, and Stella Randolph. *History by Contract.* Leutershausen, Germany: Fritz, Majer, and Sohn, 1978.

"Orville Wright Flies *Constellation.*" *Aviation News,* May 1, 1944, 15.

Parkin, J. H. *Bell and Baldwin.* Toronto: University of Toronto Press, 1964.

Penrose, Harald. *An Ancient Air: A Biography of John Stringfellow of Chard.* Washington, D.C.: Smithsonian Institution Press, 1989.

Prendergast, Curtis. *The First Aviators.* Alexandria, Va.: Time-Life Books, 1980.

Pritchard, J. Laurence. *Sir George Cayley: The Inventor of the Aeroplane.* London: Max Parrish, 1961.

Randolph, Stella. *Lost Flights of Gustave Whitehead.* Washington, D.C.: Places, 1937.

Roland, Alex. *Model Research: The National Advisory Committee for Aeronautics, 1915–1958.* Washington, D.C.: National Aeronautics and Space Administration, 1985.

Roseberry, C. R. *Glenn Curtiss: Pioneer of Flight.* Garden City. N.Y.: Doubleday, 1972.

Schwipps, Werner. *Lilienthal: Die Biographie des ersten Fliegers.* München: Aviatic Verlag, 1979.

———. *Lilienthal und die Amerikaner.* München: Deutsches Museum, 1985.

Shaw, Herbert. "Orville Wright Finds Historic Relic, Long Lost." *U.S. Air Services,* January 1947, 17–18.

Sullivan, Mark. "The Airplane Emerges." In *Our Times: The United States, 1900–1925.* Vol. 2. New York: Scribner's, 1927.

Villard, Henry Serrano. *Contact! The Story of the Early Birds.* New York: Thomas Y. Crowell, 1968.

Voisin, Gabriel. *Men, Women, and 10,000 Kites.* London: Putnam, 1963.

Walker, Percy B. *Early Aviation at Farnborough: The History of the Royal Aircraft Establishment.* Vol. 2, *The First Aeroplanes.* London: MacDonald, 1974.

Wolko, Howard S. *In the Cause of Flight.* Washington, D.C.: Smithsonian Institution Press, 1981.

———, ed. *The Wright Flyer: An Engineering Perspective.* Washington, D.C.: Smithsonian Institution Press, 1987.

Worrel, Rodney K. "The Wright Brothers' Pioneer Patent." *American Bar Association Journal,* October 1979, 1512–18.

Wright, Orville. *How We Invented the Airplane.* New York: David McKay Co., 1953.

Wright, Wilbur. *Scenes in the Church Commission during the Last Day of Its Session.* Dayton, Ohio: Wright Brothers, 1888.

Wykeham, Peter. *Santos-Dumont: A Study in Obsession.* New York: Harcourt, Brace, and World, 1962.

Zahm, Albert F. *Aerial Navigation.* New York: Appleton, 1911.

———. "The First Man-Carrying Aeroplane Capable of Sustained Free Flight: Langley's Success as a Pioneer in Aviation." In *Annual Report of the Board of Regents of the Smithsonian Institution, 1914,* 217–22. Washington, D.C.: Government Printing Office, 1915.

Photographs for this volume were drawn from the following collections.

National Air and Space Museum Archives, Smithsonian Institution, Washington, D.C.
Photos 1 (SI A-4441-A), 2 (SI A-4441), 3 (SI A-43268), 4 (SI 86-9864), 5 (SI A-21147-B), 6 (SI A-30907-H-2), 7 (SI A-30908-A), 9 (SI A-4189), 12 (SI 84-12143), 13 (SI A-42296-A), 16 (SI A-2708-D), 17 (SI A-38722), 19 (SI A-43395-A), 20 (SI A-42413-B), 22 (SI A-38618), 23 (SI A-26767-B), 24 (photo by Lorie Aceto, SI 73-860), 25 (SI 73-861), 26 (SI 84-11866), 27 (SI A-42710), 28 (SI A-317-B), 29 (SI 86-13505), 30 (SI 88-7999), 31 (SI A-31246-H), 32 (SI A-42534), 33 (SI 86-9869), 34 (SI A-42555-C), 35 (photo by Carl H. Claudy, SI A-42667-E), 36 (SI A-43009-A), 37 (SI 85-10845), 38 (SI 93-7192), 39 (SI A-42805-A), 40 (SI A-38831), 41 (SI A-31980-G), 42 (SI A-45473-E), 43 (SI 88-7997), 44 (SI A-42912-D), 45 (SI A-42970-D), 46 (SI A-52735), 47 (SI A-38527-A), 48 (SI A-38532-C), 49 (SI 98-15722), 50 (SI 76-17318), 51 (SI A-1740), 52 (SI A-38902), 53 (SI A-42288-H), 54 (SI A-38496-E), 55 (SI A-18853), 56 (SI 71-2672), 58 (A-38627), 59 (SI A-38397-B), 60 (SI A-43009-D)

Special Collections and Archives, Wright State University, Dayton, Ohio
Photos 10 (Box 15, file 5, item 25) and 14 (Box 15, file 5, item 17)

Manuscript Division, Library of Congress, Washington, D.C.
Photo 11 (McFarland boxes, 86–87, Wright Papers)

U.S. Air Force Photo Collection, courtesy of National Air and Space Museum, Smithsonian Institution, Washington, D.C.
Photos 15 (USAF 10456 AC) and 18 (USAF 10461 AC)

Science Museum, London, courtesy of National Air and Space Museum, Smithsonian Institution, Washington, D.C.
Photos 21 and 57

INDEX

A

Abbott, Charles G., 76–78, 78n2, 96, 269
Ader, Clément, 26, 168, 174, 178–84
Aerial Age Weekly: interviews with Orville Wright (1917), 57, 238–39
Aerial Experiment Association, 38, 146–47n13
Aero: article by Wilbur Wright (1910), 208–9; interview with Wilbur Wright (1912), 213; letter from Wright brothers (1912), 39
Aero and Hydro: letter from Orville Wright (1914), 213–14
Aéro-Club de France, 21n2, 37, 39, 170n2, 184n4
Aero Club of America, 148n1; 1906 exhibition, 20, 22, 287, 295n3, 297, 299n4; statement by Wright brothers (1906), 16–18
Aero Club of America Bulletin: articles by Wilbur Wright (1912), 171–87
Aerodrome A. See *Great Aerodrome*
Aerodrome No. 5 (1896 Langley aircraft), 71n7; weight sustained per horsepower, 142
Aeronautical Journal: article by Wilbur Wright (1901), 109–12
Aeronautical Society of Great Britain, 28, 116
Aeronautic Review: article by William J. Tate (1928), 278–82
Aeronautics: article by Wilbur Wright (1911), 168–69; article by Wright brothers (1908), 19–21; articles by Orville Wright (1912, 1914), 148–49, 149–56
L'Aerophile, 20, 37
Air Commerce Act (1926), 252n8
Aircraft Production Board, 231, 232–33, 236, 238; appropriation for military aviation, 231, 236–37n2; formation, 236n2; members, 232–33, 236, 237n7
Albemarle Sound, N.C.: ferry boat, 86–87, 92n4
Alcock, John, 246n3
Alphonso, King (Spain), 101
American Legion Monthly: statement by Orville Wright (1926), 72–73
Ames, Joseph S., 77
Animal Mechanism (Marey), 117, 130n12; photographs of bird flight, 130n12, 143
Annapolis, Md.: military training, 265, 266
Annual Report of the Board of Regents of the Smithsonian Institution, 1902: article by Wilbur Wright, 114–29
Annual Report of the Board of Regents of the Smithsonian Institution, 1910, 37n4, 74, 75n5; text of speech delivered by Wilbur Wright, 36
Annual Report of the Board of Regents of the Smithsonian Institution, 1924, 67, 71n6
Archdeacon, Ernest, 21n2, 37, 184n4; gliders, 19, 37–38, 184n4
Archdeacon prizes, 21n2, 176n7, 184n4
Associated Press: statement by Wright brothers (1904), 14–15
Auvours, France: flight competition (1908), 101

Avery, William, 168, 171n9
Aviation: article by Orville Wright and Charles D. Walcott (1925), 66–70
Aviation and Aeronautical Engineering: article by Orville Wright (1919), 239–42
Aviation News: interview with Orville Wright (1943), 267–69

B

Ball, Robert S.: article by, 285–95
Baltimore, Md.: aircraft manufacture, 230n5, 258, 292
Bath, England: ancient quarry, 97n2
Baum, Elijah W., 280
Beach, Stanley Y., 189
Beachem, Thomas, 45
Beachy, Lincoln, 67, 71n5
Beck, Mabel, 95, 103, 273, 296; article by, 296–99
Bell, Alexander Graham, 36, 36n3, 69, 146–47n13; formation of Aerial Experiment Association (1907), 38, 146–47n13; invention of telephone, 83, 146n13; kite experiments, 143, 146n13
Bennett, James Gordon, 101, 105n15. *See also* Gordon Bennett Cup
Berg, Hart O., 101, 105n16
Billman, Charley, 191
Birdflight as the Basis of Aviation (Lilienthal), 59n2, 125, 132n32, 164
Bishop's Boys, The: A Life of Wilbur and Orville Wright (Crouch), 1, 14
Black, Fred, 293
Blériot, Louis, 37, 168, 170n3
Blériot XI (monoplane), 148–49, 170n3
Bowen, Thomas S., 229
Boys' Life: articles (1914), 49–56
Brett, George H., 265
Bridgeport, Conn.: alleged 1901 Whitehead flight, 165, 188, 189
Bridgeport Herald, 188
Brinkley, W. C., 30, 46, 54–56, 72, 271, 276
Brookins, Walter, 209, 209n2
Brown, Arthur Whitten, 246n3
Browning, John, 33
Butler, Nicholas Murray, 258

C

Cairo (Ill.) Bulletin: article by Wilbur Wright (1909), 205
California: first transcontinental flight (1911), 292, 295–96n10. *See also* Los Angeles; San Francisco
"Capable of Flight: The Saga of the 1903 Wright Airplane" (Crouch), 14
Case, Leland D.: interview with Orville Wright, 98–104
Cayley, Sir George, 173, 175n2, 186
Cellie, Andrew, 188
Century Magazine: article by Orville Wright (1908), 5, 8, 12, 24–33
Chanute, Octave, 26–27, 164–65, 168–69; biplane glider (1896), 121, 130n13, 168, 170n7; correspondence with Wright brothers, 4, 34n12, 171n11; death (1910), 34n12, 165; double-decker concept, 117, 118, 130n13, 169, 170–71n7; encouragement of Wright brothers, 27, 34n12, 92, 164–65; glider experiments, 117, 168–69, 171n9; and Louis-Pierre Mouillard, 171, 173, 174–75; relationship with Wright brothers, 164–65, 170n2; tour of Europe (1903), 19, 37, 39, 168, 170n2; tribute by Wilbur Wright (1911), 168–69; verification of Lilienthal's tables, 51–52; as witness to Wright experiments, 27, 37, 121, 124, 169
Church of the United Brethren in Christ, 3, 79
Cincinnati, Ohio: radio broadcast by Orville Wright (1923), 247
Coffin, Howard E., 232, 237n7
Collier, Robert J., 292
Collier's Weekly: interview with John T. Daniels (1927), 274–78; interview with Orville Wright (1915), 214–18; story of Charles E. Taylor (1948), 285–95
Columbia University, New York, N.Y.: lecture series, 258
Columbus, N.Mex.: airmail service, 229; raid (1916), 230n4
Cook, Frederick A., 35, 35n2
Coolidge, Calvin, 261n8
Corsham, England: underground storage facility, 97n2
Country Life in America: article by Orville Wright (1909), 200–201
Crane, Carl J.: interview with Orville Wright, 59–62
Creel, George, 102
Curtiss, Glenn H., 38n2, 38n3; member of Aerial Experiment Association, 38, 147n13; modification and testing of 1903 Langley airplane, 13, 67, 69–70, 74; receipt of Langley Medal (1913), 71n7; use of adjustable wing tips, 37, 38; Wright patent-infringement suits against, 38n3, 71n8, 74, 76n10, 130n11
Curtiss Aeroplane and Motor Company, 38n3, 66, 67, 69

D

Daily Mail: prize offered by, 201–5
Daniels, John T.: injured by Wright Flyer, 30, 48, 56, 274, 276–77; interview with, 274–78; making of

historic photograph, 46–47, 64, 100, 272–73; as witness to first powered flight (1903), 30, 45, 46, 55, 72, 274–76
Dayton, Ohio: homecoming celebration honoring Wright brothers (1909), 192; libraries, 41, 52; military airfields, 235–36; newspapers, 3–4, 31, 217; U.S. Army demonstration flight (1944), 105n20. *See also* Hawthorn Hill; Huffman Prairie; McCook Field; Simms Station; United Brethren Church; Wright Cycle Company; Wright-Patterson Air Force Base
Dayton Press, 15n1
Dayton Tattler: article by Wright brothers (1890), 166
Dayton-Wright Airplane Company, 8, 104, 237n7, 293, 298
Deeds, Edward A., 232, 237n7
Delagrange, Léon, 19, 20, 21n3, 105n16, 168
Denver, Colo.: air show (1910), 167–68n2
DH-4 (aircraft), 105n21
Dickie, James, 188
Dodd, Townsend F., 229
Dosher, Joseph J., 273
Dough, W. S., 30, 45, 46, 55, 72, 276
Drinkwater, Alpheus W., 273–74
Dunbar, Paul Laurence, 4, 166n2
Dvorak, John J., 188–89

E

Eckener, Hugo, 259, 260n4
Empire of the Air (Mouillard), 25, 159, 172–73
Encyclopaedia Britannica, 52; article on Wilbur Wright by Orville Wright, 79–81
England: London-to-Manchester prize, 201–5; soaring experiments, 157; World War I, 215, 222, 233, 235; World War II, 94–95, 97n2. *See also* Bath; Corsham; London; Manchester
English Channel: first crossing by airplane (1909), 170n3
Esnault-Pelterie, Robert, 19, 21n2
Etheridge, A. D., 30, 46, 55, 72, 276
Europe: first public flights of powered heavier-than-air flying machine (1906), 176n7; medals and honors given to Wright brothers, 80, 101, 192; motor manufacturers, 226, 235; passenger airlines, 250; visit by Octave Chanute (1903), 37, 39, 168, 170n2; Wilbur Wright's flight demonstrations (1908), 80, 101, 192; World War I, 214–15, 222, 237n6; World War II, 94–95, 97n2. *See also* England; France; Germany
Evening Item, The, 3–4; 1890 article, 3, 165–66
Experiments in Aerodynamics (Langley), 24, 28, 59n3, 112n2

F

Farman, Henri, 20, 21n3, 101, 168
Farman airplane, 19, 37, 205n3
Flying: articles by Orville Wright (1913, 1917), 40–48, 219–21
Fly Magazine: article by Wilbur Wright (1911), 211–12
Ford, Henry: aircraft manufacture, 104, 257n3; Wright home and shop, 293, 296n17, 299n3
Ford Model T automobile, 239n2, 257n3
Fort Myer, Va.: flight trials (1908), 12, 23–24n2, 50–51, 102, 105n17, 199n5, 219n9, 290
France: Ader experiment (1897), 168, 174, 176–84; aviation studies, 19, 20, 37–38, 168, 170n2; as birthplace of aviation, 174, 175n6, 176n7; first manned balloon flight (1783), 175n6; negotiations with Wright brothers (1906), 184n6; patent laws, 39; soaring experiments, 157, 158; World War I airplane manufacture, 235; Wright brothers' contract with syndicate, 80, 198, 199n6–7. *See also* Auvours; Le Mans; Paris; Pau
Franklin Institute, Philadelphia, Pa.: address by Orville Wright (1914), 149–56; Elliott Cresson Medal, 156n1
Furnas, Charles W., 21n6, 23

G

Gardner, Lester D., 293
Gerber, Paul Edward, 295
Germany: patent laws, 39; soaring experiments, 157, 158; World War I, 222, 231, 233–35, 238, 262
Gill, Howard, 213
Glenn L. Martin Company, 230n5
Gordon Bennett Cup, 211–12
Governor's Island, New York: Hudson-Fulton flights (1909), 206, 208n3, 291
Great Aerodrome (1903 Langley airplane), 13, 66–70, 70–71n3, 74–75, 77–78; crash, 13, 54, 69, 70–71n3; display in National Museum, 13, 66, 68, 70, 75, 77; modification and testing (1914), 13, 66–70, 71n8, 74–75
Greenfield Village, Dearborn, Mich.: Wright home and shop, 293, 294, 296n17, 299n3
Guggenheim Fund, 193
Guggenheim Medal, 259, 260n4

H

Hammondsport, N.Y.: Langley airplane, 68, 69–70, 74, 75
Harper's Magazine: interview with Orville Wright (1917), 221–30
Harris, Paul, 98
Harth, Frederic, 158, 161n4

Hawthorn Hill (mansion), Dayton, Ohio, 57, 58n2, 194, 218
Hazel, John R., 38, 38n3
Hearst, William Randolph, 292
Hendrick, Burton J.: interview with Orville Wright, 221–30
Henson, Samuel, 34n9
Hentzen, Heinrich, 158, 161n2
Herring, Augustus M., 117, 130n11, 168, 171n9
Herring-Curtiss Company, 38n3, 130n11
Hindenburg (airship), 260n4
Hoxsey, Arch, 167n2, 209, 209n2
Hudson-Fulton Celebration (1909), 206, 208n2–3, 291
Huffaker, Edward C., 85, 86, 92n3, 121, 123, 168, 171n9
Huffman, Torrence, 18, 18n4, 31
Huffman Prairie (Simms Station), near Dayton, Ohio, 18n3–4, 31, 191–92, 237n8, 291, 295n6; airplane shed, 31, 235, 237n8, 291
Hughes, Charles Evans, 8

I

Independent, The, 104n5
Internal Work of the Wind, The (Langley), 59n3, 112n2, 159

J

Jacobs, Eastman N., 259
Jacobs, James, 246n2, 296–98
Johnson, Clarence L., 259, 260–61n5
Johnson, Louis, 260
Johnstone, Ralph, 167–68n2, 209, 209n2
Jones, B. Melvill, 258, 259
Jones, Jesse, 268
Journal of the Western Society of Engineers, 129n1; article by Wilbur Wright (1903), 132–45

K

Kelly, Fred C., 2, 6, 7; biography of Wright brothers, 6, 96, 101, 105n14; interviews with Orville Wright, 81–83, 214–18, 261–67
Kelly, Oakley G., 248, 251n4
Keuka, Lake, N.Y., 69–70
Kill Devil Hill: Discovering the Secret World of the Wright Brothers (Combs), 1
Kill Devil Hills, near Kitty Hawk, N.C.: dune stabilization, 261n8; fiftieth-anniversary celebration of first flights, 272; height and slope of sand hills, 120, 133, 280; mosquitoes, 85–86, 88–89; site of first powered flights (December 17, 1903), 14–15, 45–48, 55–56, 64–65, 72–73, 278n4; soaring birds, 140–42, 275; wind conditions, 216, 271, 280; Wright brothers' camp, 14, 42–43, 63–64, 84–92, 281
Kill Devil Hills Lifesaving Station, near Kitty Hawk, N.C., 23, 30, 45, 46, 55, 56, 64, 72, 271
Kittyhawk (airplane). *See* Wright Flyer
Kitty Hawk, N.C., 84–85, 279–81. *See also* Kill Devil Hills; Wright Brothers National Memorial
Knabenshue, Roy, 292, 293

L

Lamson, Charles, 168, 171n9
Langley, Samuel P.: aerodynamic research, 28, 36, 59n2, 110, 125, 126; crash of *Great Aerodrome* (1903), 13, 54, 69, 70–71n3; death (1906), 36n2, 37n4, 70n2; first successful flight of powered heavier-than-air model aircraft (1896), 71n7; friendship with Alexander Graham Bell, 36n3, 146n13; measurements of plane surfaces, 58, 73–74; propeller efficiency, 30; secretary of Smithsonian Institution, 13, 73; theory of soaring flight, 159; use of dihedral angle system, 144; Wright/Smithsonian controversy, 13, 66–70, 73–78, 95–96
Langley Aeronautical Laboratory, Washington, D.C., 71n8, 79n7
Langley Day (May 6), 67, 71n7
Langley Medal, 13, 36, 36n2, 37n4, 71n7, 74, 75n5
Lawrence Sperry Award, 259, 260n5
Le Mans, France: demonstration flights (1908), 12, 80
Library of Congress, Washington, D.C.: Wright Papers, 2, 3, 7, 8
Lilienthal, Otto, 79–80, 115–18, 164–66, 183–87; death (1896), 33n4, 79, 116, 117, 130n8; experiments with powered aircraft, 129n5; glider experiments, 79–80, 99, 105n8, 115–18, 164, 179–80, 187; humorous article by Wright brothers (1890), 3, 165–66; inaccuracy of tables, 52, 58, 119, 125, 128, 187; influence on Wright brothers, 3, 58, 117, 164; memorial tribute by Wilbur Wright, 164, 184–87; method of balance control, 26, 80, 116, 118, 122, 129n7, 187; tables of air pressure data, 110, 119, 121, 122, 130n15, 131n20, 164, 186, 187; upright position of operator, 112, 118; wing curvature, 122, 132n27
Lindbergh, Charles A., 6, 258, 277, 298–99; transatlantic flight (1927), 100, 206n3
Lockheed Constellation transportation aircraft, 102, 104n2, 105n20
London, England: first London-to-Manchester flight (1910), 205n3. *See also* Science Museum
London Magazine: article by Wilbur Wright (1909), 201–5

Long Beach, Calif.: transcontinental flight (1911), 292, 295–96n10
Los Angeles, Calif.: aircraft manufacture, 230n5, 292
Love, Rodney M., 95

M

MacArthur, Douglas, 265
Mackintosh, E. E. B., 92–95, 97n2
Macready, John A., 248, 251n4
Madden, Martin B., 255, 256n5
Manchester, England: first London-to-Manchester flight (1910), 205n3
Marey, Étienne Jules, 117, 130n12, 143
Martin, Glenn L., 229, 230–31n5, 259, 292, 296n13
Martin flying boat, 258, 260n3
Massachusetts Institute of Technology, Cambridge, Mass.: exhibition of Wright Flyer (1916), 49n12, 293, 297, 299n4
Maxim, Sir Hiram, 25, 33n7, 142, 144, 183; propeller efficiency, 30; steam-powered aircraft, 33n7, 129n3; work abandoned, 26, 99
McCook Field, Dayton, Ohio, 254, 255–56n3
McCurdy, J. A. D., 147n13
McFarland, Marvin W., 2, 4
McSurely, Alexander: interview with Orville Wright, 267–69
Means, James, 169n1
Melville, George W., 99, 104n5
Miller, Harold S., 95, 97
Miller, Ivonette Wright, 105n23
Miracle at Kitty Hawk: The Letters of Wilbur and Orville Wright (Kelly), 2
Mitchell, William, 252n7
Mobile Era, The: A Monthly Magazine Containing the General News of the Air Craft: interview with Wilbur Wright (1910), 167
Montgomery, Ala.: Wright flying school, 160, 161n7, 291
Montgomery, Robert L., 232
Moore, Johnny, 34n17, 47, 55, 56, 72, 271, 276
Morrow, Dwight W., 252, 255n2
Morrow Board. *See* President's Aircraft Board
Motor: interview with Wilbur Wright (1908), 196–99
Mouillard, Louis-Pierre, 25, 159, 171–75, 186
Munich Crisis (1938), 97n2

N

National Advisory Committee for Aeronautics, 69, 77, 79n7, 251, 259
National Aeronautic Association, 247, 251, 278, 281–82
National Aeronautic Association Review: transcription of radio message by Orville Wright (1924), 247–51
National Aeronautics and Space Administration, 79n7
National Air and Space Museum, Washington, D.C., 2, 132n29, 251n4
National Air Museum, Washington, D.C., 13
National Geographic Magazine: article (1911), 210–11
National Geographic Society, Washington, D.C.: sixth annual banquet (1911), 211n1
National Museum. *See* United States National Museum
National Parks Conference: address by Wilbur Wright (1917), 219–21
Naval Aircraft Factory, Philadelphia, Pa., 258n3
Navigating the Air: A Scientific Statement of the Progress of Aëronautical Science up to the Present Time (1907): technical paper by Wright brothers, 147–48
Nevin, Robert M., 267n2
Newcomb, Simon, 99, 104–5n5
New York: Hudson-Fulton Celebration (1909), 206, 208n2–3. *See also* Governor's Island; Hammondsport; Keuka, Lake; New York, N.Y.; West Point
New York, N.Y.: aeronautical exhibitions, 20, 22, 287, 295n3, 297–98, 299n4; airmail service, 250. *See also* Columbia University
New York Aero Club show (1906), 20, 22, 287, 295n3, 297, 299n4
New York Aero Show Program (1920), 244–46
New York Times, The: quotation by Orville Wright, 258
New York Times Magazine: interview with Orville Wright (1917), 236
North Carolina: fortieth-anniversary celebration of first flight, 283. *See also* Albemarle Sound; Kitty Hawk

O

Ohio: remarks by Wilbur Wright, 35. *See also* Cincinnati; Dayton
Ohio Society of New York: twenty-fourth annual banquet (1910), 35n1
O'Neal, Benny, 45

P

Papers of Wilbur and Orville Wright, The (McFarland), 2, 4, 113n1
Paris, France: lecture by Chanute (1903), 37, 39, 170n2. *See also* Satory
Pau, France: flight demonstrations (1908), 80, 101; Wright memorial, 101
Paulhan, Louis, 175, 205n3
Peary, Robert E., 35n2, 102, 105n22
Peltier, Thérèse, 21n3, 105n16
Pénaud, Alphonse, 33n3, 71n9, 99, 153

Pénaud tail, 67, 71n9, 112
Pennington, E. J., 166
Pershing, John J., 230n4
Pilcher, Percy, 34n11, 112, 116, 118, 129n6; area of machine, 27, 114, 121; death (1899), 26, 34n11, 116–17, 186
Popular Science Monthly: article by Orville Wright (1922), 246–47; interview with Orville Wright (1929), 256–57
Potomac River, U.S.: crash of Langley airplane (1903), 54, 68, 69
President's Aircraft Board, 255n2, 256n6; testimony of Orville Wright, 252–55
Progress in Flying Machines (Chanute), 24, 112n2, 164, 171n11, 174

Q

Quirk, Leslie W., 56n2, 57n6; articles by, 49–56

R

Read, Albert, 246n3
Reader's Digest, 188
Reed, R. Luther, 70
Renstrom, Arthur G., 2
Richard's anemometer, 17, 22–23, 46, 132n29
Rodgers, Calbraith Perry, 292, 295–96n10
Rome, Italy: flight demonstrations (1908), 80
Roosevelt, Franklin Delano, 93, 265
Rosendahl, Charles E., 259
Rotarian, The: interview with Orville Wright (1948), 98–104
Rotary Club, 98, 102, 103

S

San Francisco, Calif.: airmail service, 250
Santos-Dumont, Alberto, 20, 174, 175–76n7, 177, 188
Satory, near Paris, France: trials of Ader machine (1897), 177–84
Saunders, W. O.: interview with John T. Daniels, 272, 274–78
Science Museum, London, England: Wright Flyer: display (1928–48), 13, 49n12, 66, 69, 73–76, 298; replica, 93, 94, 97n4; return to United States (1948), 78n2, 92–93; wartime protection, 93–95, 97n2
Science News Letter: article by Orville Wright (1932), 257
Scientific American, 38, 189; article by Wilbur Wright (1908), 194–95; article by Wright brothers (1908), 21–23; interview with Wilbur Wright (1909), 206–8; letter from Wilbur Wright (1910), 37–38
Selfridge, Thomas E.: death (1908), 24n2, 50–51, 51n3, 102, 199n5, 219n9, 290; as secretary of Aerial Experiment Association, 38
Seville, Henri Paul, 148, 149
Sheepshead Bay, Long Island, N.Y., 292
Silver Dart (airplane), 147n13
Simms Station, near Dayton, Ohio: rail stop, 191, 290, 295n6. *See also* Huffman Prairie
Sines, Ed, 3, 4
Slipstream: article by Orville Wright (1925), 63–65
Smeaton, John, 132
Smeaton Coefficient, 125, 132n31
Smithsonian Institution, Washington, D.C.: acquisition of Wright Flyer, 13, 49n12, 78–79n2, 97n5, 296; 1902 annual report, 129n1; 1910 annual report, 36, 36n1, 37n4, 74, 75n5; 1924 annual report, 67; 1942 annual report, 13, 96; publications on subject of flying, 11, 25, 99; Wright/Smithsonian controversy, 13, 66–70, 73–78, 95–96, 269n2. *See also* Langley Aeronautical Laboratory; Langley Medal; National Air and Space Museum; United States National Museum
Spencer, Charles, 186, 187n6
Sperry, Lawrence, 157n8
Sperry gyroscope, 157n8
Spratt, George A., 9n1, 43, 48–49n6, 86, 121, 123
Spirit of St. Louis (airplane), 206n3
Squier, George O., 233
Steeper, Harold W., 97
St. Louis Post-Dispatch: interview with Orville Wright (1943), 261–67
Stringfellow, John, 26, 33–34n9, 169

T

Taft, William Howard, 211n1, 267n2
Tate, Addie M., 280, 281
Tate, Dan, 89, 121, 131n25, 272
Tate, William J., 84, 89, 92n2, 121, 131n25, 271–72; articles by, 278–85
Taylor, Charles E., 40, 48n3, 163, 231, 272; building of 1903 Wright Flyer engine, 40, 163, 272, 287; death (1956), 296n18; employment by Wright brothers, 48n3, 237n5, 272, 285–86; story of Wright brothers, 285–95
Taylor, David W., 77, 233
Taylor, Henrietta Webbert, 286, 292, 294, 296n14
Today: interview with Orville Wright (1934), 81–83

U

United Brethren Church, Dayton, Ohio, 103, 286
United Brethren Printing Establishment, Dayton, Ohio, 3
United States: aircraft production during World War I, 8, 236–37n2, 237n6, 237n7; airmail service, 250; entrance into World War I, 38n3, 255n3; first coast-

to-coast flight (1911), 292, 295–96n10. *See also* California; New York; North Carolina; Ohio; Potomac River; Washington, D.C.
United States National Museum, Washington, D.C., 72n10; *Great Aerodrome,* 13, 66, 68, 70, 75, 77; Wright Flyer, 74, 76, 96, 97, 97n5, 295
University of Dayton Exponent: interview with Orville Wright (1924), 59–62
U.S. Air Services: article by C. G. Abbott and Orville Wright (1928), 76–78; article by Mabel Beck (1954), 296–99; article by William J. Tate (1943), 283–85; articles by Orville Wright, 58, 73–79, 84–92, 157–61, 188–89, 242–44; interviews with Orville Wright (1938), 258–60; transcript of Morrow Board hearings (1925), 252–55
U.S. Army: banquet honoring (1911), 211; competition with Navy, 265, 266; contract with Wright brothers, 12, 290; demonstration flight (1944), 105n20; purchase of Wright airplane, 24n2, 102, 105n17
U.S. Army Signal Corps, 21–22, 23–24n2, 32
U.S. Circuit Court of Appeals, 71n4, 76n7; Wright patent decision, 66, 74, 76n10
U.S. Congress: appropriation for military aviation (1917), 236–37n2, 251; investigation of aircraft industry, 237n7; Winslow bill, 250–51, 252n8
U.S. Navy: Bureau of Aeronautics, 246n2; competition with Army, 265, 266

V

Voisin, Charles, 19, 21n2, 168
Voisin, Gabriel, 19, 21n2, 168, 170n3
Voisin biplanes, 21n2, 37, 105n16

W

Walcott, Charles D.: death (1927), 78n2, 96; role in National Advisory Committee for Aeronautics, 69, 79n7; as secretary of Smithsonian Institution, 36n2, 70n2, 78n2, 79n7; Wright/Smithsonian controversy, 66–70, 71n8, 77, 78, 78n2
Waldon, Sidney D., 232
Ward, Jesse, 34n17
War Department, 69, 211, 211n3, 215, 235, 262
Washington, D.C.: Kitty Hawk flight fortieth-anniversary dinner, 93, 267, 268; Langley Day celebrations, 67, 71n7; return of Wright Flyer (December 17, 1948), 13, 78–79n2. *See also* Library of Congress; National Geographic Society; Smithsonian Institution
Washington Herald, The: interview with Orville Wright (1938), 259–60
Webbert, Charles, 18, 18n5
Weiller, Lazare, 199n6
Weisinger, Mort, 188
Wenham, Francis Herbert, 26, 33n8, 169, 173, 186
Westcott, Robert, 45
Western Society of Engineers, 39, 108, 129n2, 145n1
West Point, N.Y.: military training, 265, 266
Wetmore, Alexander, 78n2
Whitehead, Charles, 188
Whitehead, Gustave, 165, 188–89
Wilbur and Orville: A Biography of the Wright Brothers (Howard), 1
Wilbur and Orville Wright: A Bibliography (Renstrom), 2, 6
Wilbur and Orville Wright: A Chronology (Renstrom), 2
Wilbur and Orville Wright: Pictorial Materials, a Documentary Guide (Renstrom), 2
Wilbur Wright Field, Dayton, Ohio, 236, 237n9
Williams, Al, 248, 251n5
Wilson, Woodrow, 79
Winslow bill, 250–51, 252n8
Wood, Leonard, 211, 211n2
World War I: entered by United States (1917), 38, 236n2, 255n3; government investigation of U.S. aircraft industry, 8, 237n7; role of airplane, 214–15, 218n2, 222, 231–36, 238, 261–62; U.S. aircraft production during, 102, 236–37n2, 237n6
World War II: protection of Wright Flyer during, 93–95, 97n2; role of airplane, 218n2; split-flap aircraft, 246n2
Wright, Katharine, 58n2, 254, 256n4, 273, 282n2; letters from brothers, 84–92; marriage, 289; nickname, 92n5
Wright, Lorin, 289
Wright, Milton, 3, 58n2, 83, 103; airplane flight (1910), 219n8; as bishop, 3, 79, 103, 286; toy helicopter given to sons, 24, 33n3, 99
Wright, Orville: airplane accident (1908), 23–24n2, 49–51, 102, 199n5, 219n9, 290; automatic pilot system, 157n8, 161n3; automatic record changer, 104, 105n23; as consultant, 193, 194; death (1948), 2, 13, 194; injuries, 102, 219n9; interviews with, 59–62, 81–83, 98–104, 214–18, 221–39, 256–69; medals and awards, 156n1, 157n8, 194; personality, 4–5, 6, 194, 290; retirement (1915), 193, 219n10, 292; role after brother's death, 12–13, 193–94; split flap, 104, 246n2, 297; technical papers, 148–49, 149–56, 157–61; views on military use of airplane, 102–3, 214–15, 218n2, 221–22, 231, 250, 259–60; wills, 95, 97n5; world's record for soaring, 157; Wright/Smithsonian controversy, 13, 66–70, 73–78, 95–96, 269; writing skill, 4, 5
Wright, Reuchlin, 289

Wright, Susan Koerner, 79, 256n4
Wright, Wilbur: death (1912), 5, 12–13, 81, 187n1; *Encyclopaedia Britannica* article by Wilbur Wright, 79–81; first visit to Kitty Hawk, 280–81; interviews with, 167, 206–8, 213; leadership role as older brother, 4–5; 1906 letter to Octave Chanute, 37n4, 74, 75n5, 114n3; personality, 4–5, 289–90; technical papers, 109–12, 112–13, 114–29, 132–45; winner of Michelin Prize (1908), 101; writing skill, 3, 4
Wright brothers: childhood, 3, 24, 59, 83, 99; contract with French syndicate, 80, 198, 199n6–7; cooperative association between, 269; correspondence with Octave Chanute, 4, 34n12, 171n11; efforts to protect reputation, 11–13, 193; first major public flights (1908), 12, 192, 285n2; flying exhibition team, 12, 161n7, 167, 167n2, 209n2, 213, 237n8; 1900 glider, 19, 51–52, 63, 66n2–3, 119–20, 131n19, 146n12, 281; 1901 glider, 27, 52, 120–29, 145n3, 146n10–12; 1902 glider, 29, 37, 40, 43, 52–53, 63, 91, 133–39, 143, 145n3, 146n10–12; kite experiments, 134, 145n6, 199n4, 275; method of lateral control, 129–30n7, 130n14, 149–56, 174, 184, 199n4, 263; observation of birds, 140–44, 158–60, 202, 223, 275; patent-infringement cases, 7, 38n3, 39n2, 66, 71n8, 74, 76n10, 130n11, 175, 176n10; printing and publishing, 3–4, 60, 79, 83, 166n2; propeller design and experiments, 30, 41–42, 67; receipt of Langley Medal (1910), 13, 36, 36n2, 37n4, 71n7, 74, 75n5; soaring experiments, 158, 161, 161n3; telegram announcing first flights, 216–17, 273, 289; vacations, 59, 60; wind-tunnel experiments, 28–29, 34n22, 49n6, 58, 80, 99–100, 145n3, 263, 286; wing models, 52, 56n3, 58, 60–61. *See also* Wright, Orville; Wright, Wilbur; Wright Company; Wright Cycle Company; Wright Flyer
Wright Brothers, The: A Biography Authorized by Orville Wright (Kelly), 6, 96, 101
Wright Brothers National Memorial, Kitty Hawk, N.C., 259, 261n8, 281–82
Wright Company, 12, 167n2, 291–92, 296–97; and 1911 Gordon Bennett race, 211, 212; patent issues, 81, 175; retirement of Orville Wright (1915), 193, 219n10, 292
Wright Cycle Company, Dayton, Ohio, 4, 60, 83, 285–86, 299n3; lease on shop, 219n10, 299n3; locations, 18n5, 299n3; opening of (1892), 62n2, 84n2; proceeds of business, 34n12, 288; shop moved to Greenfield Village, 293, 296n17, 299n3
Wright Field, Dayton, Ohio, 236, 237n9, 256n3, 299
Wright Flyer (1903 airplane), 40–48, 63, 80, 147–48, 296–99; cloth covering, 146n12, 298; crankshaft and flywheel, 48n5, 287, 295n3, 297, 299n4; damaged by wind, 30, 48, 56, 274, 276–77, 297; difficulty in flying, 18n2, 251n3; donation to Smithsonian Institution, 13, 49n12, 78–79n2, 97n5, 296; duration of longest flight, 15, 19, 30, 48, 57n7, 65, 80, 278n4; engine, 40–41, 53, 61, 63, 147, 287–88, 299n4; exhibited in Smithsonian museums, 2, 13, 97, 97n5, 295; first flights (December 17, 1903), 14–15, 45–48, 55–56, 64–65, 72–73, 278n4; fuel tank, 287; gasoline, 264, 287–88; greatest altitude attained, 248; greatest distance covered, 15, 19, 30, 48, 57n7, 165; horsepower, 41, 80, 147, 148, 247; launching rail, 44, 100, 274, 278n2; loaned to Science Museum in London (1928–48), 66, 69, 73–75, 93–95, 97n2, 298; making of historic photograph, 46–47, 49n11, 72, 100; patents, 38, 39, 130n14, 176n10, 192; propellers, 41–42, 48n5, 52–53, 53–54, 247, 288; return to United States (1948), 13, 49n12, 78n2, 92–97; span, 63, 66n5, 278n2; speed of longest flight, 19, 80; storage (1903–16), 49n12, 273, 293, 297, 298; weight, 60, 63, 148, 247, 278n2
Wright-Patterson Air Force Base, Dayton, Ohio, 237n8–9, 256n3

Y

Yeager, Chuck, 194

Z

Zahm, Albert F., 67, 69, 71n8, 76n11
Zeppelin airships, 215, 231, 260n4